MEANS UNIT PRICE ESTIMATING

A Comprehensive Guide

MEANS UNIT PRICE ESTIMATING

A Comprehensive Guide

Publisher
E. Norman Peterson, Jr.

Editor In Chief
William D. Mahoney

Senior Editor
Edward B. Wetherill

Contributing Editors
F. William Horsley
Arthur Thornley

Illustrator
Carl W. Linde

R.S. MEANS COMPANY, INC.
CONSTRUCTION PUBLISHERS & CONSULTANTS
100 CONSTRUCTION PLAZA
P.O. BOX 800
KINGSTON, MA 02364-0800
(617) 747-1270

Printed in the United States of America

10   9   8   7   6   5   4   3   2   1

Library of Congress Cataloging in Publication Data
ISBN 0-87629-027-6

TABLE OF CONTENTS

FOREWORD	vii
INTRODUCTION	viii
CHAPTER ONE: ESTIMATE TYPES	2
Order of Magnitude Estimates	3
Square Foot and Cubic Foot Estimates	3
Systems (or Assemblies) Estimates	5
Unit Price Estimates	7
CHAPTER TWO: BEFORE STARTING THE ESTIMATE	12
CHAPTER THREE: THE QUANTITY TAKEOFF	20
CHAPTER FOUR: PRICING THE ESTIMATE	26
Sources of Cost Information	26
Types of Costs	27
The Paperwork	46
The Estimate Summary	48
CHAPTER FIVE: PRE-BID SCHEDULING	54
CHAPTER SIX: UPON COMPLETING THE ESTIMATE	62
Bidding Strategies	62
Cost Control and Analysis	66
Productivity and Efficiency	71
Retainage and Cash Flow	73
Life Cycle Costs	76
CHAPTER SEVEN: USING *Means Building Construction Cost Data*	80
Format and Data	80
Unit Price Section	82
Square Foot and Cubic Foot Costs	93
Repair and Remodeling	96
City Cost Indexes	98
Circle Reference Numbers	101
CHAPTER EIGHT: ESTIMATING BY UCI DIVISION	106
Project Description: Sample Estimate	107
Division 1: General Requirements	123
Sample Estimate	130
Division 2: Site Work	133
Sample Estimate	141
Division 3: Concrete	153
Sample Estimate	168

CHAPTER EIGHT: *Continued*

Division 4: Masonry	179
Sample Estimate	192
Division 5: Metals	195
Sample Estimate	199
Division 6: Wood and Plastics	200
Sample Estimate	213
Division 7: Moisture and Thermal Control	215
Sample Estimate	223
Division 8: Doors, Windows and Glass	227
Sample Estimate	236
Division 9: Finishes	245
Sample Estimate	256
Division 10: Specialties	262
Sample Estimate	263
Division 11: Architectural Equipment	263
Division 12: Furnishings	265
Division 13: Special Construction	265
Division 14: Conveying Systems	265
Sample Estimate	266
Division 15: Mechanical	266
Sample Estimate	278
Division 16: Electrical	287
Sample Estimate	292
Estimate Summary	295
APPENDIX A: SPEC-AID	310
APPENDIX B: CARPENTRY TABLES	346

FOREWORD

For over 45 years, R.S. Means Co., Inc. has been compiling and publishing construction cost data. On the basis of this experience, a series of estimating texts, manuals, and guides is now being presented to aid the construction professional in understanding the estimating process. This series of books is designed to benefit all who are involved with the construction industry: the owner, developer, architect, engineer, designer, contractor or facilities manager.

This book, the latest in the series, explains and demonstrates the methods and procedures of Unit Price Estimating, from the plans and specifications to the estimate summary. All aspects of the estimate, including the site visit, the quantity takeoff, pricing and bidding are covered in detail. A complete sample estimate is presented to demonstrate the application of .these estimating practices.

All construction costs used in this book are from the 1986 edition of Means' *Building Construction Cost Data*. Many pages, tables and charts from the annual cost guide are reproduced in order to show the origin and development of the cost data used in the estimating examples. *Building Construction Cost Data* is the leading source of thorough and up-to-date costs for the construction industry.

This book follows the logical progression of the estimating process. Initial chapters include analysis of the plans and specifications, the site visit, and evaluation of collected site data. The quantity takeoff, determination of costs, and final pricing are thoroughly covered, reflecting the importance and required attention to detail for each procedure. Also included are some strategies and principles that may be applied upon completion of the estimate. In addition, the format and origin of costs in Means' *Building Construction Cost Data* are explained.

The final section of the book is devoted to a detailed discussion of estimating for each UCI (Uniform Construction Index) division. A sample building project estimate is carried out, by division, to the estimate summary. This process demonstrates the proven estimating techniques described in the book. These are the techniques used by a majority of construction estimators and represent sound estimating practice.

INTRODUCTION

Every cost estimate requires three basic components. Without all three, the estimate cannot be completed. The first is the establishment of standard "units" of measure. In construction, such units could be as detailed as a square foot of drywall or as all-encompassing as a square foot of floor area. In auto repair, a unit could be an individual spark plug or a complete engine. Depending upon the estimator's intended use, the designation of the "unit" may imply only an isolated entity or may describe the unit as "in place". In building construction, these units are described as "material only" or "installed". The "installed" unit includes both material and labor.

The second component of an estimate is the determination of the quantity of units, an actual counting process: how many square feet of drywall, how many spark plugs. The third component, and perhaps the most difficult to obtain, is the determination of a reasonable cost for each unit. If costs for units were to remain constant and if there were no variables in construction, then there would be no need for estimates or estimators. Prices do fluctuate, however, and labor productivity varies; no two projects are exactly alike.

Essential Components of All Estimates

1. Designation of a "unit" of measure.
2. Determination of quantity of units.
3. Establishment of a reasonable cost per unit.

The first part of the estimate, the designation of units, is the step which determines and defines the detail, and thus the degree of accuracy of a cost estimate. The choice of units also determines the time required to do an estimate. The term "estimating accuracy" is a relative concept. What is the correct or accurate cost of a given construction project? Is it the total price that the owner pays to the contractor? Might not another reputable contractor perform the same work for a different cost, whether higher or lower? There is no *one* correct estimated cost for a given project. There are too many variables in construction. At best, the estimator can determine a very close approximation of what the final costs to the owner will be. The resulting accuracy of this approximation is directly affected by the amount of detail provided and the amount of time spent on the estimate.

The second component of every estimate, the determination of quantity, is oversimplified as the counting of units. In construction, this process is called the "quantity takeoff". In order to perform this function successfully, the estimator should have a working knowledge of construction materials and methods. This knowledge helps to assure that each quantity is correctly tabulated, and that items are not forgotten or omitted. The estimator with a sound construction knowledge is also more likely to account for all required work in the estimate. Experience is, therefore, invaluable.

The third component, determination of unit costs, is significantly responsible for variations in estimating. Even though material costs for framing lumber may be the same for competing contractors, the labor costs for installing the material can vary because of a difference in productivity. Labor rates may also vary àccording to pay scales in different areas. The use of specialized equipment can decrease installation time and, therefore, cost. Material prices fluctuate with the market. These cost differences occur from city to city and even from supplier to cross town supplier. It is the experienced and well prepared estimator who can keep track of these variations and fluctuations and use them to best advantage when preparing accurate estimates.

Estimating for building construction is certainly not as simple as applying the three components above and arriving at a "magic figure". Detailed estimates for large projects require many weeks of hard work. The purpose of this text is to make the estimating process easier and more organized for the experienced estimator, and to provide those who are less experienced with a basis for sound estimating practice.

We begin with a discussion of the different types of estimates.

Chapter 1
ESTIMATE TYPES

Chapter 1
ESTIMATE TYPES

Construction estimators use four basic types of estimates. These types may be referred to by different names and may not be recognized by all as definitive, but most estimators will agree that each type has its place in the construction estimating process. Figure 1.1 graphically demonstrates the relationship of required time versus resulting accuracy for these four basic estimate types.

1. **Order of Magnitude Estimates:** The order of magnitude estimate could be loosely described as an educated guess. It can be completed in a matter of minutes. Accuracy is plus or minus 20%.

2. **Square Foot and Cubic Foot Estimates:** This type is most often useful when only the proposed size and use of a planned building is known. Very little information is required. Accuracy is plus or minus 15%.

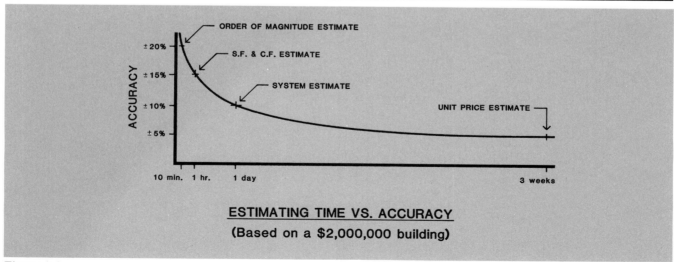

ESTIMATING TIME VS. ACCURACY
(Based on a $2,000,000 building)

Figure 1.1

3. **Systems (or Assemblies) Estimate:** A systems estimate is best used as a budgetary tool in the planning stages of a project. Accuracy is expected at plus or minus 10%.
4. **Unit Price Estimate:** Working drawings and full specifications are required to complete a unit price estimate. It is the most accurate of the four types but is also the most time consuming. Used primarily for bidding purposes, accuracy is plus or minus 5%.

Order of Magnitude Estimates

The Order of Magnitude estimate can be completed with only a minimum of information. The proposed use and size of the planned structure should be known and may be the only requirement. The "units", as described in the introduction to this book, can be very general, and need not be well defined. For example: "An office building for a small service company in a suburban industrial park will cost about $500,000." This type of statement (or estimate) can be made after a few minutes of thought used to draw upon experience and to make comparisons with similar projects from the past. While this rough figure might be appropriate for a project in one region of the country, an adjustment may be required for a change of location and for cost changes over time (price changes, inflation, etc.).

Figure 1.2, from Means' *Building Construction Cost Data*, shows examples of a different approach to the Order of Magnitude estimate. This format is based on unit of use. Please note at the bottom of the categories "Hospitals" and "Housing" that costs are given "per bed or person", "per rental unit" and "per apartment". This data does not require that details of the proposed project be known in order to determine rough costs; the only required information is the intended use of the building and its approximate size. What is lacking in accuracy (plus or minus 20%) is more than compensated by the minimal time required to complete the Order of Magnitude estimate, a matter of minutes.

Square Foot and Cubic Foot Estimates

The use of Square Foot and Cubic Foot Estimates is most appropriate prior to the preparation of plans or preliminary drawings, when budgetary parameters are being analyzed and established. Please refer again to Figure 1.2 and note that costs for each type of project are presented first as "Total project costs" by square foot and by cubic foot. These costs are then broken down into different construction components, and then into the relationship of each component to the project as a whole, in terms of costs per square foot. This breakdown enables the designer, planner or estimator to adjust certain components according to the unique requirements of the proposed project.

Historical data for square foot costs of new construction are plentiful (see *Building Construction Cost Data*, Division 17). However, the best source of square foot costs is the estimator's own cost records for similar projects, adjusted to the parameters of the project in question. While helpful for preparing preliminary budgets, Square Foot and Cubic Foot estimates can also be useful as checks against other, more detailed estimates. While slightly more time is required than with Order of Magnitude estimates, a greater accuracy (plus or minus 15%) is achieved due to more specific definition of the project.

17.1 S.F., C.F. and % of Total Costs	UNIT	UNIT COSTS			% OF TOTAL		
		1/4	MEDIAN	3/4	1/4	MEDIAN	3/4
900 Per car, total cost	Car	4,975	6,800	9,550			
950 Total: Mechanical & Electrical	"	355	535	660			
43-001 GYMNASIUMS	S.F.	40.90	55	70.45			
002 Total project costs	C.F.	2.07	2.66	3.62			
180 Equipment	S.F.	.94	1.76	3.09	2%	3.20%	6.70%
272 Plumbing		2.52	3.43	4.34	4.80%	7.20%	8.50%
277 Heating, ventilating, air conditioning		2.68	4.64	7.60	7.40%	9.70%	14%
290 Electrical		3.44	4.26	6.25	6.20%	9%	10.70%
310 Total: Mechanical & Electrical	▼	6.50	11.55	15	16.60%	21.80%	27%
350 See also division 11.1-49							
46-001 HOSPITALS	S.F.	90.30	111	147			
002 Total project costs	C.F.	6.65	7.95	11.10			
112 Roofing	S.F.	.66	1.64	2.67	.50%	1.20%	2.90%
132 Finish hardware		.89	.97	1.17	.60%	1%	1.20%
154 Floor covering		.62	1.13	2.84	.50%	1.10%	1.60%
180 Equipment		2.09	4.12	6.10	1.50%	3.80%	5.30%
272 Plumbing		7.95	10.15	13.75	7.50%	9.10%	10.70%
277 Heating, ventilating, air conditioning		8.65	14.40	19.80	8.40%	13%	16.60%
290 Electrical		9.30	12.65	19.20	10.30%	12.30%	15.20%
310 Total: Mechanical & Electrical	▼	27.30	37.20	55.05	26.90%	37.70%	40.30%
900 Per bed or person, total cost	Bed	27,100	41,800	62,700			
990 See also division 11.1-37							
48-001 HOUSING For the Elderly	S.F.	43.70	54.90	69.05			
002 Total project costs	C.F.	3.08	4.28	5.60			
010 Sitework	S.F.	3.19	4.74	6.70	6.10%	8.20%	12%
050 Masonry		1.32	4.76	7.45	2%	6.50%	10.70%
073 Miscellaneous metals		.91	1.72	2.40	1.20%	2.10%	2.40%
112 Roofing		.85	1.50	2.60	1.20%	2.10%	3%
114 Dampproofing		.25	.34	.79	.20%	.40%	.70%
134 Windows		.60	1.01	2.18	1.10%	1.50%	2.40%
135 Glass & glazing		.14	.45	.81	.20%	.40%	.90%
153 Drywall		2.61	3.42	5.50	3.70%	4.10%	4.60%
154 Floor covering		.71	1.04	1.51	.90%	1.40%	1.90%
157 Tile & marble		.33	.49	.73	.50%	.60%	.80%
158 Painting		1.41	1.98	3.08	2%	2.60%	3.10%
180 Equipment		1.02	1.41	2.24	1.80%	3.20%	4.40%
251 Conveying systems		1.04	1.41	1.87	1.80%	2.30%	2.80%
272 Plumbing		3.32	4.60	6.85	8.30%	9.70%	10.90%
273 Heating, ventilating, air conditioning		1.49	2.30	3.24	3.20%	5.60%	7.10%
290 Electrical		3.20	4.51	6.35	7.50%	9%	10.60%
291 Electrical incl. electric heat		3.69	6.95	8.25	9.60%	11%	13.30%
310 Total: Mechanical & Electrical	▼	8.05	11.30	14.65	18.40%	21.90%	24.60%
900 Per rental unit, total cost	Unit	38,800	45,900	50,500			
950 Total: Mechanical & Electrical	"	7,700	9,650	11,400			
50-001 HOUSING Public (low-rise)	S.F.	33.15	46.10	62.95			
002 Total project costs	C.F.	2.79	3.63	4.55			
010 Sitework	S.F.	4.79	6.50	10.35	9%	11.70%	16.40%
180 Equipment		.95	1.69	2.56	2.20%	3.20%	4.20%
272 Plumbing		2.41	3.33	4.27	7.10%	9%	11.50%
273 Heating, ventilating, air conditioning		1.28	2.41	2.73	4.40%	6%	6.40%
290 Electrical		2.11	3.05	4.28	4.90%	6.50%	8.20%
310 Total: Mechanical & Electrical	▼	6.45	9.30	12.15	15.70%	19.20%	22.10%
900 Per apartment, total cost	Apt.	36,800	41,700	52,100			
950 Total: Mechanical & Electrical	"	6,175	8,475	10,600			
51-001 ICE SKATING RINKS	S.F.	31.40	43.90	72.05			
002 Total project costs	C.F.	1.78	2.23	2.63			
272 Plumbing	S.F.	.94	1.39	2.13	3.10%	3.20%	4.60%
290 Electrical		2.48	3.25	4.51	5.70%	7%	10.10%
310 Total: Mechanical & Electrical	▼	4.49	6.37	9.59	12.40%	16.40%	25.90%

Figure 1.2

Systems (or Assemblies) Estimates

Rising design and construction costs in recent years have made budgeting and cost efficiency increasingly important in the early stages of building projects. Never before has the estimating process had such a crucial role in the initial planning. Unit Price Estimating, because of the time and detailed information required, is not suited as a budgetary or planning tool. A faster and more cost effective method is needed for the planning phase of a building project; this is the "Systems", or "Assemblies Estimate".

The Systems method is a logical, sequential approach which reflects how a building is constructed. Twelve "Uniformat" divisions organize building construction into major components that can be used in Systems estimates. These Uniformat divisions are listed below:

Systems Estimating Divisions:

Division 1 — Foundations
Division 2 — Substructures
Division 3 — Superstructure
Division 4 — Exterior Closure
Division 5 — Roofing
Division 6 — Interior Construction
Division 7 — Conveying
Division 8 — Mechanical
Division 9 — Electrical
Division 10 — General Conditions
Division 11 — Special
Division 12 — Site Work

Each division is further broken down into systems. Each of these systems incorporates several different items into an assemblage that is commonly used in building construction. Figure 1.3 is an example of a typical system, in this case "Drywall Partitions/Stud Framing" (see *Means Assemblies Cost Data*).

In the Systems format, a construction component may appear within more than one division. For example, concrete is found in Division 1 — Foundations, as well as in Divisions 2, 3, 5 and 12 (see list above). Conversely, each division may incorporate many different areas of construction, and the labor of different trades.

A great advantage of the Systems Estimate is that the estimator/designer is able to substitute one system for another during design development and can quickly determine the cost differential. The owner can then anticipate accurate budgetary requirements before final details and dimensions are established.

Final design details of the building project are required for a Unit Price Estimate. The Systems method does not require such details, but the estimators who use it must have a solid background knowledge of construction materials and methods, Building Code requirements, design options, and budgetary restrictions.

The Systems Estimate should not be used as a substitute for the Unit Price Estimate. While the Systems approach can be an invaluable tool in the planning stages of a project, it should be supported by Unit Price Estimating when greater accuracy is required.

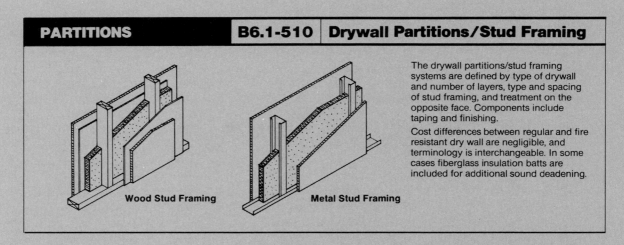

Wood Stud Framing   **Metal Stud Framing**

The drywall partitions/stud framing systems are defined by type of drywall and number of layers, type and spacing of stud framing, and treatment on the opposite face. Components include taping and finishing.

Cost differences between regular and fire resistant dry wall are negligible, and terminology is interchangeable. In some cases fiberglass insulation batts are included for additional sound deadening.

System Components			COST PER S.F.		
	QUANTITY	UNIT	MAT.	INST.	TOTAL
SYSTEM 06.1-510-1250					
DRYWALL PARTITION,5/8" F.R.1 SIDE,5/8" REG.1 SIDE,2"X4"STUDS16" O.C.					
Gypsum plasterboard, nailed/screwed to studs, 5/8"F.R. fire resistant	1.000	S.F.	.28	.27	.55
Gypsum plasterboard, nailed/screwed to studs, 5/8" regular	1.000	S.F.	.26	.28	.54
Taping and finishing joints	2.000	S.F.	.04	.46	.50
Framing, 2 x 4 studs @ 16" O.C., 10' high	1.000	S.F.	.30	.48	.78
TOTAL			.88	1.49	2.37

6.1-510	Drywall Partitions/Wood Stud Framing							
						COST PER S.F.		
	FACE LAYER	BASE LAYER	FRAMING	OPPOSITE FACE	INSULATION	MAT.	INST.	TOTAL
1200	5/8" FR drywall	none	2 x 4, @ 16" O.C.	same	0	.90	1.48	2.38
1250				5/8" reg. drywall	0	.88	1.49	2.37
1300				nothing	0	.60	.98	1.58
1400		1/4" SD gypsum	2 x 4 @ 16" O.C.	same	1-1/2" fiberglass	1.63	2.21	3.84
1450				5/8" FR drywall	1-1/2" fiberglass	1.46	1.96	3.42
1500				nothing	1-1/2" fiberglass	1.16	1.46	2.62
1600		resil. channels	2 x 4 @ 16", O.C.	same	1-1/2" fiberglass	1.49	2.83	4.32
1650				5/8" FR drywall	1-1/2" fiberglass	1.39	2.27	3.66
1700				nothing	1-1/2" fiberglass	1.09	1.77	2.86
1800		5/8" FR drywall	2 x 4 @ 24" O.C.	same	0	1.39	1.93	3.32
1850				5/8" FR drywall	0	1.11	1.66	2.77
1900				nothing	0	.81	1.16	1.97
1950		5/8" FR drywall	2 x 4, @ 16" O.C.	same	0	1.46	2.02	3.48
1955				5/8" FR drywall	0	1.18	1.75	2.93
2000				nothing	0	.88	1.25	2.13
2010			staggered, 6" plate	same	0	1.77	2.52	4.29
2015				5/8" FR drywall	0	1.49	2.25	3.74
2020				nothing	0	1.19	1.75	2.94
2200		5/8" FR drywall	2 rows-2 x 4	same	2" fiberglass	2.28	2.73	5.01
2250			16"O.C.	5/8" FR drywall	2" fiberglass	2.00	2.46	4.46
2300				nothing	2" fiberglass	1.70	1.96	3.66
2400	5/8" WR drywall	none	2 x 4, @ 16" O.C.	same	0	1.06	1.50	2.56
2450				5/8" FR drywall	0	.98	1.49	2.47
2500				nothing	0	.68	.99	1.67
2600		5/8" FR drywall	2 x 4, @ 24" O.C.	same	0	1.55	1.95	3.50
2650				5/8" FR drywall	0	1.19	1.67	2.86
2700				nothing	0	.89	1.17	2.06

Figure 1.3

Unit Price Estimates

The Unit Price Estimate is the most accurate and detailed of the four estimate types and therefore takes the most time to complete. Detailed working drawings and specifications must be available to the unit price estimator. All decisions regarding the building's materials and methods must be made in order to complete this type of estimate. There are fewer variables, and the estimate can, therefore, be more accurate. The working drawings and specifications are needed to determine the quantities of materials, equipment, and labor. Current and accurate costs for these items (unit prices) are also necessary. These costs can come from different sources. Wherever possible the estimator should use prices based on experience or cost figures from similar projects. If no records are available, prices may be determined instead from an up-to-date industry source book such as Means' *Building Construction Cost Data*.

Because of the detail involved and the need for accuracy, Unit Price Estimates require a great deal of time and expense to complete properly. For this reason, Unit Price Estimating is best suited for construction bidding. It can also be effective for determining certain detailed costs in conceptual budgets or during design development.

Most construction specification manuals and cost reference books such as Means' *Building Construction Cost Data* divide all unit price information into the sixteen Uniform Construction Index (UCI) divisions as adopted by the Construction Specifications Institute, Inc.:

Uniform Construction Index Divisions:

Division 1   — General Requirements
Division 2   — Site Work
Division 3   — Concrete
Division 4   — Masonry
Division 5   — Metals
Division 6   — Wood & Plastics
Division 7   — Moisture-Thermal Control
Division 8   — Doors, Windows & Glass
Division 9   — Finishes
Division 10 — Specialties
Division 11 — Equipment
Division 12 — Furnishings
Division 13 — Special Construction
Division 14 — Conveying Systems
Division 15 — Mechanical
Division 16 — Electrical

This method of organizing the various components of construction provides a standard of uniformity that is widely used by construction industry professionals: architects, engineers, material suppliers, and contractors. An example page from the 1986 Means' *Building Construction Cost Data* is shown in Figure 1.4. This page lists various types of formwork. (Please note that the heading "3.1 Formwork" denotes the UCI subdivision classification for these items in Division 3 — Concrete.) Each page contains a wealth of information useful in Unit Price Estimating. The type of work to be performed is described in detail: typical crew makeup, daily output, and separate costs for material and installation. Total costs are extended to include the installing contractor's overhead and profit.

3.1 Formwork		CREW	DAILY OUTPUT	UNIT	BARE COSTS			TOTAL INCL O&P
					MAT.	INST.	TOTAL	
500 ㉝	Spread footings, 1 use	C-1	305	S.F.C.A.	.88	2.08	2.96	3.95
505	2 use		371		.50	1.71	2.21	3
510	3 use		401		.39	1.58	1.97	2.70
515	4 use		414		.32	1.53	1.85	2.55
600	Supports for dowels, plinths or templates, 2' x 2'		25	Ea.	2.60	25	27.60	39
605	4' x 4' footing		22		5.65	29	34.65	48
610	8' x 8' footing		20		11.40	32	43.40	58
615	12' x 12' footing		17		18.50	37	55.50	74
700	Plinths, 1 use		250	S.F.C.A.	1.42	2.53	3.95	5.20
710	4 use		270		.41	2.34	2.75	3.82
50-001	FORMS IN PLACE, GRADE BEAM 1 use	C-2	530		1.25	1.84	3.09	4.03
005	2 use		580		.71	1.69	2.40	3.20
010	3 use		600		.53	1.63	2.16	2.93
015	4 use		605		.44	1.62	2.06	2.81
52-001	FORMS IN PLACE, MAT FOUNDATION 1 use		290		1.17	3.37	4.54	6.15
005	2 use		310		.65	3.15	3.80	5.25
010	3 use		330		.47	2.96	3.43	4.78
012	4 use		350		.38	2.79	3.17	4.43
55-001	FORMS IN PLACE, SLAB ON GRADE							
100	Bulkhead forms with keyway, 1 use, 2 piece	C-1	510	L.F.	.34	1.24	1.58	2.16
105	3 piece (see also edge forms)		400		.43	1.58	2.01	2.74
110	4 piece		350		.62	1.81	2.43	3.28
200	Curb forms, wood, 6" to 12" high, on grade, 1 use		215	S.F.C.A.	1.10	2.94	4.04	5.45
205	2 use		250		.63	2.53	3.16	4.33
210	3 use		265		.47	2.39	2.86	3.95
215	4 use		275		.40	2.30	2.70	3.74
300	Edge forms, to 6" high, 4 use, on grade		600	L.F.	.16	1.06	1.22	1.69
305	7" to 12" high, 4 use, on grade		435	S.F.C.A.	.51	1.46	1.97	2.65
350	For depressed slabs, 4 use, to 12" high		300	L.F.	.42	2.11	2.53	3.49
355	To 24" high		175		.50	3.62	4.12	5.75
400	For slab blockouts, 1 use to 12" high		200		.42	3.17	3.59	5
405	To 24" high		120		.50	5.30	5.80	8.10
500	Screed, 24 ga. metal key joint, see division 3.1-10							
502	Wood, incl. wood stakes, 1" x 3"	C-1	900	L.F.	.26	.70	.96	1.30
505	2" x 4"		900	"	.79	.70	1.49	1.88
600	Trench forms in floor, 1 use		160	S.F.C.A.	1.26	3.96	5.22	7.05
605	2 use		175		.68	3.62	4.30	5.95
610	3 use		180		.49	3.52	4.01	5.60
615	4 use		185		.39	3.42	3.81	5.35
60-001	FORMS IN PLACE, STAIRS (Slant length x width), 1 use	C-2	165	S.F.	2.18	5.90	8.08	10.90
005	2 use		170		1.27	5.75	7.02	9.65
010	3 use		180		.97	5.45	6.42	8.90
015	4 use		190		.81	5.15	5.96	8.30
100	Alternate pricing method (0.7 L.F./S.F.), 1 use		100	LF Riser	3.17	9.80	12.97	17.55
105	2 use		105		1.95	9.30	11.25	15.55
110	3 use		110		1.54	8.90	10.44	14.45
115	4 use		115		1.33	8.50	9.83	13.70
200	Stairs, cast on sloping ground (length x width), 1 use		220	S.F.	1.44	4.44	5.88	7.95
210	4 use		240	"	.89	4.07	4.96	6.85
65-001	FORMS IN PLACE, WALLS							
002								
010	Box out for wall openings, to 16" thick, to 10 S.F.	C-2	24	Ea.	12.20	41	53.20	72
015	Over 10 S.F. (use perimeter)	"	280	L.F.	1.15	3.49	4.64	6.30
025	Brick shelf, 4" wide, add to wall forms, use wall area							
026	above shelf, 1 use	C-2	240	S.F.C.A.	1.20	4.07	5.27	7.20
030	2 use		275		.71	3.55	4.26	5.90
035	4 use		300		.47	3.26	3.73	5.20
050	Bulkhead forms for walls, with keyway, 1 use, 2 piece		265	L.F.	1.37	3.69	5.06	6.80
055	3 piece		175	"	1.78	5.60	7.38	10

Figure 1.4

Figure 1.5 is a Means' "Condensed Estimate Summary" form. This form can be used after each division has been separately estimated. It serves as a checklist to assure that estimators have included all divisions, and is a concise means for determining the total costs of the Unit Price Estimate. Please note at the top of the form the items: Total Area, Total Volume, Cost per Square Foot, and Cost per Cubic Foot. This information can prove valuable when the estimator needs Order of Magnitude, or Square Foot and Cubic Foot Estimates for budgeting. This data will also serve as a cross-check for similar projects in the future.

A fifth type of estimate, more accurate than unit price, warrants mention: the Scheduling Estimate. This type involves the application of realistic manpower allocation. A complete unit price estimate is a prerequisite for the preparation of a scheduling estimate. A thorough discussion of scheduling estimating is beyond the scope of this book, but a brief discussion is included in Chapter Five, and a complete discussion may be found in *Means' Scheduling Manual*, 2nd edition, by F. William Horsley.

	MEANS CONDENSED ESTIMATE SUMMARY						
						SHEET NO.	
PROJECT						ESTIMATE NO.	
LOCATION			TOTAL AREA/VOLUME			DATE	
ARCHITECT			COST PER S.F./C.F.			NO. OF STORIES	
PRICES BY:			EXTENSIONS BY:			CHECKED BY:	

DIV.	DESCRIPTION	MATERIAL	LABOR	EQUIPMENT	SUBCONTRACT	TOTAL
1.0	General Requirements					
2.0	Site Work					
3.0	Concrete					
4.0	Masonry					
5.0	Metals					
6.0	Carpentry					
7.0	Moisture & Thermal Protection					
8.0	Doors, Windows, Glass					
9.0	Finishes					
10.0	Specialties					
11.0	Equipment					
12.0	Furnishings					
13.0	Special Construction					
14.0	Conveying Systems					
15.0	Mechanical					
16.0	Electrical					
	Subtotals					
	Sales Tax %					
	Overhead %					
	Subtotal					
	Profit %					
	Contingency %					
	Adjustments					
	TOTAL BID					

Figure 1.5

Chapter 2
BEFORE STARTING THE ESTIMATE

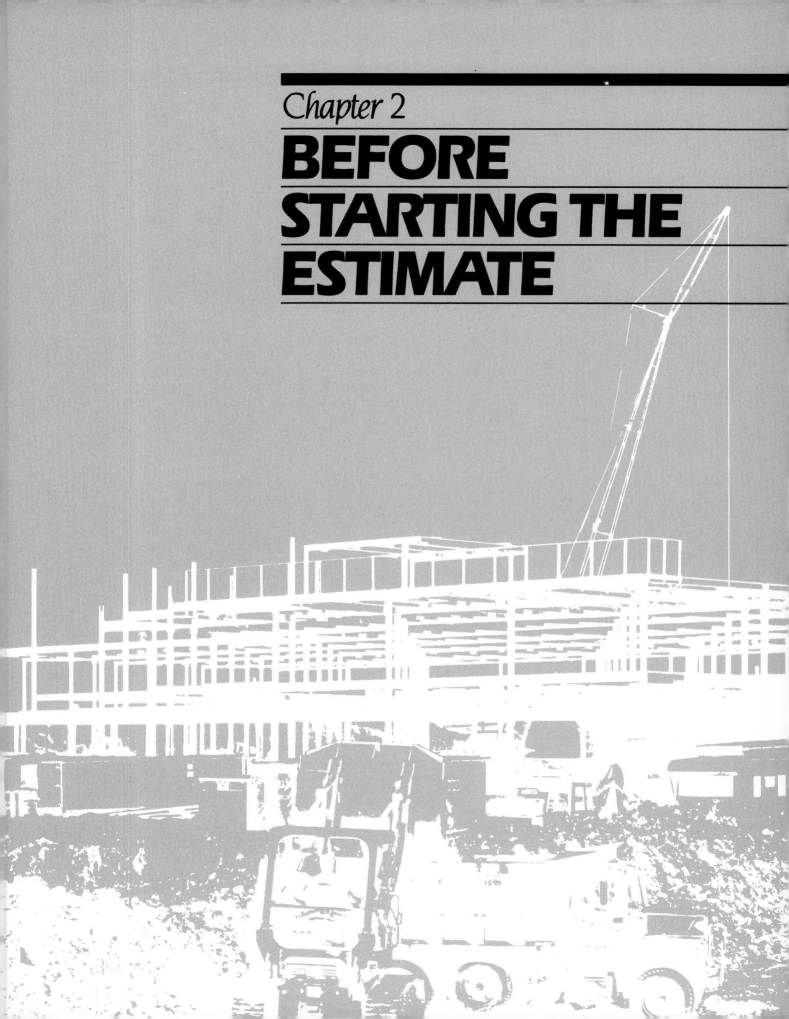

Chapter 2

BEFORE STARTING THE ESTIMATE

The "Invitation to Bid" — To the contractor, this can mean the prospect of weeks of hard work with only a chance of bidding success. It can also mean the opportunity to obtain a contract for a successful and lucrative building project. It is not uncommon for the contractor to bid ten or more jobs in order to win just one. The success rate most often depends upon estimating accuracy and thus, the preparation, organization and care that go into the estimating process.

The first step before starting the estimate is to obtain copies of the plans and specifications in *sufficient quantities*. Most estimators mark up plans with colored pencils and make numerous notes and references. For one trade to estimate from plans that have been used by another is difficult at best and may easily lead to errors. Most often two complete sets are provided by the architect. More sets must be purchased, if needed.

The estimator should be aware of and note any instructions to bidders, which may be included in the specifications or in a separate document. To avoid future confusion, the bid due date, time and place should be clearly stated and understood upon receipt of the construction documents (plans and specifications). The due date should be marked on a calendar and a schedule. Completion of the estimate should be made as soon as possible, to avoid confusion at the last minute.

If bid security, or a bid bond, is required, then time must be allowed and arrangements made, especially if the bonding capability or capacity of a contractor has not previously been established.

All pre-bid meetings with the owner or architect should be attended, preferably *after* a review of the plans and specifications. Important points are often brought up at such meetings and details clarified. Attendance by all bidders is important, not only to show the owner an interest in the project, but also to assure equal and competitive bidding. It is to the estimator's advantage to examine and review the plans and specifications before any such meetings and before the initial site visit. It is important to become familiar with the project as soon as possible.

In recent years, specifications, or project manuals, have become massive volumes containing a wealth of information. This author cannot stress enough the importance of reading all contract documents thoroughly. They exist to protect all parties involved in the construction process. The contract documents are written so that the estimators will be bidding equally and competitively, ensuring that all items in a project are included. The contract documents protect the designer (the architect or engineer) by ensuring that all work is supplied and installed as specified. The owner also benefits from thorough and complete construction documents, being guaranteed a measure of quality control and a complete job. Finally, the contractor benefits because the scope of work is well defined, eliminating the gray areas of what is implied but not stated. "Extras" are more readily avoided. Change orders, if required, are accepted with less argument if the original contract documents are complete, well stated, and most importantly, read by all concerned parties. Appendix A of this book contains a reproduction of a SPEC-AID, an R.S. Means Co., Inc. publication. This document was created not only to assist designers and planners when developing project specifications, but also as an aid to the estimator. The sections, arranged by UCI division, list thousands of components and variables of the building construction process. The estimator can use this form as a means of documenting a project's requirements, and as a checklist to be sure that all items have been included.

During the first review of the specifications, all items to be priced should be identified and noted. All work to be subcontracted should be examined for "related work" required from other trades. Such work is usually referenced and described in a thorough project specification. "Work by others" or "Not in Contract" should be clearly defined as well as delineated on the drawings. Certain materials are often specified by the designer and purchased by the owner to be installed (labor only) by the contractor. These items should be noted and the responsibilities of each party clearly understood.

The General Conditions, Supplemental Conditions and Special Conditions sections of the specifications should be examined carefully. These sections describe the items that have a direct bearing on the proposed project, but may not be part of the actual, physical construction. An office trailer, temporary utilities, and testing are examples of these kinds of items. Also included in these sections is information regarding completion dates, payment requirements (e.g. retainage), allowances, alternates, and other important project requirements. All of these requirements have a significant bearing on the ultimate costs of the project and must be known and understood prior to performing the estimate. A more detailed discussion of General Conditions is included in Chapter 8.

While analyzing the plans and specifications, the estimator should evaluate the different portions of the project to determine which areas warrant the most attention. For example, if a building is to have a steel framework with a glass and aluminum frame skin, then more time should be spent estimating Division 5 – Metals, and Division 8 – Doors, Windows and Glass, than Division 6 – Woods and Plastics.

Figures 2.1 and 2.2 are charts showing the relative percentage of different construction components by UCI Division and Systems Division, respectively. These charts have been developed to represent the average percentages for new construction as a whole. All commonly used building types are included. The estimator should determine, for a given project, the relative proportions of each component, and time should be allocated accordingly. Using the percentages in Figure 2.1, a 10% error in Division 6 would result in approximately a 0.2% error in the project as a whole, while a 10% error in Division 15 would result in an approximate 2% error overall. Thus, more time and care should be given to estimating those areas which contribute more to the cost of the project.

When the overall scope of the work has been identified, the drawings should be examined to confirm the information in the specifications. This is the time to clarify details while reviewing the general content. The estimator should note which sections, elevations and detail drawings are for which plans. At this point and throughout the whole estimating process, the estimator should note and list any discrepancies between the plans and specifications, as well as any possible omissions. It is often stated in bid documents that bidders are obliged to notify the owner or architect/engineer of any such discrepancies. When so notified, the

Component Contribution by UCI Division

No.	Division	%	No.	Division	%	No.	Division	%
1.5	CONTRACTOR EQUIP.*	6.8%	5.1	Structural Metals	2.2%	9.1	Lath & Plaster	0.4%
2.3	Earthwork	1.7	5.2	Metal Joists & Deck	1.5	9.2	Drywall	4.7
2.4	Caissons & Pilings	0.7	5.4	Misc. & Ornamental Metals	2.6	9.3	Tile & Terrazzo	1.1
2.5	Site Utilities	0.6	5	METALS	6.4	9.5	Acoustical Work	0.8
2.6	Roads & Walks	0.8	6.1	Rough Carpentry	1.6	9.6	Flooring	1.4
2.7	Site Improvements	0.1	6.2	Finish Carpentry	0.1	9.8	Painting	2.2
2.8	Landscaping	1.2	6	WOOD & PLASTICS	1.8	9	FINISHES	10.5
2	SITEWORK	5.1	7.1	Water & Dampproofing	0.7		DIVISIONS 10-14	8.3
3.1	Formwork	5.8	7.2	Insulation	0.6	15.1	Plumbing	5.0
3.2	Reinforcing	2.4	7.3	Shingles	0.3	15.5	Fire Protection	2.5
3.3	Cast in Place Concrete	9.8	7.4	Roofing & Siding	3.3	15.6	Heating	7.2
3.4	Precast Concrete	0.3	7.6	Sheet Metal Work	0.2	15.7	Air Condit. & Vent.	4.4
3.5	Cementitious Decks	0.1	7	MOISTURE PROTECTION	5.0	15	MECHANICAL	19.0
3	CONCRETE	18.5	8.1	Doors & Frames	1.5	16	ELECTRICAL	9.5
4.1	Mortar & Accessories	0.3	8.6	Windows	2.5		TOTAL	100.0%
4.2	Brick Masonry	2.7	8.8	Glass & Glazing	1.8			
4.3	Block & Tile Work	6.6	8	DOORS, WINDOWS, GLASS	5.8			
4.4	Stone	0.4						
4	MASONRY	10.0						

*Percentage for contractor equipment is spread among divisions and included above for information only.

Figure 2.1

Cost Distribution by System Division

Division No.	Building System	Percentage	Division No.	Building System	Percentage
1 & 2	Foundation & Substructure	9.8%	7	Conveying	4.8%
3	Superstructure	17.9	8	Mechanical	19.4
4	Exterior Closure	15.8	9	Electrical	9.7
5	Roofing	3.2	11	Equipment	3.3
6	Interior Construction	11.7	12	Sitework	4.4
				Total weighted index (Div. 1-12)	100.0%

Figure 2.2

designer will most often issue an addendum to the contract documents in order to properly notify all parties concerned and to assure equal and competitive bidding.

Once familiar with the contract documents, the estimator should notify appropriate subcontractors and vendors to solicit bids. Those subcontractors whose work is affected by the site conditions should accompany the estimator on the job site visit. At least one such visit (and often two or more) is extremely important, especially in cases of renovation and remodeling where existing conditions can have a significant effect on the cost of a project. During the site visit, the estimator should take notes, and possibly photographs, of all information pertinent to the construction and therefore to the project estimate. Pre-printed forms, such as the Job Site Analysis shown in Figures 2.3 and 2.4, can be useful to ensure that all items are included. Please note that most aspects of site work are included, in addition to such items as utilities, taxes, material and labor availability. This kind of form can be very helpful as a checklist to prevent the omission of items which may be less obvious. If unusual site conditions exist or if questions arise during the takeoff, a second site visit is recommended.

In some areas, questions are likely to arise that cannot be answered clearly by the plans and specifications. Certain items may be omitted, or there may be conflicts or discrepancies within the contract documents. It is crucial that the owner or responsible party be notified quickly (usually in writing) so that these questions may be resolved before causing unnecessary problems. A proper estimate cannot be completed until all such questions are answered.

Perhaps the best way for an estimator to approach a project is to begin with a clear mind and a clear desk. Clutter and confusion in either case can have detrimental effects on the efficiency and accuracy of the estimate.

MEANS JOB SITE ANALYSIS

SHEET NO. _____

PROJECT _____ BID DATE _____

LOCATION _____ NEAREST TOWN _____

ARCHITECT	ENGINEER	OWNER

Access, Highway _____ Surface _____ Capacity _____
 Railroad Siding _____ Freight Station _____ Bus Station _____
 Airport _____ Motels/Hotels _____ Hospital _____
 Post Office _____ Communications _____ Police _____
 Distance & Travel Time to Site _____ Dock Facilities _____

Water Source _____ Amount Available _____ Quality _____
 Distance from Site _____ Pipe/Pump Required? _____ Tanks Required? _____
 Owner _____ Price (MG) _____ Treatment necessary? _____
 Natural Water Availability _____ Amount _____

Power Availability _____ Location _____ Transformer _____
 Distance _____ Amount Available _____
 Voltage _____ Phase _____ Cycle _____ KWH or HP Rate _____

Temporary Roads _____ Lengths & Widths _____
 Bridges/Culverts _____ Number & Size _____
 Drainage Problems _____
 Clearing Problems _____
 Grading Problems _____
 Fill Availability _____ Distance _____
 Mobilization Time _____ Cost _____
 Camps or Housing _____ Size of Work Force _____
 Sewage Treatment _____
 Material Storage Area _____ Office & Shed Area _____

Labor Source _____ Union Affiliation _____
 Common Labor Supply _____ Skilled Labor Supply _____
 Local Wage Rates _____ Fringe Benefits _____
 Travel Time _____ Per Diem _____

Taxes, Sales _____ Facilities _____ Equipment _____
 Hauling _____ Transportation _____ Property _____
 Other _____

Material Availability: Aggregates _____ Cement _____
 Ready Mix Concrete _____
 Reinforcing Steel _____ Structural Steel _____
 Brick & Block _____ Lumber & Plywood _____
 Building Supplies _____ Equipment Repair & Parts _____

Demolition: Type _____ Number _____
 Size _____ Equip. Required _____
 Dump Site _____ Distance _____ Dump fees _____
 Permits _____

Figure 2.3

16

Clearing: Area	Timber	Diameter	Species
Brush Area	Burn on Site		Disposal Area
Saleable Timber	Useable Timber		Haul
Equipment Required			

Weather: Mean Temperatures

Highs		Lows	
Working Season Duration		Bad Weather Allowance	
Winter Construction			
Average Rainfall	Wet Season		Dry Season
Stream or Tide Conditions			
Haul Road Problems			
Long Range Weather			

Soils: Job Borings Adequate?		Test Pits	
Additional Borings Needed	Location		Extent
Visible Rock			
U.S. Soil & Agriculture Maps			
Bureau of Mines Geological Data			
Conty/State Agriculture Agent			
Tests Required			
Ground Water			

Construction Plant Required

Alternate Method

Equipment Available

Rental Equipment	Location

Miscellaneous: Contractor Interest

Sub Contractor Interest

Material Fabricator Availability

Possible Job Delays

Political Situation

Construction Money Availability

Unusual Conditions

Summary

Figure 2.4

Chapter 3
THE QUANTITY TAKEOFF

Chapter 3
THE QUANTITY TAKEOFF

Traditionally, quantities are taken off, or surveyed from the drawings in sequence as the building would be built. Recently, however, the sequence of take off and estimating is more often based on the sixteen divisions of the Uniform Construction Index (UCI) format. A thorough and detailed discussion, by UCI division, is included in Chapter 8.

Quantities may be taken off by one person if the project is not too large and time allows. For larger projects, the plans are often split into several disciplines (or divisions) and the work assigned to two or more quantity surveyors. In this case a project leader is assigned to coordinate and assemble the estimate.

When working with the plans during the quantity takeoff, consistency is the most important consideration. If each job is approached in the same manner, a pattern will develop, such as moving from the lower floors to the top, clockwise or counterclockwise. The choice of method is not important, but consistency is. The purpose of being consistent is to avoid duplications as well as omissions and errors. Pre-printed forms provide an excellent means for developing consistent patterns. Figures 3.1 and 3.2 are examples of such forms. The Quantity Sheet (Figure 3.1) is designed purely for quantity takeoff. Note that one set of dimensions can be used for up to four different items. A good example of the use of this form is shown in Figure 8.37. Figure 3.2, a Consolidated Estimate sheet, is designed to be used for both quantity takeoff and pricing on one form.

Every contractor might benefit from designing custom forms which would be appropriate for specific uses. If employees within the same company all use the same types of forms, then communication, interaction and coordination of the estimating process will proceed more smoothly. One estimator will be able to understand the work of another. R.S. Means has published a book completely devoted to forms and their use, entitled *Means' Forms for Building Construction Professionals*. Scores of forms, examples and instructions for use are included.

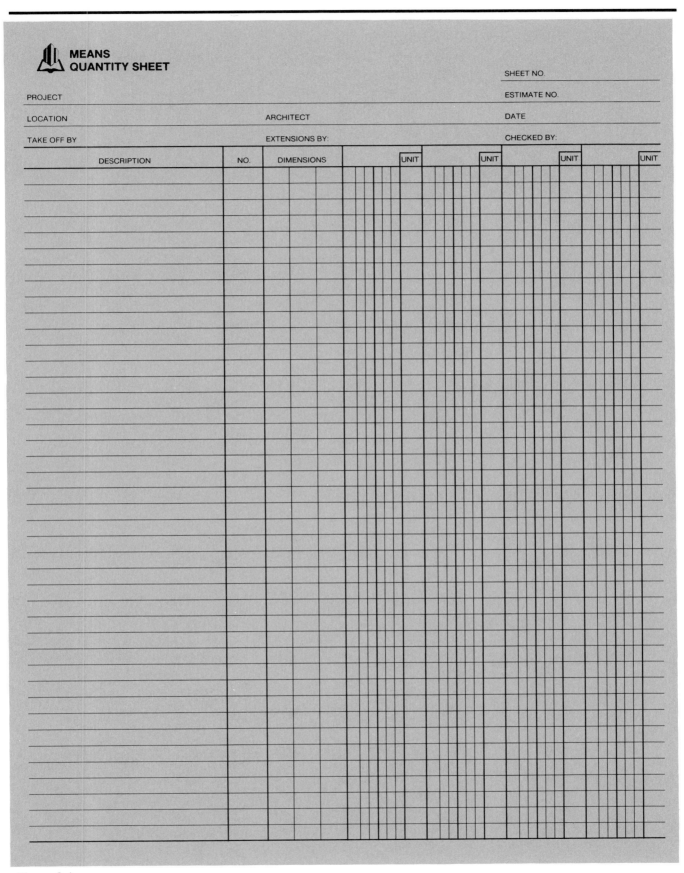

Figure 3.1

MEANS CONSOLIDATED ESTIMATE

PROJECT ________ CLASSIFICATION ________ SHEET NO. ________

LOCATION ________ ARCHITECT ________ ESTIMATE NO. ________

TAKE OFF BY ________ QUANTITIES BY ________ PRICES BY ________ EXTENSIONS BY ________ DATE ________

CHECKED ________

DESCRIPTION	SOURCE/DIMENSIONS			QUANTITY	UNIT	MATERIAL		LABOR		EQUIPMENT		SUBCONTRACT		
						UNIT COST	TOTAL	UNIT COST	TOTAL	UNIT COST	TOTAL	UNIT COST	TOTAL	

Figure 3.2

If approached logically and systematically, there are a number of short cuts which can help to save time without sacrificing accuracy. Abbreviations simply save the time of writing things out. An abbreviations list, similar to that in the back of Means' *Building Construction Cost Data*, might be posted in a conspicuous place, providing a consistent pattern of definitions for use within an office.

All dimensions – whether printed, measured, or calculated – that can be used for determining quantities for more than one item should be listed on a separate sheet and posted for easy reference. Posted gross dimensions can also be used to quickly check for order of magnitude errors.

Measurements should be converted to decimal equivalents before calculations are performed to extend the quantities. A chart similar to that shown in Figure 3.3, serves as a quick reference for such conversions. Whether converting from feet and inches to decimals, or from cubic feet to cubic yards, use good judgement and common sense to determine significant digits. Rounding off, or decreasing the number of significant digits, should be done only when it will not statistically affect the resulting product.

The estimator must use good judgement to determine when rounding is appropriate. An overall two or three percent variation in a competitive market can often be the difference between getting or losing a job, or between profit or no profit. The estimator should establish rules for rounding to achieve a consistent level of precision. As a general rule, it is best to not round numbers until the final summary of quantities. The final summary is also the time to convert units (square feet of paving to square yards, linear feet of lumber to board feet).

Conversion of Inches to Decimal Parts per Foot												
	0	1″	2″	3″	4″	5″	6″	7″	8″	9″	10″	11″
0	0	.08	.17	.25	.33	.42	.50	.58	.67	.75	.83	.92
1/8″	.01	.09	.18	.26	.34	.43	.51	.59	.68	.76	.84	.93
1/4″	.02	.10	.19	.27	.35	.44	.52	.60	.69	.77	.85	.94
3/8″	.03	.11	.20	.28	.36	.45	.53	.61	.70	.78	.86	.95
1/2″	.04	.12	.21	.29	.37	.46	.54	.62	.71	.79	.87	.96
5/8″	.05	.14	.22.	30	.39	.47	.55	.64	.72	.80	.89	.97
3/4″	.06	.15	.23	.31	.40	.48	.56	.65	.73	.81	.90	.98
7/8″	.07	.16	.24	.32	.41	.49	.57	.66	.74	.82	.91	.99

Figure 3.3

Figure 3.4 illustrates an example of the effects of premature rounding. If all items of a projects were similarly rounded up for "safety", total project costs may included an unwarranted, or at least unaccountable allowance. An extra 5% may remove a bid from the competition.

Be sure to quantify and include "labor only" items that are not shown on plans. Such items may or may not be indicated in the specifications and might include cleanup, special labor for handling materials, etc.

In general, the quantity takeoff should be organized so that information gathered can be used to future advantage. Scheduling can be made easier if items are taken off and listed by construction phase, or by floor. Material purchasing will similarly benefit.

Units for each item should be used consistently throughout the whole project — from takeoff to cost control. In this way, the original estimate can be equitably compared to progress and final cost reports more easily. It will be easier to keep track of a job.

The following list is a summation of the suggestions mentioned above plus a few more rules which will be helpful during the quantity takeoff:

- Use preprinted forms.
- Transfer carefully and make clear notations of sums carried from one sheet to the next.
- List dimensions consistently.
- Use printed dimensions, otherwise measure dimensions carefully if the scale is known and accurate.
- Add printed dimensions for a single entry.
- Convert feet and inches to decimal feet.
- Do not round off until the final summary of quantities.
- Mark drawings as quantities are determined.
- Be alert for changes in scale, or notes such as "N.T.S." (not to scale).
- Include required items which may not appear in the plans and specs.

And perhaps the four most important points:

- Write legibly.
- Be organized.
- Use common sense.
- Be consistent.

Effect of Rounding off Measurements at Quantity Take-off		Actual	Rounded Off	% Difference
	Length of partition	96'-8"	100'	3.4%
	Height of partition	11'-9"	12'	2.1%
	Total S.F.	1135.87 S.F.	1200 S.F.	5.6%
	Cost ($3.83/S.F.)	$4350.38	$4596.00	5.6%
	+15% overhead	$5002.94	$5285.40	5.6%
	+10% profit	$5503.23	$5813.94	5.6%
	Total cost difference (incl. O&P) $310.71			

Figure 3.4

Chapter 4
PRICING THE ESTIMATE

Chapter 4
PRICING THE ESTIMATE

When the quantities have been determined, then prices, or unit costs, must be applied in order to determine the total costs. Depending upon the chosen estimating method (and thus the degree of accuracy required) and the level of detail, these unit costs may be direct or bare costs, or may include overhead, profit or contingencies. In Unit Price Estimating, the unit costs most commonly used are "bare", or "unburdened". Items such as overhead and profit are usually added to the total direct costs on the bottom line, at the time of the estimate summary.

Sources of Cost Information

One of the most difficult aspects of the estimator's job is determining accurate and reliable bare cost data. Sources for such data are varied, but can be categorized in terms of their relative reliability. The most reliable source of any cost information is the accurate, up-to-date, well-kept records of the estimator's own company. There is no better cost for a particular construction item that the *actual* cost to the contractor of that item from another recent job, modified (if necessary) to meet the requirements of the project being estimated.

Bids from *responsible* subcontractors are the second most reliable source of cost data. Any estimating inaccuracies are essentially absorbed by the subcontractor. A subcontract bid is a known, fixed cost, prior to the project. Whether the price is "right" or "wrong" does not matter (as long as it is a responsible bid with no gross errors). The bid is what the appropriate portion of the work will cost. No estimating is required of the prime contractor, except for possible verification of the quote.

Quotations by vendors for material costs are, for the same reasons, as reliable as subcontract bids. In this case, however, the estimator must apply estimated labor costs. Thus the "installed" price for a particular item may be more variable. Whenever possible, all price quotations from vendors or subcontractors should be obtained in writing. Qualifications and exclusions should be clearly stated. Inclusions should be checked to be sure that they are complete and as specified. One way to assure these requirements is to prepare a form on which all subcontractors and vendors must submit quotations. This form can ask all appropriate questions and provide a consistent source of information for the estimator.

The above procedures are ideal, but often in the realistic haste of estimating and bidding, quotations are received verbally, in person or by telephone. The importance of gathering all pertinent information is heightened because omissions are more likely. A preprinted form, such as the one shown in Figure 4.1, can be extremely useful to assure that all required information and qualifications are obtained and understood. How often has the subcontractor stated, "I didn't know that I was supposed to include that?" With the help of such forms, the appropriate questions are asked and answered. An example of the use of this form is shown in Figure 8.34.

If the estimator has no cost records for a particular item and is unable to obtain a quotation, then the next most reliable source of price information is current unit price cost books such as Means' *Building Construction Cost Data*. Means presents all such data in the form of national averages; these figures must be adjusted to local conditions. This procedure will be explained in Chapter 7. In addition to being a source of primary costs, unit price books can be useful as a reference or cross check for verifying costs obtained elsewhere.

Lacking cost information from any of the above-mentioned sources, the estimator may have to rely on data from old books or adjusted records from an old project. While these types of costs may not be very accurate, they may be better than the final alternative-guesswork.

No matter which source of cost information is used, the system and sequence of pricing should be the same as that used for the quantity takeoff. This consistent approach should continue through both accounting and cost control during construction of the project.

Types of Costs

Unit price estimates for building construction may be organized according to the 16 divisions of the UCI format. Within each division, the components or individual construction items are identified, listed, and priced. This kind of definition and detail is necessary to complete an accurate estimate. In addition, each "item" can be broken down further into material, labor and equipment components.

All costs included in a unit price estimate can be divided into two types: direct and indirect. Direct costs are those directly linked to the physical construction of a project, those costs without which the project could not be completed. The material, labor and equipment costs mentioned above, as well as subcontract costs are all direct costs. These may also be referred to as "bare", or "unburdened" costs.

Indirect costs are usually added to the estimate at the summary stage and are most often calculated as a percentage of the direct costs. They include such items as sales tax on materials, overhead, profit and contingencies, etc. It is the indirect costs that generally account for the greatest variation in estimating.

Types of Costs in a Construction Estimate

Direct Costs	Indirect Costs
Material	Taxes
Labor	Overhead
Equipment	Profit
Subcontractors	Contingencies
Project Overhead	

MEANS
TELEPHONE QUOTATION

DATE _____

PROJECT _____ TIME _____

FIRM QUOTING _____ PHONE (   ) _____

ADDRESS _____ BY _____

ITEM QUOTED _____ RECEIVED BY _____

WORK INCLUDED	AMOUNT OF QUOTATION

DELIVERY TIME **TOTAL BID**

DOES QUOTATION INCLUDE THE FOLLOWING: If ☐ NO is checked, determine the following:

STATE & LOCAL SALES TAXES	☐ YES	☐ NO	MATERIAL VALUE
DELIVERY TO THE JOB SITE	☐ YES	☐ NO	WEIGHT
COMPLETE INSTALLATION	☐ YES	☐ NO	QUANTITY
COMPLETE SECTION AS PER PLANS & SPECIFICATIONS	☐ YES	☐ NO	DESCRIBE BELOW

EXCLUSIONS AND QUALIFICATIONS

ADDENDA ACKNOWLEDGEMENT **TOTAL ADJUSTMENTS**

ADJUSTED TOTAL BID

ALTERNATES

ALTERNATE NO.
ALTERNATE NO.
ALTERNATE NO.
ALTERNATE NO.
ALTERNATE NO.
ALTERNATE NO.
ALTERNATE NO.

Figure 4.1

Direct Costs

On the list above, Project Overhead has been listed as a direct cost. Project Overhead represents those costs of a construction project which are usually included in Division One – General Requirements. Typical items are the job site office trailer, supervisory labor costs, daily and final cleanup, and temporary heat and power. While these items may not be directly part of the physical structure, the project could not be completed without them. Project Overhead, like all other direct costs, can be separated into material, labor and equipment components. Figures 4.2 and 4.3 are examples of a form that can help ensure that all appropriate costs are included. Project Overhead will be further discussed below and in Chapter 8.

Material: When quantities have been carefully taken off, estimates of material cost can be very accurate. In order to maintain a high level of accuracy the unit prices for materials must be reliable and current. The most reliable source of material costs is a quotation from a vendor for the particular job in question. Ideally, the vendor should have access to the plans and specifications for verification of quantities and specified products.

Material pricing appears relatively simple and straightforward. There are, however, certain considerations that the estimator must address when analyzing material quotations. The reputation of the vendor is a significant factor. Can the vendor "deliver", both figuratively and literally? Often estimators may choose not to rely on a "competitive" lower price from an unknown vendor, but will instead use a slightly higher price from a known, reliable vendor. Experience is the best judge for such decisions.

There are many questions that the estimator should ask. How long is the price guaranteed? At the end of that period, is there an escalation clause? Does the price include delivery or sales tax, if required? Note that most of these questions are addressed on the form in Figure 4.1. But more information should be obtained to assure that a quoted price is accurate and competitive.

The estimator must be sure that the quotation or obtained price is for the materials as per plans and specifications. Architects and engineers may write into the specifications that: a) the particular type or brand of product must be used with no substitution, b) the particular type or brand of product is recommended, but alternate brands may be accepted *upon approval,* or c) no particular type or brand is specified. Depending upon the options, the estimator may be able to find an acceptable, less expensive alternative. In some cases, these substitutions can substantially lower the cost of a project.

When the estimator has received material quotations, there are still other considerations which should have a bearing on the final choice of a vendor. Lead time – the amount of time between order and delivery – must be determined and considered. It does not matter how competitive or low a quote is if the material cannot be delivered to the job site on time. If a delivery date is promised, is there a guarantee, or a penalty clause for late delivery?

The estimator should also determine if there are any unusual payment requirements. Cash flow for a company can be severely affected if a large material purchase, thought to be payable in 30 days (90 days 10 years ago!) is delivered C.O.D. Truck drivers may not allow unloading until

MEANS PROJECT OVERHEAD SUMMARY

MEANS PROJECT OVERHEAD SUMMARY							SHEET NO.			
PROJECT							ESTIMATE NO.			
LOCATION		ARCHITECT					DATE			
QUANTITIES BY:	PRICES BY:		EXTENSIONS BY:				CHECKED BY:			

DESCRIPTION	QUANTITY	UNIT	MATERIAL/EQUIPMENT		LABOR		TOTAL COST	
			UNIT	TOTAL	UNIT	TOTAL	UNIT	TOTAL
Job Organization: Superintendent								
Project Manager								
Timekeeper & Material Clerk								
Clerical								
Safety, Watchman & First Aid								
Travel Expense: Superintendent								
Project Manager								
Engineering: Layout								
Inspection/Quantities								
Drawings								
CPM Schedule								
Testing: Soil								
Materials								
Structural								
Equipment: Cranes								
Concrete Pump, Conveyor, Etc.								
Elevators, Hoists								
Freight & Hauling								
Loading, Unloading, Erecting, Etc.								
Maintenance								
Pumping								
Scaffolding								
Small Power Equipment/Tools								
Field Offices: Job Office								
Architect/Owner's Office								
Temporary Telephones								
Utilities								
Temporary Toilets								
Storage Areas & Sheds								
Temporary Utilities: Heat								
Light & Power								
Water								
PAGE TOTALS								

Figure 4.2

DESCRIPTION	QUANTITY	UNIT	MATERIAL/EQUIPMENT		LABOR		TOTAL COST	
			UNIT	TOTAL	UNIT	TOTAL	UNIT	TOTAL
Total Brought Forward								
Winter Protection: Temp. Heat/Protection								
Snow Plowing								
Thawing Materials								
Temporary Roads								
Signs & Barricades: Site Sign								
Temporary Fences								
Temporary Stairs, Ladders & Floors								
Photographs								
Clean Up								
Dumpster								
Final Clean Up								
Punch List								
Permits: Building								
Misc.								
Insurance: Builders Risk								
Owner's Protective Liability								
Umbrella								
Unemployment Ins. & Social Security								
Taxes								
City Sales Tax								
State Sales Tax								
Bonds								
Performance								
Material & Equipment								
Main Office Expense								
Special Items								
TOTALS:								

Figure 4.3

payment has been received. Such requirements must be determined during the estimating stage so that the cost of borrowing money, if necessary, can be included.

If unable to obtain the quotation of a vendor from whom the material would be purchased, the estimator has other sources for obtaining material prices. These include, in order of reliability:

1. Current price lists from manufacturer's catalogues. Be sure to check that the list is for "contractor prices".
2. Cost records from previous jobs. Historical costs must be updated for present conditions.
3. Reputable and current, annual unit price cost books, such as *Building Construction Cost Data*. Such books usually represent national averages and must be factored to local markets.

No matter which price source is used, the estimator must be sure to include any costs over the actual cost of the material. The above-mentioned concerns regarding vendor quotations should also be taken into consideration.

Labor: In order to determine the labor cost for each unit of construction, the estimator must know two pieces of information: first, the labor rate (hourly wage or salary) of the worker, and second, how many units this worker can produce or install in a given time period — in other words, the output or productivity. Wage rates are known going into a project but productivity may be very hard to determine. The best source of labor productivity (and therefore labor costs) is the estimator's well-kept records from previous projects.

To estimators working for contractors, construction labor rates for employers will be known, well-documented and constantly updated. Estimators for owners, architects, or engineers must determine labor rates from outside sources. Unit price data books, such as Means' *Building Construction Cost Data*, provide national average labor rates by trade as and base the unit costs for labor on these averages. Figure 4.4 shows national average *union* rates for the construction industry (based on January 1, 1986). Figure 4.5 lists national average *non-union* rates, again based on January 1, 1986.

If more accurate rates are required, the estimator has alternate sources. Union locals can provide rates (as well as negotiated increases) for a particular location. This source requires the estimator to call the union hall for each trade. Employer bargaining groups can usually provide labor cost data, but this data may not be continually updated. R.S. Means Co., Inc. publishes *Labor Rates for the Construction Industry* on an annual basis. This book lists the labor rates by trade for over 300 U.S. and Canadian cities.

The above sources are for union rates. Determination of non-union, or "open shop" rates is much more difficult. There are often organizations in larger cities representing non-union contractors. These organizations may have records of local pay scales, but ultimately the wage rates are determined by each contractor.

Unit labor costs are the least predictable of all costs for building projects. It is important to determine as accurately as possible both the prevailing wages and the productivity. If there are no company records for productivity, cost data books, such as Means' *Building Construction Cost Data*, and productivity reference books, such as Means' *Man-Hour*

Standards, can be invaluable. Included with the listing for each individual construction item is the designation of typical crew make-up, together with the productivity or output — the amount of work that the crew will produce. Figure 4.6, a typical page from Means' Man-Hour Standards, includes this data and indicates the required number of man-hours for each "unit" of work for the appropriate task.

Abbr.	Trade	Base Rate Incl. Fringes		Work-ers' Comp. Ins.	Average Fixed Over-head	Subs Over-head	Subs Profit	Subs Total Overhead & Profit		Rate with Subs O & P	
		Hourly	Daily					%	Amount	Hourly	Daily
Skwk	Skilled Workers Average (35 trades)	$20.50	$164.00	9.3%	13.8%	12.8%	10%	45.9%	$ 9.40	$29.90	$239.20
	Helpers Average (5 trades)	15.55	124.40	9.8		13.0		46.6	7.25	22.80	182.40
	Foremen Average, Inside (50¢ over trade)	21.00	168.00	9.3		12.8		45.9	9.65	30.65	245.20
	Foremen Average, Outside ($2.00 over trade)	22.50	180.00	9.3		12.8		45.9	10.35	32.85	262.80
Clab	Common Building Laborers	15.90	127.20	10.1		11.0		44.9	7.15	23.05	184.40
Asbe	Asbestos Workers	22.75	182.00	7.7		16.0		47.5	10.80	33.55	268.40
Boil	Boilermakers	22.75	182.00	6.6		16.0		46.4	10.55	33.30	266.40
Bric	Bricklayers	20.50	164.00	7.6		11.0		42.4	8.70	29.20	233.60
Brhe	Bricklayer Helpers	16.00	128.00	7.6		11.0		42.4	6.80	22.80	182.40
Carp	Carpenters	20.00	160.00	10.1		11.0		44.9	9.00	29.00	232.00
Cefi	Cement Finishers	19.20	153.60	5.9		11.0		40.7	7.80	27.00	216.00
Elec	Electricians	22.40	179.20	4.0		16.0		43.8	9.80	32.20	257.60
Elev	Elevator Constructors	22.65	181.20	5.5		16.0		45.3	10.25	32.90	263.20
Eqhv	Equipment Operators, Crane or Shovel	21.05	168.40	7.2		14.0		45.0	9.45	30.50	244.00
Eqmd	Equipment Operators, Medium Equipment	20.60	164.80	7.2		14.0		45.0	9.25	29.85	238.80
Eqlt	Equipment Operators, Light Equipment	19.45	155.60	7.2		14.0		45.0	8.75	28.20	225.60
Eqol	Equipment Operators, Oilers	17.50	140.00	7.2		14.0		45.0	7.90	25.40	203.20
Eqmm	Equipment Operators, Master Mechanics	21.80	174.40	7.2		14.0		45.0	9.80	31.60	252.80
Glaz	Glaziers	20.15	161.20	7.9		11.0		42.7	8.60	28.75	230.00
Lath	Lathers	20.10	160.80	6.3		11.0		41.1	8.25	28.35	226.80
Marb	Marble Setters	20.10	160.80	7.6		11.0		42.4	8.50	28.60	228.80
Mill	Millwrights	20.75	166.00	6.6		11.0		41.4	8.60	29.35	234.80
Mstz	Mosaic and Terrazzo Workers	19.90	159.20	5.4		11.0		40.2	8.00	27.90	223.20
Pord	Painters, Ordinary	19.25	154.00	7.7		11.0		42.5	8.20	27.45	219.60
Psst	Painters, Structural Steel	20.00	160.00	27.0		11.0		61.8	12.35	32.35	258.80
Pape	Paper Hangers	19.50	156.00	7.7		11.0		42.5	8.30	27.80	222.40
Pile	Pile Drivers	20.10	160.80	17.0		16.0		56.8	11.40	31.50	252.00
Plas	Plasterers	19.90	159.20	7.7		11.0		42.5	8.45	28.35	226.80
Plah	Plasterer Helpers	16.50	132.00	7.7		11.0		42.5	7.00	23.50	188.00
Plum	Plumbers	22.55	180.40	4.8		16.0		44.6	10.05	32.60	260.80
Rodm	Rodmen (Reinforcing)	21.75	174.00	16.8		14.0		54.6	11.90	33.65	269.20
Rofc	Roofers, Composition	18.80	150.40	18.2		11.0		53.0	9.95	28.75	230.00
Rots	Roofers, Tile & Slate	18.95	151.60	18.2		11.0		53.0	10.05	29.00	232.00
Rohe	Roofer Helpers (Composition)	13.75	110.00	18.2		11.0		53.0	7.30	21.05	168.40
Shee	Sheet Metal Workers	22.70	181.60	6.3		16.0		46.1	10.45	33.15	265.20
Spri	Sprinkler Installers	23.25	186.00	5.5		16.0		45.3	10.55	33.80	270.40
Stpi	Steamfitters or Pipefitters	22.75	182.00	4.8		16.0		44.6	10.15	32.90	263.20
Ston	Stone Masons	20.30	162.40	7.6		11.0		42.4	8.60	28.90	231.20
Sswk	Structural Steel Workers	21.70	173.60	19.3		14.0		57.1	12.40	34.10	272.80
Tilf	Tile Layers (Floor)	19.75	158.00	5.4		11.0		40.2	7.95	27.70	221.60
Tilh	Tile Layer Helpers	15.60	124.80	5.4		11.0		40.2	6.30	21.90	175.20
Trlt	Truck Drivers, Light	16.35	130.80	8.6		11.0		43.4	7.10	23.45	187.60
Trhv	Truck Drivers, Heavy	16.60	132.80	8.6		11.0		43.4	7.20	23.80	190.40
Sswl	Welders, Structural Steel	21.70	173.60	19.3		14.0		57.1	12.40	34.10	272.80
Wrck	*Wrecking	15.90	127.20	20.7	▼	11.0	▼	55.5	8.80	24.70	197.60

*Not included in Averages.

Figure 4.4

33

The estimator who has neither company records nor the sources described above must put together the appropriate crews and determine the expected output or productivity. This type of estimating should only be attempted based upon strong experience and considerable exposure to construction methods and practices.

Equipment: Over recent years, construction equipment has become much more sophisticated, not only because of the incentive of reduced labor costs, but also as a response to new, highly technological construction methods and materials. As a result, equipment costs represent an increasing percentage of total project costs in building construction. Estimators must carefully address the equipment and all related expenses. Costs for equipment can be divided into two categories.

Abbr.	Trade	Base Rate Incl. Fringes		Workers' Comp. Ins.	Average Fixed Overhead	Subs Overhead	Subs Profit	Subs Total Overhead & Profit		Rate with Subs O & P	
		Hourly	Daily					%	Amount	Hourly	Daily
Skwk	Skilled Workers Average	$10.05	$ 80.40	9.3%	13.8%	22.8%	10%	55.9%	$ 5.60	$15.65	$125.20
	Helpers Average ($2.00 under trade)	8.05	64.40	9.8		23.0		56.6	4.55	12.60	100.80
	Foremen Average, ($2.00 over trade)	12.05	96.50	9.3		22.8		55.9	6.75	18.80	150.40
Clab	Laborers	6.95	55.60	10.1		21.0		54.9	3.80	10.75	86.00
Asbe	Pipe or Duct Insulators	9.95	79.60	7.7		26.0		57.5	5.70	15.65	125.20
Boil	Boilermakers	11.85	94.80	6.6		26.0		56.4	6.70	18.55	148.40
Bric	Brick or Block Masons	9.25	74.00	7.6		21.0		52.4	4.85	14.10	112.80
Carp	Carpenters	10.30	82.40	10.1		21.0		54.9	5.65	15.95	127.60
Cefi	Cement Finishers	9.65	77.20	5.9		21.0		50.7	4.90	14.55	116.40
Elec	Electricians	11.15	89.20	4.0		26.0		53.8	6.00	17.15	137.20
Elev	Elevator Constructors	11.30	90.40	5.5		26.0		55.3	6.25	17.55	140.40
Eqhv	Equipment Operators, Crane	11.75	94.00	7.2		24.0		55.0	6.45	18.20	145.60
Eqmd	Equipment Operators	9.45	75.60	7.2		24.0		55.0	5.20	14.65	117.20
Eqmm	Equipment Mechanics	11.75	94.00	7.2		24.0		55.0	6.45	18.20	145.60
Glaz	Glaziers	9.75	78.00	7.9		21.0		52.7	5.15	14.90	119.20
Lath	Lathers	10.30	82.40	6.3		21.0		51.1	5.25	15.55	124.40
Mill	Millwrights	10.30	82.40	6.6		21.0		51.4	5.30	15.60	124.80
Pord	Painters	9.50	76.00	7.7		21.0		52.5	5.00	14.50	116.00
Pile	Pile Drivers	10.30	82.40	17.0		26.0		66.8	6.90	17.20	137.60
Plas	Plasterers	9.25	74.00	7.7		21.0		52.5	4.85	14.10	112.80
Plum	Plumbers	12.75	102.00	4.8		26.0		54.6	6.95	19.70	157.60
Rodm	Rodmen (Reinforcing)	7.75	62.00	16.8		24.0		64.6	5.00	12.75	102.00
Rofc	Roofers	10.40	83.20	18.2		21.0		63.0	6.55	16.95	135.60
Shee	Sheet Metal Workers	9.95	79.60	6.3		26.0		56.1	5.60	15.55	124.40
Spri	Sprinkler Installers	12.90	103.20	5.5		26.0		55.3	7.15	20.05	160.40
Stpi	Pipefitters	11.85	94.80	4.8		26.0		54.6	6.50	18.35	146.80
Ston	Stone Masons	9.25	74.00	7.6		21.0		52.4	4.85	4.10	112.80
Sswk	Structural Steel Erectors	12.25	98.00	19.3		24.0		67.1	8.20	20.45	163.60
Tilf	Flooring Installers	10.40	83.20	5.4		21.0		50.2	5.20	15.60	124.80
Trhv	Truck Drivers	8.10	64.80	8.6		21.0		53.4	4.35	12.45	99.60
Wrck	Wreckers	6.95	55.60	20.7		21.0		65.5	4.55	11.50	92.00

Figure 4.5

5.1 Structural Metals		CREW	MAKEUP	DAILY OUTPUT	MAN-HOURS	UNIT
2210	Rectangular structural tubing, 5" x 3"	E-2	1 Foreman (outside)	58	.966	Ea.
			4 Struc. Steel Workers			
			1 Equipment Oper. (crane)			
			1 Equipment Oper. Oiler			
			1 Crane, 90 Ton			
2220	6" x 4"			54	1.037	Ea.
2230	8" x 4"			54	1.037	Ea.
2240	10" x 6"			50	1.120	Ea.
2250	12" x 8"	↓	↓	48	1.167	Ea.
3600	Prefabricated fireproof with steel jackets and one coat					
3611	shop paint, 2 to 4 hour rated	E-2	1 Foreman (outside)	27,000	.002	Lb.
			4 Struc. Steel Workers			
			1 Equipment Oper. (crane)			
			1 Equipment Oper. Oiler			
			1 Crane, 90 Ton			
300	LIGHT FRAMING, angle framing, 4" and larger	E-4	1 Foreman (outside)	3,000	.011	Lb.
			3 Struc. Steel Workers			
			1 Gas Weld. Mach., 300AMP			
0450	Less than 4" angles			1,800	.018	Lb.
0600	Channel framing, 8" and larger	↓	↓	3,500	.009	Lb.
0650	Less than 8" channels			2,000	.016	Lb.
1000	Continuous slotted channel framing system, minimum	2 Sswk	2 Struc. Steel Workers	2,400	.007	Lb.
1200	Maximum	"	"	1,600	.010	Lb.
1301	Cross bracing rods	E-3	1 Foreman (outside)	700	.034	Lb.
			1 Struc. Steel Worker			
			1 Welder			
			1 Gas Weld. Mach., 300AMP			
			1 Torch, Gas & Air			
1330	Angle, 5" x 5" x 3/8"	↓	↓	2,800	.009	Lb.
1350	Hanging lintels, average			850	.028	Lb.
1380	Roof frames, 3'-0" square, 5' span	E-2	1 Foreman (outside)	4,200	.013	Lb.
			4 Struc. Steel Workers			
			1 Equipment Oper. (crane)			
			1 Equipment Oper. Oiler			
			1 Crane, 90 Ton			
1401	Tie rod, 1-1/2" to 4" diameter, with turnbuckle	2 Sswk	2 Struc. Steel Workers	800	.020	Lb.
1650	Tubular aluminum framing for window wall, minimum			600	.027	Lb.
1800	Maximum	↓	↓	500	.032	Lb.
350	PRE-ENGINEERED STEEL BUILDINGS					
0100	Building shell above the foundations with 26 ga. colored					
0111	Roofing and siding, minimum	E-2	1 Foreman (outside)	1,800	.031	S.F.Flr.
			4 Struc. Steel Workers			
			1 Equipment Oper. (crane)			
			1 Equipment Oper. Oiler			
			1 Crane, 90 Ton			
0200	Maximum	"	"	1,000	.056	S.F.Flr.
0801	Accessory items: add to the basic building above					
1000	Eave overhang, 2' wide, 26 ga., with soffit	E-2	1 Foreman (outside)	360	.156	L.F.
			4 Struc. Steel Workers			
			1 Equipment Oper. (crane)			
			1 Equipment Oper. Oiler			
			1 Crane, 90 Ton			
1200	4 ft. wide without soffit			300	.187	L.F.
1300	With soffit			250	.224	L.F.
1500	6 ft. wide without soffit			250	.224	L.F.
1600	With soffit			200	.280	L.F.
1800	Entrance canopy incl. frame, 4' x 4'			25	2.240	Ea.
1900	4' x 8'			19	2.947	Ea.
2100	End wall roof overhang, 4 ft. wide without soffit			850	.066	L.F.
2200	With soffit	↓	↓	500	.112	L.F.

Figure 4.6

1. Rental, lease or ownership costs. These costs may be determined based up on hourly, daily, weekly, monthly or annual increments. These fees or payments only buy the "right" to use the equipment.
2. Operating costs. Once the "right" of use is obtained, costs are incurred for actual use, or operation. These costs include fuel, lubrication, maintenance and parts.

Equipment costs as described above do not include the labor expense of operators. However, some cost books and suppliers may include the operator in the quoted price for equipment as an "operated" rental cost. The estimator must be aware of what is and what is not included.

Quotations for equipment rental or lease costs can be obtained from local dealers and suppliers, or even from manufacturers. These costs can fluctuate and should be updated regularly. Ownership costs must be determined within a company. There are many considerations beyond the up-front purchase price; these facts must be taken into account when figuring the cost of owning equipment. Interest rates and amortization schedules should be studied prior to the purchase. Insurance costs, storage fees, maintenance, taxes and licenses, all added together, can become a significant percentage of the cost of owning equipment. These costs must be anticipated prior to purchase in order to properly manage the ownership.

When purchasing equipment, the owner should be aware of some basic principles of accounting (or hire a good accountant). In particular, various methods of depreciation (a way of quantifying loss of value to the owner over time) can have varied effects at tax time.

Figure 4.7 shows the effects of three "textbook" examples of depreciation methods: "Straight Line", "Sum of Years Digit", and "Declining Balance". Notice that different dollar amounts are depreciated in different years. These are very simplistic examples. A tax planning strategy should be developed in order to determine the appropriate and most advantageous method. An accountant should be consulted due to the current, complicated, ever-changing tax laws. The possibilities of accelerated methods, investment tax credits and other incentives should also be considered.

Depreciation Strategies for Equipment-Based upon a $15,000 Purchase Price with No Allowance for Salvage.

Year	Methods of Depreciation		
	Straight Line	Sum of Years Digit	Declining Balance
1	$ 3,000	$ 5,000	$ 6,000.00
2	3,000	4,000	3,600.00
3	3,000	3,000	2,160.00
4	3,000	2,000	1,296.00
5	3,000	1,000	777.60
Total	$15,000	$15,000	$13,833.60

Figure 4.7

Equipment ownership costs apply to both leased and owned equipment. The operating costs of equipment, whether rented, leased or owned, are available from the following sources (listed in order of reliability):

1. The company 's own records.
2. Annual cost books containing equipment operating costs, such as *Building Construction Cost Data.*
3. Manufacturers' estimates.
4. Textbooks dealing with equipment operating costs.

These operating costs consist of fuel, lubrication, expendable parts replacement, minor maintenance, transportation and mobilizing costs. For estimating purposes, the equipment ownership and operating costs should be listed separately. In this way, the decision to rent, lease or purchase can be decided project by project.

There are two commonly used methods for including equipment costs in a construction estimate. The first is to include the equipment as a part of the construction task for which it is used. In this case, costs are included in each line item as a separate unit price. The advantage of this method is that costs are allocated to the division or task that actually incurs the expense. As a result, more accurate records can be kept for each construction component. The disadvantage of this method occurs in the pricing of equipment (e.g., tower crane, personnel hoist, etc.) that may be used by many different trades for different tasks. Duplication of costs can occur in this instance.

The second method for including equipment costs in the estimate is to keep all such costs separate and to include them in Division 1 as a part of Project Overhead. The advantage of this method is that all equipment costs are grouped together, and that items used by all trades are included (without duplication). The disadvantage is that for future estimating purposes, equipment costs will be known only by job and not by unit of construction. Under these circumstances, omissions can easily occur.

Whichever method is used, the estimator must be consistent, and must be sure that all equipment costs are included, but not duplicated. The estimating method should be the same as that chosen for cost monitoring and accounting, so that the data will be available for future projects.

Subcontractors: In essence, subcontractor quotations should be solicited and analyzed in the same way as material quotes. A primary concern is that the bid covers the work as per plans and specifications, and that all appropriate work alternates and allowances are included. Any exclusions should be clearly stated and explained. If the bid is received verbally, a form such that in Figure 4.1 will help to assure that all is included. Any unique scheduling or payment requirements must be noted and evaluated prior to submission of the prime bid. Such requirements could affect or restrict the normal progress of the project, and should therefore be known in advance.

The estimator should note how long the subcontract bid will be honored. This time period usually varies from 30 to 90 days and is often included as a condition in complete bids. The general contractor may have to define the time limits of the prime bid based upon certain subcontractors. The estimator must also note any escalation clauses that may be included in subcontractor bids.

Reliability is another factor to be considered when soliciting and evaluating subcontractor bids. Reliability cannot be measured or priced until the project is actually under construction. Most general contractors stay with the same subcontractors for just this reason. A certain unspoken communication exists in these established relationships and usually has a positive effect on the performance of the work. Such familiarity, however, can often erode the competitive nature of bidding. To be competitive with the prime bid, the estimator should always obtain comparison subcontract prices, whether these prices come from another subcontractor or are prepared by the estimator.

The estimator should question and verify the bonding capability and capacity of unfamiliar subcontractors. Taking such action may be necessary when bidding in a new location. Other than word of mouth, these inquiries may be the only way to confirm subcontractor reliability.

For major subcontract items such as mechanical, electrical, and conveying systems, it may be necessary to make up spread sheets in order to tabulate inclusions and omissions. This procedure ensures that all cost considerations are included in the ''adjusted'' quotation. Time permitting, the estimator should make a takeoff and price these major subcontract items to compare with the sub-bids. If time does not permit a detailed takeoff, the estimator should at least budget the work. A Systems Estimate is ideal for this purpose.

Project Overhead: Project overhead includes those items as specified in Division 1 – General Requirements. It also includes those items required for the actual construction of the project, but not necessarily applicable to another specific UCI division. As seen in Figures 4.2 and 4.3, project overhead covers items from project supervision to clean-up, from temporary utilities to permits. All may not agree that certain items (such as equipment or scaffolding) should be included as Project Overhead, and might prefer to list such items in another division. Ultimately, it is not important, *where* each item is incorporated into the estimate but that *every item is included somewhere*.

Project overhead often includes time-related items; equipment rental, supervisory labor, and temporary utilities are examples. The cost for these items depends upon the duration of the project. A preliminary schedule should, therefore, be developed *prior* to completion of the estimate so that time-related items can be properly counted. This will be further discussed in Chapter 5.

Bond requirements for a project are usually specified in the General Conditions portion of the specification. Costs for bonds are based on total project costs and are determined at the estimate summary stage. A discussion of different types of bonds is included below.

Indirect Costs
The direct costs of a project must be itemized, tabulated and totalled before the indirect costs can be applied to the estimate. The indirect costs are almost always defined as a percentage of direct costs and include:

1. Sales tax (if required)
2. Office or Operating Overhead (vs. Project Overhead)
3. Profit
4. Contingencies
5. Bonds (often included as Project Overhead)

Sales Tax: Sales tax varies from state to state and often from city to city within a state (see Figure 4.8). Larger cities may have a sales tax in addition to the state sales tax. Some localities also impose separate sales taxes on labor and equipment.

When bidding takes place in unfamiliar locations, the estimator should check with local agencies regarding the amount, and the method of payment of sales tax. Local authorities may require owners to withhold payments to out-of-state contractors until payment of all required sales tax has been verified. Sales tax is often taken for granted or even omitted and, as can be seen in Figure 4.8, can be as much as 7.9% of material costs. Indeed, this can represent a significant portion of the project's total cost. Conversely, some clients and/or their projects may be tax exempt. If this fact is unknown to the estimator, a large dollar amount for sales tax might be needlessly included in a bid.

Office or Operating Overhead: Office overhead, or the cost of doing business, is perhaps one of the main reasons why so many contractors are unable to realize a profit, or even to stay in business. If a contractor does not know the costs of operating the business, then, more than likely, these costs will not be recovered. Many companies survive, and even turn a profit, by simply adding a certain percentage for overhead to each job, without knowing how the percentage is derived or what is included. When annual volume changes significantly, whether by increase or decrease, the previously used percentage for overhead may no longer be valid. Often when such a volume change occurs, the owner finds that the company is not doing as well as before and cannot determine the reasons. Chances are, overhead costs are not being fully recovered. As an example, Figure 4.9 lists office costs and expenses for a "typical" construction company for a year. It is assumed that the anticipated annual volume of the company is $10 million. Each of the items is described briefly below:

Sales Tax Percentages on Materials by State (as of 7/85)

State	Tax	State	Tax	State	Tax	State	Tax
Alabama	4%	Illinois	5%	Montana	0%	Rhode Island	6%
Alaska	0	Indiana	5	Nebraska	3.5	South Carolina	5
Arizona	5	Iowa	4	Nevada	5.75	South Dakota	4
Arkansas	4	Kansas	3	New Hampshire	0	Tennessee	5.5
California	6	Kentucky	5	New Jersey	6	Texas	4
Colorado	3	Louisiana	4	New Mexico	3.75	Utah	5.5
Connecticut	7.5	Maine	5	New York	4	Vermont	4
Delaware	0	Maryland	5	North Carolina	3	Virginia	4
District of Columbia	6	Massachusetts	5	North Dakota	4	Washington	7.9
Florida	5	Michigan	4	Ohio	5.5	West Virginia	5
Georgia	3	Minnesota	6	Oklahoma	3	Wisconsin	5
Hawaii	4	Mississippi	6	Oregon	0	Wyoming	3
Idaho	4	Missouri	6.125	Pennsylvania	6	Average	4.28%

Figure 4.8

ANNUAL MAIN OFFICE EXPENSES

Salaries

Owner	$ 70,000
Engineer/Estimator	45,000
Assistant Estimator	30,000
Project Manager	60,000
General Superintendent	50,000
Bookkeeper/Office Manager	24,000
Secretary/Receptionist	18,000

Office Worker Benefits

Workers Compensation		
FICA & Unemployment	37% of	
Medical Insurance	salaries	109,890
Miscellaneous Benefits		

Physical Plant

Office & Warehouse	30,000
Utilities	2,400
Telephone	3,000
Office Equipment	2,500
Office Supplies	1,000
Auto & Truck (4 vehicles)	24,000

Professional Services

Accounting	1,500
Legal	1,500
Advertising	4,000

Miscellaneous

Dues	1,000
Seminars & Travel	2,000
Entertainment & Gifts	3,000
Uncollected Receivables (2%)	200,000
TOTAL ANNUAL EXPENSES	**$682,790**

Figure 4.9

40

Owner: This includes only a reasonable base salary and does not include profits.

Engineer/Estimator: Since the owner is primarily on the road getting business, this is the person who runs the daily operation of the company and is responsible for estimating.

Assistant Estimator: This person is the "number cruncher", performing most quantity takeoffs and some pricing.

Project Manager: This is the person who runs the projects from the office and acts as the liason between the owner and the field.

General Superintendent: The general super's post is perhaps the most important position in the company. This person is responsible for the day-to-day progress of all projects, the nuts and bolts. All field personnel are handled by this person.

Bookkeeper/Office Manager: This is the overworked, underpaid person who actually runs the company. Every company must have one.

Secretary/Receptionist: This is the assistant to the person who actually runs the company.

Office Worker Insurance & Taxes: These costs are for main office personnel only and, for this example, are calculated as 37% of the total salaries based on the following breakdown:

Worker's Compensation	6%
FICA	7%
Unemployment	4%
Medical & other insurance	10%
Profit sharing, pension, etc.	10%
	37%

Physical Plant Expenses: Whether the office, warehouse and yard are rented or owned, roughly the same costs are incurred. Telephone and utility costs will vary depending on the size of the building and the type of business. Office equipment includes items such as copy machine rental, typewriters, etc.

Professional Services: Accountant fees are primarily for quarterly audits. Legal fees go towards collecting and contract disputes. Advertising includes the Yellow Pages, promotional materials, etc.

Miscellaneous: There are many expenses that could be placed in this category. Included in the example are just a few.

Uncollected Receivables: This amount can vary greatly, often depending upon the overall economic climate. Depending upon the timing of "uncollectables", cash flow can be severely restricted and can cause serious financial problems, even for large companies. Sound cash planning and anticipation of such possibilities can help to prevent severe repercussions.

While the office example used here is feasible within the industry, keep in mind that it is hypothetical and that conditions and costs vary from company to company.

In order for this company to stay in business without losses (profit is not yet a factor), not only must all direct construction costs be paid, but an additional $682,790 must be recovered during the year in order to operate the office. Remember that the anticipated volume is $10 million for the year. Office overhead costs, therefore, will be approximately 6.8%

of annual volume for this example. The most common method for recovering these costs is to apply this percentage to each job over the course of the year. The percentage may be applied in two ways:

1. Office overhead applied as a percentage of total project costs. This is probably the most commonly used method and is appropriate where material and labor costs are not separated.

2. Office overhead applied as a percentage of labor costs only . This method requires that labor and material costs be estimated separately. As a result material handling charges are also more easily applied.

The second method described above allows for more precision in the estimate. This method assumes that office expenses are more closely related to labor costs than to total project costs. For example, assume that two companies have the same total annual volume. Company A builds projects that are material intensive (90% materials, 10% labor). Company B builds projects that are very labor intensive (10% materials, 90% labor). In order to manage the large labor force, the office (and overhead) expense of Company B will be much greater than that of Company A. As a result, the applicable overhead percentage of B is greater than that of A based on equal annual volumes. For argument's sake, the overhead percentage of *total costs* for Company A is 3%, for Company B, 10%. If company A then gets projects that are more labor intensive, an allowance of 3% becomes too low and costs will not be recovered. Likewise, if Company B starts to build material intensive projects, 10% will be too high an overhead figure and bids may no longer be competitive. Office overhead may be more precisely recovered if it is figured as a percentage of labor costs, rather than total costs. In order to do this, a company must determine the ratio of material to labor costs from its historical records. In the example of Figure 4.9, assume that for this company, the ratio is 50/50. Total annual labor costs would be anticipated to be $4,508,500, as calculated below. As a percentage of labor, office overhead will be:

Annual Volume	$10,000,000
Anticipated Overhead (6.83%)	− 683,000
Anticipated Profit (3%)	− 300,000
Total Bare Costs	9,017,000
Labor (50% of Bare Costs)	$ 4,508,500

$$\frac{\$682,790}{\$4,508,500} = 15.14\%$$

By applying this overhead percentage (15.14%) to labor costs, the company is assured of recovering office expenses even if the ratio of material to labor changes significantly.

The estimator must also remember that if volume changes significantly then the percentage for office overhead should be recalculated for current conditions. The same is true if there are changes in office staff. Remember that salaries are the major portion of office overhead costs. It should be noted that a percentage is commonly applied to material costs, for handling, in addition to and regardless of the method of recovering office overhead costs. This percentage is more easily calculated if material costs are estimated and listed separately.

Profit: Determining a fair and reasonable percentage to be included for profit is not an easy task. This responsibility is usually left to the owner or chief estimator. Experience is crucial in anticipating what profit the market will bear. The economic climate, competition, knowledge of the project, and familiarity with the architect or owner, all affect the way in which profit is determined. Chapter 6 will show one way to mathematically determine profit margin based on historical bidding information. As with all facets of estimating, experience is the key to success.

Contingencies: Like profit, contingencies can be difficult to quantify. Especially appropriate in preliminary budgets, the addition of a contingency is meant to protect the contractor as well as to give the owner a realistic estimate of project costs.

A contingency percentage should be based on the number of "unknowns" in a project. This percentage should be inversely proportional to the amount of planning detail that has been done for the project. If complete plans and specifications are supplied, and the estimate is thorough and precise, then there is little need for a contingency. Figure 4.10, from Means' *Building Construction Cost Data*, lists suggested contingency percentages that may be added to an estimate based on the stage of planning and development.

As an estimate is priced and each individual item is rounded up or "padded", this is, in essence, adding a contingency (see Figure 3.4). This method can cause problems, however, because the estimator can never be quite sure of what is the actual cost and what is the "padding", or safety margin for each item. At the summary, the estimator cannot determine exactly how much has been included as a contingency for the whole project. A much more accurate and controllable approach is the precise pricing of the estimate and the addition of one contingency amount at the bottom line.

Bonds: Bonding requirements for a project will be specified in Division 1 – General Requirements, and will be included in the construction contract. Various types of bonds may be required. Listed below are a few common types:

> **Bid Bond.** A form of bid security executed by the bidder or principle and by a surety (bonding company) to guarantee that the bidder will enter into a contract within a specified time and furnish any required Performance or Labor and Material Payment bonds.

> **Completion Bond.** Also known as "Construction" or "Contract" bond. The guarantee by a surety that the construction contract will be completed and that it will be clear of all liens and encumbrances.

> **Labor and Material Payment Bond.** The guarantee by a surety to the owner that the contractor will pay for all labor and materials used in the performance of the contract as per the construction documents. The claimants under the bond are those having direct contracts with the contractor or any subcontractor.

1.1 Overhead		CREW	DAILY OUTPUT	UNIT	BARE COSTS			TOTAL INCL O&P
					MAT.	INST.	TOTAL	
02-001	**ARCHITECTURAL FEES** New construction, minimum			Project				4.90%
005	Maximum							16%
010	⑩ For alteration work, to $500,000, add to fee			↓				50%
015	Over $500,000, add to fee							25%
04-001	**CLEANING UP** After job completion, allow			Job Cost				.30%
003	Rubbish removal, see division 2.1-43							
005	Cleanup of floor area, continuous, per day	A-5	12	M.S.F.	1.49	25	26.49	38
010	Final	"	11.50	"	1.58	26	27.58	39
06-001	**CONSTRUCTION COST INDEX** (Div. 19) for 162 major U.S. and							
002	Canadian cities, total cost, min. (Greensboro NC)			%				81.00
005	Average							100%
010	Maximum (Anchorage, AK)			↓				134.10
08-001	㊿ **CONSTRUCTION ECONOMIES**							
09-001	**CONSTRUCTION MANAGEMENT FEES** $1,000,000 job, minimum			Project				4.50%
005	Maximum							7.50%
030	$5,000,000 job, minimum			↓				2.50%
035	Maximum							4%
10-001	⑨ **CONSTRUCTION TIME** Requirements							
11-001	**CONTINGENCIES** Allowance to add at conceptual stage			Project				15%
005	Schematic stage							10%
010	Preliminary working drawing stage			↓				7%
015	Final working drawing stage							2%
12-001	⑬ ⑰ **CONTRACTOR EQUIPMENT** See division 1.5							
14-001	**CREWS** For building construction, see p. viii-xxiv							
010								
15-001	**ENGINEERING FEES** Educational planning consultant, minimum			Project				.50%
010	Maximum			"				2.50%
020	⑪ Electrical, minimum			Contract				4.10%
030	Maximum							10.10%
040	Elevator & conveying systems, minimum							2.50%
050	Maximum							5%
060	Food service & kitchen equipment, minimum							8%
070	Maximum							12%
080	Landscaping & site development, minimum							2.50%
090	Maximum							6%
100	Mechanical (plumbing & HVAC), minimum			↓				4.10%
110	Maximum							10.10%
120	Structural, minimum			Project				1%
130	Maximum			"				2.50%
16-001	**HISTORICAL COST INDEXES** (Div. 19) Back to 1942							
18-001	**INSURANCE** Builders risk, standard, minimum			Job Cost				.10%
005	Maximum							.50%
020	② All-risk type, minimum							.12%
025	Maximum			↓				.68%
040	Contractor's equipment floater, minimum			Value				.50%
045	Maximum			"				2.50%
060	Public liability, average			Job Cost				.82%
061								
080	⑦ Workers' compensation & employer's liability, average							
085	by trade, carpentry, general			Payroll	10.10%			
090	Clerical				.57%			
095	Concrete				8.77%			
100	Electrical				4%			
105	Excavation				6.87%			
110	Glazing				7.90%			
115	Insulation			↓	7.35%			

Figure 4.10

44

Performance Bond. (1) A guarantee that a contractor will perform a job according to the terms of the contracts. (2) A bond of the contractor in which a surety guarantees to the owner that the work will be performed in accordance with the contract documents. Except where prohibited by statute, the performance bond is frequently combined with the labor and material payment bond. Figure 4.11 shows typical average rates for performance bonds for building construction.

Surety Bond. A legal instrument under which one party agrees to answer to another party for the debt, default or failure to perform of a third party.

Building Construction Contract Amount	Average Cost Performance Bonds
First $ 500,000 bid	$9.00 per M
Next 2,000,000 bid	$ 4,500 plus $5.85 per M
Next 2,500,000 bid	16,200 plus 4.90 per M
Next 2,500,000 bid	28,450 plus 4.20 per M
Over 7,500,000 bid	38,950 plus 4.10 per M

Performance Bond Rates
The table shows examples of performance bond rates for jobs scheduled to be completed in about 24 months. The rates are "preferred" rates which are offered to contractors that the bonding company considers financially sound and capable of doing the work.

Contractors should prequalify through a bonding company agency before submitting a bid on a contract which requires a bond. This is only an example. Costs will vary by company, location and project type.

Figure 4.11

The Paperwork

At the pricing stage of the estimate, there is typically a large amount of paperwork that must be assembled, analyzed and tabulated. Generally, the information contained in this paperwork is covered by the following major categories:

- Quantity takeoff sheets for all general contractor items (Figure 3.1)
- Material supplier written quotations
- Material supplier telephone quotations (Figure 4.1)
- Subcontractor written quotations
- Equipment supplier quotations
- Cost Analysis or Consolidated Cost Analysis Sheets (Figures 4.12 and 4.13)
- Estimate Summary Sheet (Figures 4.14, 4.15 and 4.16)

A system is needed to efficiently handle this mass of paperwork and to ensure that everything will get transferred (and only once) from the quantity takeoff to the cost analysis sheets. Some general rules for this procedure are:

- Write on only one side of any document where possible.
- Code each sheet with a large division number in a consistent place, preferably near one of the upper corners.
- Use Telephone Quotation forms for uniformity in recording prices received from any source, not only telephone quotes.
- Document the source of every quantity and price.
- Keep each type of document in its pile (Quantities, Material, Subcontractors, Equipment) filed in order by division number.
- Keep the entire estimate in one or more compartmented folders.
- When an item is transferred to the cost analysis sheet, check it off.
- If gross subcontractor quantities are known, pencil in the resultant unit prices to serve as a guide for future projects.

All subcontract costs should be properly noted and listed separately. These costs contain the subcontractor's markups, and will be treated differently from other direct costs when the estimator calculates the general contractor's overhead, profit and contingency allowance.

After all the unit prices, subcontractor prices, and allowances have been entered on the Cost Analysis sheets, the costs are extended. In making the extensions, ignore the cents column and round all totals to the nearest dollar. In a column of figures, the cents will average out and will not be of consequence. Indeed, for budget-type estimates, the extended figures could be rounded to the nearest $10, or even $100, with the loss of only a small amount of precision. Finally, each subdivision is added and the results checked, preferably by someone other than the person doing the extensions.

It is important to check the larger items for order of magnitude errors. If the total subdivision costs are divided by the building area, the resultant square foot cost figures can be used to quickly pinpoint areas that are out of line with expected square foot costs.

The takeoff and pricing method as discussed has been to utilize a Quantity Sheet for the material takeoff (see Figure 3.1), and to transfer the data to a Cost Analysis form for pricing the material, labor, and subcontractor items (see Figure 4.12).

MEANS COST ANALYSIS

PROJECT		SHEET NO.
LOCATION		ESTIMATE NO.
ARCHITECT		DATE
QUANTITIES BY	PRICES BY:	EXTENSIONS BY:	CHECKED BY:

DESCRIPTION	QUANTITY	UNIT	MATERIAL		LABOR		EQUIPMENT		SUBCONTRACT	
			UNIT COST	TOTAL	UNIT COST	TOTAL	UNIT COST	TOTAL	UNIT COST	TOTAL

Figure 4.12

An alternative to this method is a consolidation of the takeoff task and pricing on a single form. An example, the Consolidated Cost Analysis Form, is shown in Figure 4.13. The same sequences and recommendations for completing the Quantity Sheet and Cost Analysis form are to be followed when using the Consolidated Cost Analysis form to price the estimate.

The Estimate Summary

When the pricing of all direct costs is complete, the estimator has two choices: all further price changes and adjustments can be made on the Cost Analysis or Consolidated Estimate sheets, *or* total costs for each subdivision can be transferred to an Estimate Summary sheet so that all further price changes, until bid time, will be done on one sheet.

Unless the estimate has a limited number of items, it is recommended that costs be transferred to an Estimate Summary sheet. This step should be double-checked since an error of transposition may easily occur. Pre-printed forms can be useful. A plain columnar form, however, may suffice.

If a company has certain standard listings that are used repeatedly, it would save valuable time to have a custom Estimate Summary sheet printed with the items that need to be listed. The Estimate Summary in Figures 4.14 and 4.15 is an example of a commonly used form. The printed UCI division and subdivision headings act as a checklist to assure that all required costs are included. Figure 4.16 is a Condensed Estimate Summary form. Appropriate column headings or categories for any estimate summary form are:

1. Material
2. Labor
3. Subcontractor (can also be used for Equipment)
4. Total

As items are listed in the proper columns, each category is added and appropriate markups applied to the total dollar values. Generally, the sum of each column has different percentages added near the end of the estimate for the indirect costs:

1. Sales tax
2. Overhead
3. Profit
4. Contingencies

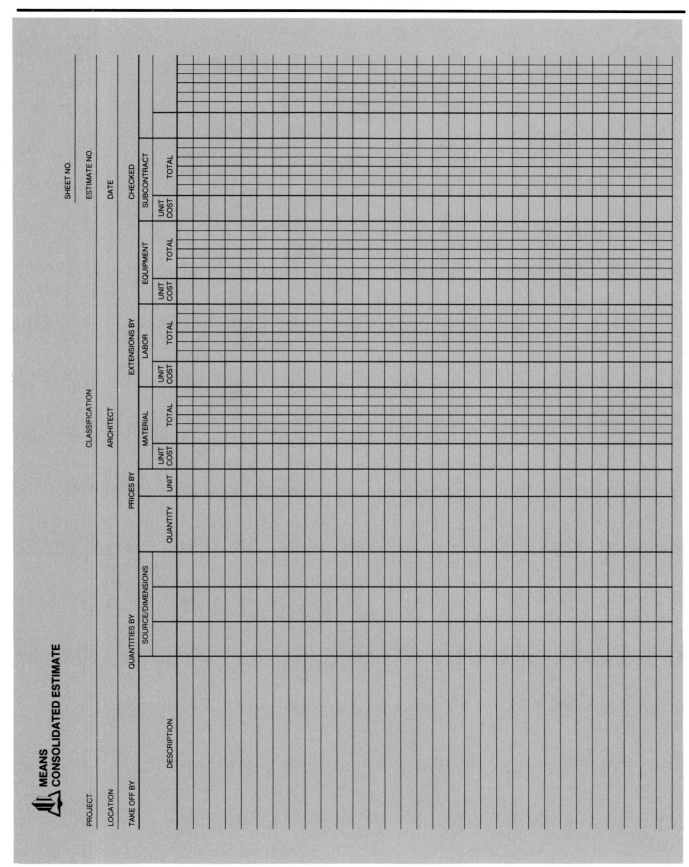

Figure 4.13

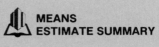

MEANS ESTIMATE SUMMARY

		SHEET NO.
PROJECT		ESTIMATE NO.
LOCATION	TOTAL AREA/VOLUME	DATE
ARCHITECT	COST PER S.F./C.F.	NO. OF STORIES
PRICES BY:	EXTENSIONS BY:	CHECKED BY:

DIV.	DESCRIPTION	MATERIAL	LABOR	EQUIPMENT	SUBCONTRACT	TOTAL
1.0	**General Requirements**					
	Insurance, Taxes, Bonds					
	Equipment & Tools					
	Design, Engineering, Supervision					
2.0	**Site Work**					
	Site Preparation, Demolition					
	Earthwork					
	Caissons & Piling					
	Drainage & Utilities					
	Paving & Surfacing					
	Site Improvements, Landscaping					
3.0	**Concrete**					
	Formwork					
	Reinforcing Steel & Mesh					
	Foundations					
	Superstructure					
	Precast Concrete					
4.0	**Masonry**					
	Mortar & Reinforcing					
	Brick, Block, Stonework					
5.0	**Metal**					
	Structural Steel					
	Open-Web Joists					
	Steel Deck					
	Misc. & Ornamental Metals					
	Fasteners, Rough Hardware					
6.0	**Carpentry**					
	Rough					
	Finish					
	Architectural Woodwork					
7.0	**Moisture & Thermal Protection**					
	Water & Dampproofing					
	Insulation & Fireproofing					
	Roofing & Sheet Metal					
	Siding					
	Roof Accessories					
8.0	**Doors, Windows, Glass**					
	Doors & Frames					
	Windows					
	Finish Hardware					
	Glass & Glazing					
	Curtain Wall & Entrances					
	PAGE TOTALS					

Figure 4.14

DIV.	DESCRIPTION	MATERIAL	LABOR	EQUIPMENT	SUBCONTRACT	TOTAL
	Totals Brought Forward					
9.0	**Finishes**					
	Studs & Furring					
	Lath, Plaster & Stucco					
	Drywall					
	Tile, Terrazzo, Etc.					
	Acoustical Treatment					
	Floor Covering					
	Painting & Wall Coverings					
10.0	**Specialties**					
	Bathroom Accessories					
	Lockers					
	Partitions					
	Signs & Bulletin Boards					
11.0	**Equipment**					
	Appliances					
	Dock					
	Kitchen					
12.0	**Furnishings**					
	Blinds					
	Seating					
13.0	**Special Construction**					
	Integrated Ceilings					
	Pedestal Floors					
	Pre Fab Rooms & Bldgs.					
14.0	**Conveying Systems**					
	Elevators, Escalators					
	Pnuematic Tube Systems					
15.0	**Mechanical**					
	Pipe & Fittings					
	Plumbing Fixtures & Appliances					
	Fire Protection					
	Heating					
	Air Conditioning & Ventilation					
16.0	**Electrical**					
	Raceways					
	Conductors & Grounding					
	Boxes & Wiring Devices					
	Starters, Boards & Switches					
	Transformers & Bus Duct					
	Lighting					
	Special Systems					
	Subtotals					
	Sales Tax %					
	Overhead %					
	Subtotal					
	Profit %					
	Adjustments/Contingency					
	TOTAL BID					

Figure 4.15

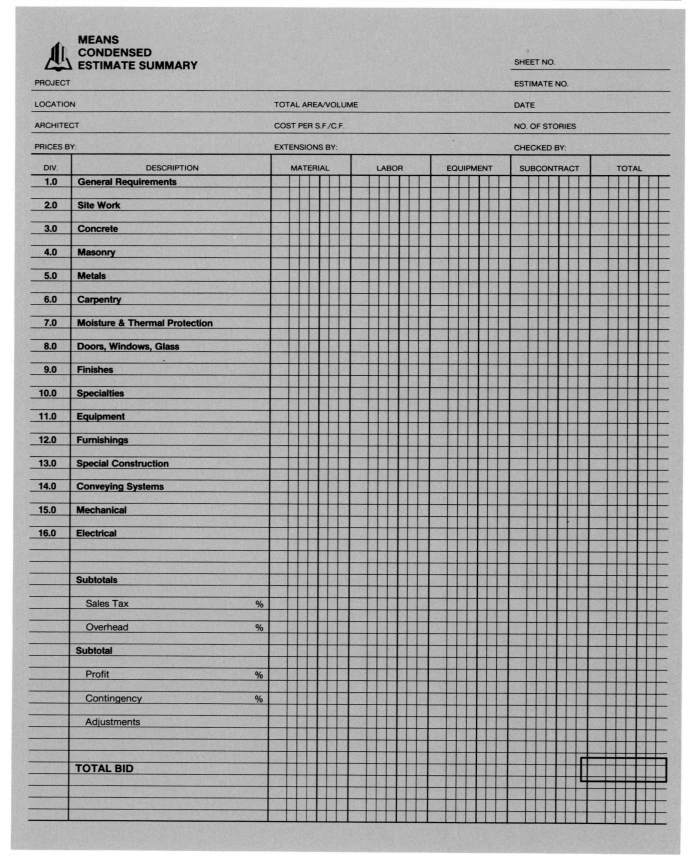

Figure 4.16

Chapter 5
PRE-BID
SCHEDULING

Chapter 5
PRE-BID SCHEDULING

The need for planning and scheduling is clear once the contract is signed and work commences on the project. However, some scheduling is also important during the bidding stage for the following reasons:

1. To determine if the project can be completed in the allotted or specified time.
2. To determine the time requirements for general conditions items, such as supervision, field office, and watchman.
3. To determine when the building will be enclosed in order to anticipate possible temporary heat and power requirements.

The schedule produced prior to bidding may be a simple bar chart or network diagram that includes overall quantities, probable delivery times and available manpower. Network scheduling methods, such as the Critical Path Method (CPM) and the Precedence Chart simplify prebid scheduling because they do not require scaled diagrams.

In the CPM Diagram, the activity is represented by the arrow. The Precedence Diagram, on the other hand, shows the activity in a node with arrows used to denote precedence relationships between the activities. The precedence arrows may be used in different configurations to represent the sequential relationships between activities. Examples of CPM and Precedence diagrams are shown in Figures 5.1 and 5.2, respectively. In both systems, duration times are indicated along each path. The sequence of activities requiring the most total time represents the shortest possible time in which those activities may be completed.

For example, in Figure 5.1, activities A, B, and C require 20 successive days for completion before activity G can begin. Activity paths for D and E, and for F are shorter and can be easily fit into the 20 day sequence. Therefore, this 20 day sequence is the shortest possible time for completion of these activities before activity G can begin.

Past experience or a prepared rough schedule may suggest that the allotted time specified in the bidding documents is insufficient to complete the required work. In such cases, a more comprehensive schedule should be produced prior to bidding; this schedule should include the calculations for added overtime or premium time work costs required to meet the completion date.

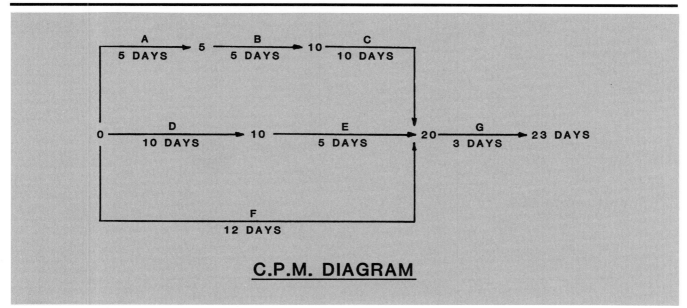

C.P.M. DIAGRAM

Figure 5.1

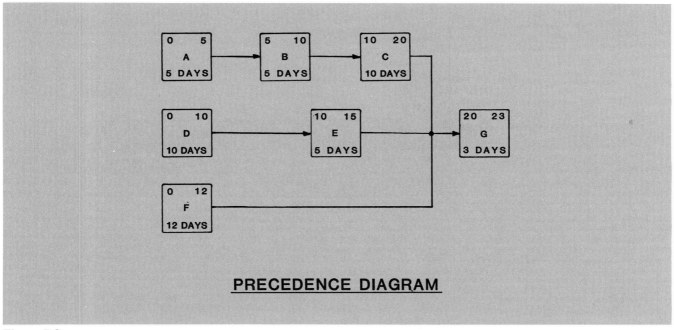

PRECEDENCE DIAGRAM

Figure 5.2

The following simple example is of a 100' x 200', four-story flat plate building with a basement and 25' square bays. It is based on the data listed below.

Description	Quantity / Output	Duration
Earthwork:		
Bulk Excavation	$\dfrac{7228\ CY}{1000\ CY/Day}$	7 Days
Footing Excavation	$\dfrac{1300\ CY}{200\ CY/Day}$	7 Days
Backfill Bulk	$\dfrac{1300\ CY}{240\ CY/Day}$	5 Days
Backfill Footings	$\dfrac{770\ CY}{240\ CY/Day}$	3 Days
Forms:		
Spread and Continuous Footings	$\dfrac{5894\ SF}{400\ SF/Day}$	15 Days
Walls and Pilasters	$\dfrac{10,176\ SF}{600\ SF/Day}$	17 Days

Figure 5.3 shows a preliminary schedule for excavation and the foundation. Note that a one day duration time has been added to the estimated time to complete the forming operation for both the footings and walls. The established duration time to excavate, form, reinforce and place the concrete for the foundation is 32 days, not including a factor for weather.

Our next major category on the schedule is the poured-in-place concrete structure. Because of the large amount of formwork required, a rough schedule may help to produce a more reliable quotation. The most efficient and economical quantity of the forms and number of uses can be determined. Assume the specifications require seven days curing time for the concrete slabs before the forms may be stripped and the slabs reshored. Also assume a twelve man carpenter crew is available with additional laborers to support the carpenters. Durations for each task are developed from derived quantities, productivity rates and assumed crew sizes. The calculations are shown in Figure 5.4.

A preliminary schedule may be developed to determine the minimum time requirements for forming, reinforcing and placing the concrete. The schedule will also help determine how many sets of forms are required for the most efficient use in the specified curing time. Figure 5.5 is an example of this kind of preliminary schedule.

Repeating the cycle for the roof slab and assuming that one set of floor forms (enough for one floor of the building) is available, the structure would take approximately sixty-eight working days to complete with no allowance for weather. A *quick*, rough estimate of time to erect the same structure may be derived by using the formula below. Exercise care when using the quick method to estimate the duration times of activities that may be overlapped or done concurrently. Crew output is the product of the output per man per day times the number of men.

$$\frac{\text{Form Area}}{\text{Crew Output}} + \frac{\text{Final Reinf.}}{\text{Duration}} + \frac{\text{Final Conc.}}{\text{Duration}} = \text{Total Duration}$$

$$\frac{25{,}060 \text{ SFCA}}{1080 \text{ SF/Day}} + \frac{75{,}200 \text{ SFCA}}{1680 \text{ SF/Day}} + 2 \text{ Days} + 1 \text{ Day} = 71 \text{ Days}$$

(first floor)　　　(upper floors)

Only the final reinforcing and concrete durations are included because previous durations are not limiting activities. If the same formula is applied to the foundations, approximate total duration time can be determined as follows:

$$\frac{5894 \text{ SFCA}}{400 \text{ SF/Day}} + \frac{10{,}176 \text{ SFCA}}{600 \text{ SF/Day}} + 1 \text{ Day} + 1 \text{ Day} = 34 \text{ Days}$$

To complete the schedule, probable duration times are derived from the estimated quantities for the remaining divisions of the estimate. The precedence format works well for the preliminary schedules because of the advantage of using arrow placement to show precedence relationships between activities. The relationships between activity nodes (rectangles) can be shown with the arrow configurations as in Figure 5.6.

The computations used in precedence schedules can become complicated. Finish-to-start connectors with lag times are convenient and make calculations easier. The polygons on the diagram are used to show logical delivery times for materials, allowing adequate turn-around time for shop drawings.

Once the preliminary schedule has been developed using a no-scale network diagram depicting activity dependencies, a simple bar chart for the project can be drawn to condense the information.

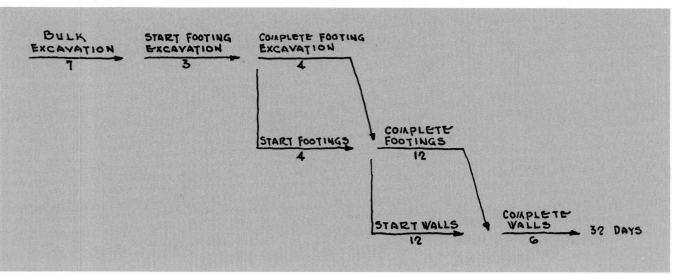

Figure 5.3

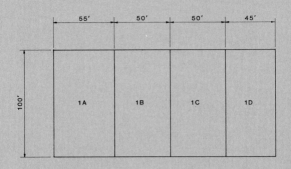

Placement Plan

Duration Derivation

Columns Each

Forms $\dfrac{90 \text{ sfca Ea}}{60 \text{ sfca/day x 12 Carp}} = .125$ days Ea (1st use)

Reinforcing $\dfrac{.13 \text{ tons Ea}}{.375 \text{ tons/day x 4 Rdmn}} = .087$ days Ea

Concrete $\dfrac{1.67 \text{ cy Ea}}{11.5 \text{ cy/day x 8 men}} = .018$ days Ea

Slab Forms 1st Floor

"1A"   Slab Form   5500 sfca
          Edge Form   168 sfca
          $\overline{\phantom{168 \text{ sfca}}}$
          $\dfrac{5668 \text{ sfca}}{90 \text{ sfca/day x 12 Carp}} = 5$ days

"1B & 1C" Slab Form   5000 sfca
           Edge Form   158 sfca
           $\overline{\phantom{158 \text{ sfca}}}$
           $\dfrac{5158 \text{ sfca}}{90 \text{ sfca/day x 12 Carp}} = 4.78$ days

           Columns 10 Ea x .125 days Ea $= \dfrac{1.25 \text{ days}}{6.0 \text{ days}}$

"1D"   Slab Form   4500 sfca
           Edge Form   150 sfca
           $\overline{\phantom{150 \text{ sfca}}}$
           $\dfrac{4650 \text{ sfca}}{90 \text{ sfca/day x 12 Carp}} = 4.3$ days

           Columns 10 Ea x .125 days Ea $= \dfrac{1.25 \text{ days}}{6.0 \text{ days}}$

Reinforcing @ 2.8 psf

"1A" $\dfrac{5500 \text{ sf x 2.8 psf}}{2000}$ $\dfrac{7.7 \text{ tons}}{.7 \text{ tons/day x 5 Rdmn}} = 2$ days

"1B & 1C" $\dfrac{5000 \text{ sf x 2.8 psf}}{2000}$ $\dfrac{7.0 \text{ tons}}{.7 \text{ tons/day} = 5 \text{ Rdmn}} = 2$ days

"1D" $\dfrac{4500 \text{ sf x 2.8 psf}}{2000}$ $\dfrac{6.3 \text{ tons}}{.7 \text{ tons/day x 5 Rdmn}} = 2$ days

Concrete (Average)

$\dfrac{150 \text{ cy}}{16.5 \text{ cy/day x 9 men}} = 1$ day

2nd & 3rd Floors & Roof

Forms "A" $\dfrac{5668 \text{ sfca}}{140 \text{ sfca/day x 12 Carp}} = 4$ days

"B & C" $\dfrac{5158 \text{ sfca}}{140 \text{ sfca/day x 12 Carp}} = 3$ days

"D" $\dfrac{4650 \text{ sfca}}{140 \text{ sfca/day x 12 Carp}} = 3$ days

Reinforcing and concrete placement durations are the same as the 1st floor.

Figure 5.4

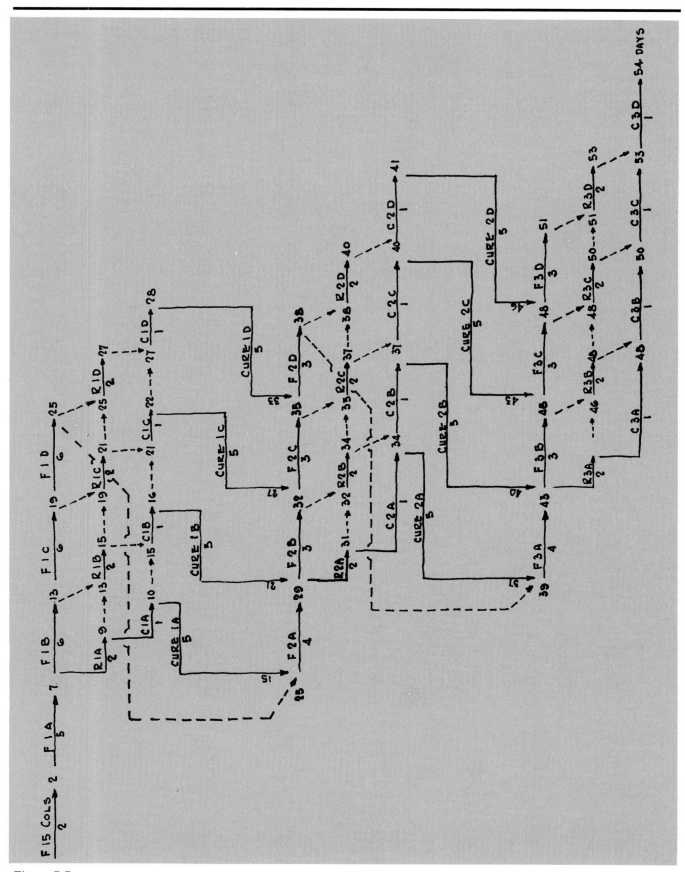

Figure 5.5

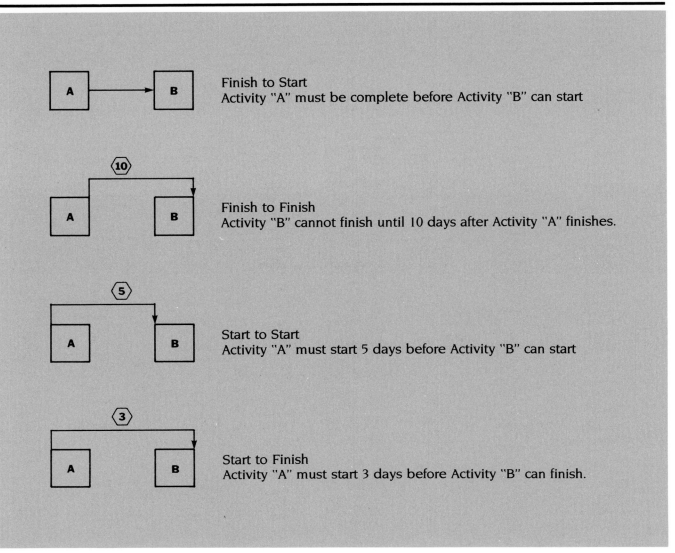

Figure 5.6

Chapter 6
UPON COMPLETING THE ESTIMATE

Chapter 6
UPON COMPLETING THE ESTIMATE

Bidding Strategies

The goal of most contractors is to make as much money as possible on each job, but more importantly, to maximize return on investment on an annual basis. This means making more money by taking fewer jobs at a higher profit.

One measure of successful bidding is how much money is "left on the table," the difference between the low bid and next lowest bid. The contractor who consistently takes jobs by a wide margin below the next bidder, is obviously not making as much money as possible. Information on competitive public bidding is accessible. Thus, the amount of money left on the table is easily determined and can be the basis for fine-tuning a future bidding strategy.

Since a contractor cannot physically bid every type of job in a geographic area, a selection process must determine which projects should be bid. This selective process should begin with an analysis of the strengths and weaknesses of the contractor. The following items that must be considered as objectively as possible are:

- Individual strengths of the company's top management.
- Management experience with the type of construction involved, from top management to project superintendents.
- Cost records adequate for the appropriate type of construction.
- Bonding capability and capacity.
- Size of projects with which the company is "comfortable".
- Geographic area that can be managed effectively.
- Unusual corporate assets such as:
  - Specialized equipment availability
  - Reliable and timely cost control systems
  - Strong balance sheet

Market Analysis

Most contractors tend to concentrate on one, or a few, fairly specialized types of construction. From time to time, the company should step back and examine the total picture of the industry they are serving. During this process, the following items should be carefully analyzed:

- Historical trend of the market segment.
- Expected future trend of the market segment.
- Geographic expectations of the market segment.

- Historical and expected competition among other builders.
- Risk involved in the particular market segment.
- Typical size of projects in this market.
- Expected return on investment from the market segment.

If several of these areas are experiencing a downturn, then it might be appropriate to examine an alternate market.

Certain steps should be taken to develop a bid strategy for a particular market. The first is to obtain the bid results of jobs in the prospective geographic area. These results should be set up on a tabular basis. This is fairly easy to do in public jobs since the bid results are normally published (or at least available) from the agency responsible for the project. In private work this step is very difficult, since the bid results are not normally divulged by the owner.

For example, assume a public market where all bid prices and the total number of bidders is known. For each "type" of market sector, create a chart showing the percentage left on the table versus the total number of bidders. When the median figure (percent left on the table) for each number of bidders is connected with a smooth curve, the usual shape of the curve is shown in Figure 6.1.

The exact shape and magnitude of the amounts left on the table will depend on how much risk is involved with that type of work. If the percentages left on the table are high, then the work can be assumed to be very risky; if the percentages are low, the work is probably not too risky.

Bidding Analysis

If a company has been bidding in a particular market, certain information should be collected and recorded as a basis for a bidding analysis. The percentage left on the table should be tabulated, along with the number of bidders for the projects in that market on which the company was the low bidder. By probability, half the bids should be above the median line and half below. (See Figure 6.1.) If more than half are below the line, the company is doing well; if more than half are above, the bidding strategy should be examined. Once the bidding track record for the company has been established, the next step is to reduce the historical percentage left on the table. One method is to create a chart showing, for instance, the

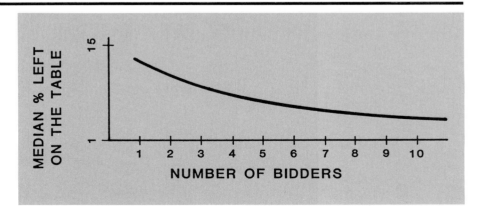

Figure 6.1

last ten jobs on which the company was low bidder and the dollar spread between the low and second lowest bid. Next, rank the percentage differences from one to ten (one being the smallest and ten being the largest left on the table). An example is shown in Figure 6.2.

The company's "costs" ($17,170,000) are derived from the company's low bid ($18,887,000) assuming a 10% profit ($1,717,000). The "second bid" is the next lowest bid. The "difference" is the dollar amount between the low bid and the second bid. The differences are then ranked based on the percentage of job "costs" left on the table for each.

$$\text{Median \% Difference} = \frac{5.73 + 6.44}{2} = 6.09\%$$

From Figure 6.2, the median percentage left on the table is 6.09%. To maximize the potential returns on a series of competitive bids, a useful formula for pricing profit is needed. The following formula has proven effective.

$$\text{Normal Profit \%} + \frac{\text{Median \% Difference}}{2} = \text{Adjusted Profit \%}$$

$$10.00 \quad + \quad \frac{6.09}{2} \quad = \quad 13.05\%$$

Now apply this adjusted profit % to the same list of ten jobs as shown in Figure 6.3. Note that the job "costs" remain the same, but that the low bids have been revised. Compare the bottom line results of Figure 6.2 to those of Figure 6.3 based on the two profit margins, 10% and 13.05%, respectively.

Total volume *drops* from $18,887,000 to $17,333,900.

Job No.	"Cost"	Low Bid	Second Bid	Difference	% Diff	% Rank	Profit (Assumed at 10%)
1	$ 918,000	$ 1,009,800	$1,095,000	$ 85,200	9.28	10	$ 91,800
2	1,955,000	2,150,500	2,238,000	87,500	4.48	3	195,500
3	2,141,000	2,355,100	2,493,000	137,900	6.44	6	214,100
4	1,005,000	1,105,500	1,118,000	12,500	1.24	1	100,500
5	2,391,000	2,630,100	2,805,000	174,900	7.31	8	239,100
6	2,782,000	3,060,200	3,188,000	127,800	4.59	4	278,200
7	1,093,000	1,202,300	1,282,000	79,700	7.29	7	109,300
8	832,000	915,200	926,000	10,800	1.30	2	83,200
9	2,372,000	2,609,200	2,745,000	135,800	5.73	5	237,200
10	1,681,000	1,849,100	2,005,000	155,900	9.27	9	168,100
	$17,170,000	$18,887,000		$1,008,000			$1,717,000 = 10% of Cost

Figure 6.2

Net profits *rise* from $1,717,000 to $2,000,900.

Profits rise while volume drops. If the original volume is maintained or even increased, profits would rise even faster. Note how this occurs. By determining a reasonable increase in profit margin, the company has, in effect, raised all bids. By doing so, the company loses two jobs to the second bidder (jobs 4 and 8 in Figure 6.3).

A positive effect of this volume loss is reduced exposure to risk. Since the profit margin is higher, the remaining eight jobs collectively produce more profit than the ten jobs based on the original, lower profit margin. From where did this money come? The money "left on the table" has been reduced from $1,008,000 to $517,100. The whole purpose is to systematically lessen the dollar amount difference between the low bid and the second low bid. This is a hypothetical approach based upon a number of assumptions:

- Bidding must be done within the same market in which data for the analysis was gathered.
- Economic conditions should be stable from the time the data is gathered until the analysis is used in bidding. If conditions change, use of such an analysis should be reviewed.
- Each contractor must make roughly the same number of bidding mistakes. For higher numbers of jobs in the sample, this requirement becomes more probable.
- The company must bid additional jobs if total annual volume is to be maintained or increased. Likewise, if net total profit margin is to remain constant, fewer jobs need be bid.

Even though the accuracy of this strategy is based on these criteria, the concept is valid and can be applied, with appropriate and reasonable judgment, to many bidding situations.

Job No.	Company's "Cost"	Revised Low Bid	Second Bid	Adj. Diff.	Profit [10% + 3.05%]	Total
1	$ 918,000	$ 1,037,800	$1,095,000	$ 57,200	$ 91,800 + $28,000	$ 119,800
2	1,955,000	2,210,100	2,238,000	$ 27,900	$195,500 + 59,600	255,100
3	2,141,000	2,420,400	2,493,000	$ 72,600	214,100 + 65,300	279,400
4	(1,005,000)	(1,136,100)	1,118,000 (L)	—	100,500 + 30,600	0
5	2,391,000	2,703,000	2,805,000	102,000	239,100 + 72,900	312,000
6	2,782,000	3,145,100	3,188,000	42,900	278,200 + 84,900	363,100
7	1,093,000	1,235,600	1,282,000	46,400	109,300 + 33,300	142,600
8	(832,000)	(940,600)	926,000 (L)	—	83,200 + 25,400	0
9	2,372,000	2,681,500	2,745,000	63,500	237,200 + 72,300	309,500
10	1,681,000	1,900,400	2,005,000	104,600	168,100 + 51,300	219,400
	$15,333,000	$17,333,900		$517,100		$2,000,900

Figure 6.3

Cost Control and Analysis

An internal accounting system should be used by the contractor to logically allocate and track the gathered costs of a construction project. With this information, a cost analysis can be made about each cost center. The cost centers of a project are the major items of construction (e.g., concrete) that can be subdivided by component. This subdivision should coincide with the system and methods of the quantity takeoff. The major purposes of cost control and analysis are:

- To provide management with a system to monitor costs and progress.
- To provide cost feedback to the estimator(s).
- To determine the costs of change orders.
- To be used as a basis for submitting payment requisitions to the owner or his representative.
- To manage cash flow.

A cost control system should be established that is uniform throughout the company and from job to job. The various costs are then consistently allocated. The cost control system might be simplified with a code that provides a different designation for each part of a component cost. The following information should be recorded for each component cost.

- Labor charges in dollars and man-hours, summarized from weekly time cards, are distributed by code.
- Equipment rental costs are derived from purchase orders or from weekly charges from an equipment company.
- Material charges are determined from purchase orders.
- Appropriate subcontractor charges are allocated.
- Job overhead items may be listed separately or by component.
- Quantities completed to date must also be recorded in order to determine unit costs.

Each component of costs – labor, materials and equipment – is now calculated on a unit basis by dividing the quantity to date (percentage complete) into the component cost to date. This procedure establishes the actual unit costs to date. The remaining quantities of each component to be completed should be estimated at a unit cost approximating the costs to date. The actual costs to date and the predicted costs are added together to represent the anticipated costs at the end of the project. Typical forms that may be used to develop a cost control system are shown in Figures 6.4 to 6.7.

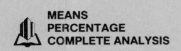

MEANS PERCENTAGE COMPLETE ANALYSIS

PAGE _____

PROJECT _____ ARCHITECT _____ DATE _____

LOCATION _____ BY _____ FROM _____ TO _____

NO.	DESCRIPTION	ACTUAL OR ESTIMATED	TOTAL PROJECT	THIS PERIOD		PERCENT TOTAL TO DATE											
				QUANTITY	%	QUANTITY	10	20	30	40	50	60	70	80	90	100
		ACTUAL														
		ESTIMATED														
		ACTUAL														
		ESTIMATED														
		ACTUAL														
		ESTIMATED														
		ACTUAL														
		ESTIMATED														
		ACTUAL														
		ESTIMATED														
		ACTUAL														
		ESTIMATED														
		ACTUAL														
		ESTIMATED														
		ACTUAL														
		ESTIMATED														
		ACTUAL														
		ESTIMATED														
		ACTUAL														
		ESTIMATED														
		ACTUAL														
		ESTIMATED														
		ACTUAL														
		ESTIMATED														
		ACTUAL														
		ESTIMATED														
		ACTUAL														
		ESTIMATED														
		ACTUAL														
		ESTIMATED														
		ACTUAL														
		ESTIMATED														
		ACTUAL														
		ESTIMATED														
		ACTUAL														
		ESTIMATED														
		ACTUAL														
		ESTIMATED														
		ACTUAL														
		ESTIMATED														
		ACTUAL														
		ESTIMATED														

Figure 6.4

67

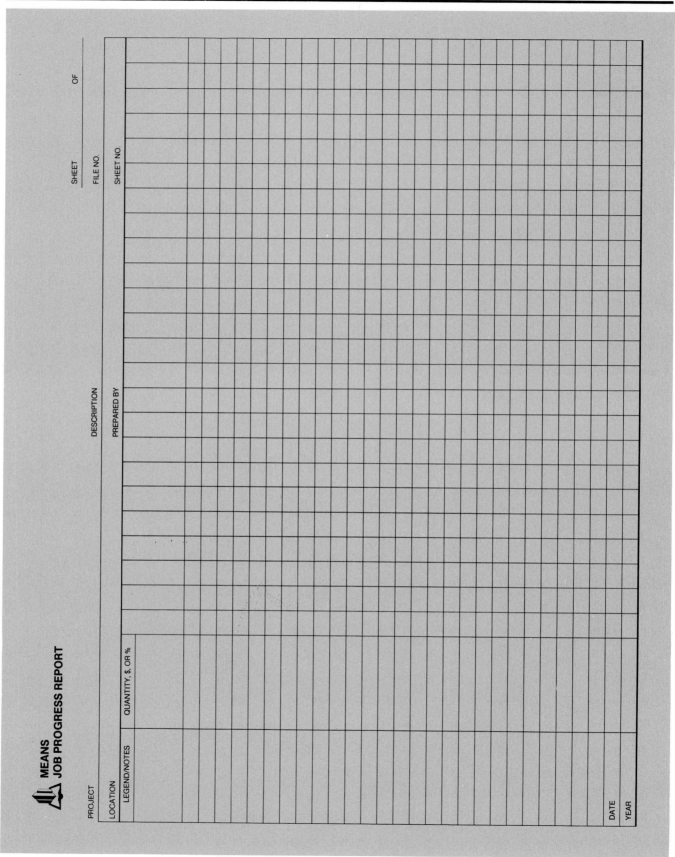

Figure 6.5

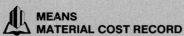

MEANS
MATERIAL COST RECORD

SHEET NO. _____

PROJECT _____

LOCATION _____

DATE	NUMBER	VENDOR/DESCRIPTION	QTY.	UNIT PRICE	AMOUNT	QTY.	UNIT PRICE	AMOUNT	QTY.	UNIT PRICE	AMOUNT

Figure 6.6

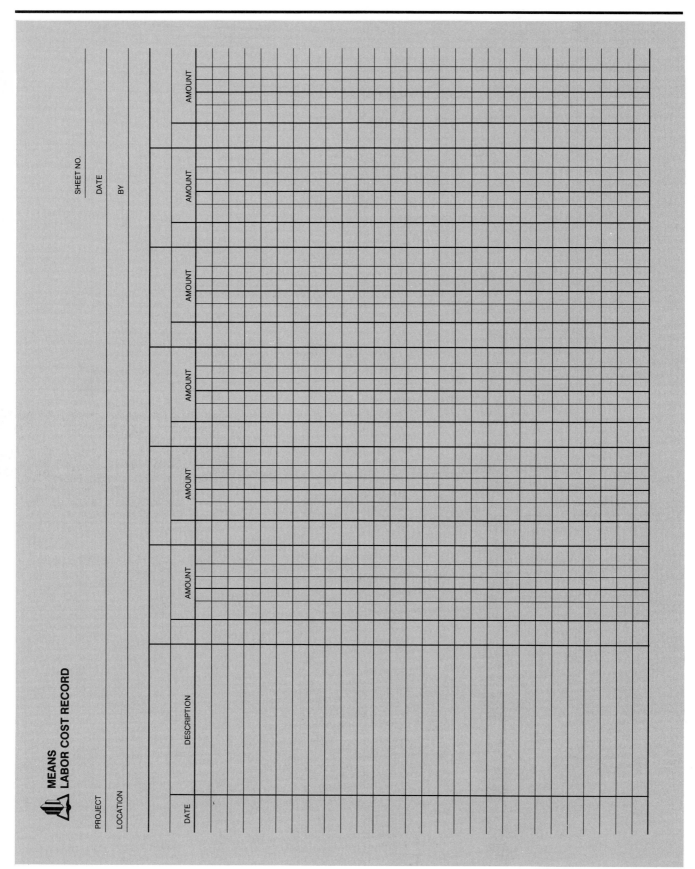

Figure 6.7

70

The analysis of cost centers serves as a useful management tool, providing information on a current basis. Immediate attention is attracted to any center that is operating at a loss. Management can concentrate on this item in an attempt to make it profitable or to minimize the expected loss.

The estimating department can use the unit costs developed in the field as background information for future bidding purposes. Particularly useful are unit labor costs and unit man-hours (productivity) for the separate components. Current unit man-hours and labor costs should be integrated into the accumulated historical data.

Frequently, items are added to or deleted from the contract. Accurate cost records are an excellent basis for determining cost changes that result from change orders and requests for additional work.

Cost records require the determination of completed quantities in order to calculate unit costs. These calculations are used to determine the percent completion of each cost center. This percentage is used to calculate the billing of completed items for payment requisitions.

A cost system is only as good as the people responsible for coding and recording the required information. Simplicity is the key word. Do not try to break down the code into very small items unless there is a specific need. Continuous updating of costs is important so that operations which are not in control can be immediately brought to the attention of management.

Productivity and Efficiency

When using a cost control system such as the one described above, the derived unit costs should reflect standard practices. Productivity should be based on a five day, eight hour per day (during daylight hours) work week unless a company's requirements are particularly and normally unique. Installation costs should be derived using normal minimum crew sizes, under normal weather conditions, during the normal construction season. Costs and productivity should also be based on familiar types of construction.

All unusual costs incurred or expected should be separately recorded for each component of work. For example, an overtime situation might occur on every job and in the same proportion. In this case, it would make sense to carry the unit price adjusted for the added cost of premium time. Likewise, unusual weather delays, strike activity or owner/architect delays should have separate, identifiable cost contributions; these are applied as isolated costs to the activities affected by the delays. This procedure serves two purposes:

- To identify and separate the cost contribution of the delay so that job estimates will not automatically include an allowance for these "non-typical" delays, and
- To serve as a basis for an extra compensation claim and/or as justification for reasonable extension of the job.

The use of long-term overtime on almost any construction job is counter-productive; that is, the longer the period of overtime, the lower the actual production rate. There have been numerous studies conducted which come up with slightly different numbers, but all have the same conclusion.

As illustrated in Figure 6.8, there can be a difference between the actual payroll cost per hour and the *effective* cost per hour for overtime work. This is due to the reduced production efficiency with the increase in weekly hours beyond 40. This difference between actual and effective cost is for overtime over a prolonged period. Short-term overtime does not result in as great a reduction in efficiency, and in such cases, cost premiums would approach the payroll costs rather than the effective hourly costs listed in Figure 6.8. As the total hours per week are increased on a regular basis, more time is lost by absenteeism and the accident rate increases.

As an example, assume a project where workers are working 6 days a week, 10 hours per day. From Figure 6.8 (based on productivity studies), the actual productive hours are 51.1 hours. This represents a theoretical production efficiency of 51.1/60 or 85.2%.

Depending upon the locale, overtime work is paid at time and a half or double time. In both cases, the overall *actual* payroll cost (including regular and overtime hours) is determined as follows:

For time and a half:

$$\frac{40 \text{ reg. hrs.} + (20 \text{ overtime hrs.} \times 1.5)}{60 \text{ hrs}} = 1.167$$

Based on 60 hrs., the payroll cost per hour will be 116.7% of the normal rate at 40 hrs. per week.

Efficiency and Cost Effects of Prolonged Overtime Work								
Days per Week	Hours per Day	Total Hours Worked	Actual Productive Hours	Production Efficiency	Payroll Cost per Hour Overtime after 40 hrs.		Effective Cost per Hour Overtime after 40 hrs.	
					@ 1-1/2 times	@ 2 times	@ 1-1/2 times	@ 2 times
5	8	40	40.0	100.0%	100.0%	100.0%	100.0%	100.0%
	9	45	43.4	96.5	105.6	111.1	109.4	115.2
	10	50	46.5	93.0	110.0	120.0	118.3	129.0
	11	55	49.2	89.5	113.6	127.3	127.0	142.3
	12	60	51.6	86.0	116.7	133.3	135.7	155.0
6	8	48	46.1	96.0	108.3	116.7	112.8	121.5
	9	54	48.9	90.6	113.0	125.9	124.7	139.1
	10	60	51.1	85.2	116.7	133.3	137.0	156.6
	11	66	52.7	79.8	119.7	139.4	149.9	174.6
	12	72	53.6	74.4	122.2	144.4	164.2	194.0
7	8	56	48.8	87.1	114.3	128.6	131.1	147.5
	9	63	52.2	82.8	118.3	136.5	142.7	164.8
	10	70	55.0	78.5	121.4	142.9	154.5	181.8
	11	77	57.1	74.2	124.0	148.1	167.3	199.6
	12	84	58.7	69.9	126.2	152.4	180.6	218.1

Figure 6.8

For double time:

$$\frac{40 \text{ reg. hrs.} + (20 \text{ overtime hrs.} \times 2)}{60 \text{ hrs.}} = 1.33$$

Payroll cost will be 133% of the normal rate.

However, because the actual productive hours (and thus production efficiency) are reduced to 51.1 hours, the *effective* cost of overtime is:

For time and a half:

$$\frac{40 \text{ reg. hrs.} + (20 \text{ overtime hrs.} \times 1.5)}{51.1 \text{ hrs.}} = 1.37$$

Payroll cost will be 137% of the normal rate.

For double time:

$$\frac{40 \text{ reg. hrs.} + (20 \text{ overtime hrs.} \times 2)}{51.1 \text{ hrs.}} = 1.566$$

Payroll cost will be 156.6% of the normal rate.

Thus, when figuring overtime, the actual cost per unit of work will be higher than the apparent overtime payroll dollar increase, due to the reduced productivity of the longer work week. These calculations are true only for those pay costs which are determined by hours worked. Costs which are applied weekly or monthly, such as some fringe benefits, will not be similarly affected.

Retainage and Cash Flow

The majority of construction projects have some percentage of retainage held back by the owner until the job is complete. This retainage can range from 5% to as high as 15% or 20% in unusual cases. The most typical retainage is 10%. Since the profit on a given job may be less than the amount of withheld retainage, the contractor must wait longer before a positive cash flow is achieved than if there were no retainage.

Figures 6.9 and 6.10 are graphic and tabular representations of the projected cash flow for a small project. With this kind of projection, the contractor is able to anticipate cash needs throughout the course of the job. Note that at the eleventh of May, before the second payment is received, the contractor has paid out about $25,000 more than has been received. This is the maximum amount of cash (on hand or financed) that is required for the whole project. At this stage of planning, the contractor can determine if there will be adequate cash available or if a loan is needed. In the latter case, the expense of interest could be anticipated and included in the estimate. On larger projects, the projection of cash flow becomes crucial, because unexpected interest expense can quickly erode profit margin.

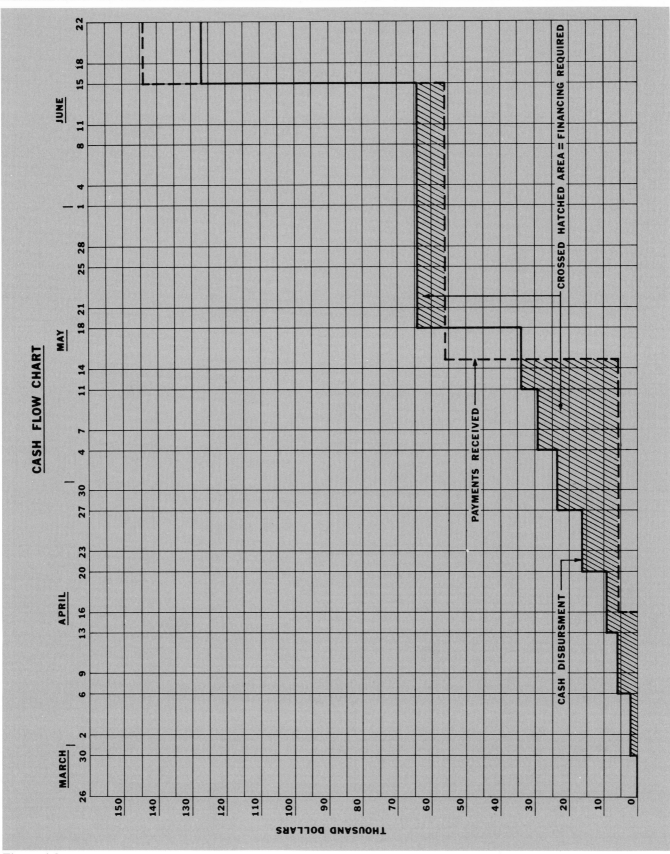

Figure 6.9

Figure 6.10

Date		Payroll Incl Taxes	Workers Comp	Monthly Billing	Retainage	Subs Billing + Payment	Retainage	Material Incl Taxes	Equip Incl Taxes	Payments	Accumulated Costs $
3-30	Payroll	1926	148								− 1926
3-30	monthly Billing			4558							
4-6	Payroll	3346	253								− 5172
4-13	Payroll	4197	311								− 9369
4-16	Payment									4558	− 4811
4-20	Pay Sub					708	506				− 5519
4-20	Pay material					708		515			− 6304
4-20	Pay Equipment								965		− 6999
4-30	Payroll	3827	275								− 10826
4-27	Payroll	4525	333								− 15351
4-30	monthly Billing			51330							
5-4	Payroll	5535	508			592	5104				− 20876
5-11	Payroll	3531	370								− 24407
5-15	Payment									51330	+ 26993
5-18	Payroll	2613	243								+ 24310
5-18	Pay Sub					5245		22118			+ 19065
5-18	Pay material										+ 3053
5-18	Pay Equipment								719		+ 3833
6-1	Final Billing			88883		48915	9816				
6-15	Payment									88883	+ 85051
6-15	Pay Subs					48915		12685			+ 36136
6-15	Pay material								738		+ 23451
6-15	Pay Equipment										+ 22713
		$ 29330	$ 2441	$ 1144771	16086	54868	6094	35318	2482	$ 1144771	

General Conditions
Permit   150 @300
Supervision- Carpenter Foreman 35 days @ $170
Temp. Power & Water
Temp. Office & Storage   6 wks @ $30
Clean Up Laborer   2 days @ $100

Cash
Retainage
Pay Workers Comp
Pay Subs Retainage
Gen. Conditions

Material Incl Taxes
22713
16086
38799
36358
60294
30204
7024
23340

The General Conditions section of the specifications usually explains the responsibilities of both the owner and the contractor with regard to billing and payments. Even the best planning and projections are contingent upon the owner paying requisitions as anticipated. There is an almost unavoidable adversary relationship between contractor and owner regarding payment during the construction process. However, it is in the best interest of the owner that the contractor be solvent so that delays, complications, and difficulties can be avoided prior to final completion of the project. The interest of both parties is best served if information is shared and communication is open. Both are working toward the same goal: the timely and successful completion of the project.

Life Cycle Costs

Life cycle costing is a valuable method of evaluating the total costs of an economic unit during its entire life. Regardless of whether the unit is a piece of excavating machinery or a manufacturing building, life cycle costing gives the owner an opportunity to look at the economic consequences of a decision. Today, the initial cost of a unit is often not the most important; the operation and maintenance costs of some building types far exceed the initial outlay. Hospitals, for example, may have operating costs within a three-year period that exceed the original construction costs.

Estimators are in the business of initial costs. But what about the other costs that affect any owner: taxes, fuel, inflation, borrowing, estimated salvage at the end of the facility's lifespan, and expected repair or remodeling costs. These costs that may occur at a later date need to be evaluated in advance. The thread that ties all of these costs together is the time value of money. The value of money today is quite different from what it will be tomorrow. $1,000 placed in a savings bank at 5% interest will, in four years, have increased to $1,215.50. Conversely, if $1,000 is needed four years from now, then $822.70 should be placed in an account today. Another way of saying the same thing is that at 5% interest, the value of $1,000 four years from now is only worth $822.70 today.

Using interest and time, future costs are equated to the present by means of a present worth formula. Standard texts in engineering economics have outlined different methods for handling interest and time. A present worth evaluation could be used, or all costs might be converted into an equivalent, uniform annual cost method.

As an example, assume that an excavating machine is purchased for $20,000. Hourly gas and oil charges will be $6.20. A major overhaul of the engine will be needed in three years at a cost of $4,000. After six years, the trade-in value will be $1,500. What is the total *present worth* of the machine over its six-year life if money is borrowed at 12%?

First Cost of the Machine:

Purchase Price =	$20,000.00
Total present worth of Operating and Maintenance @ $6.20/hour = 1,500 hours x $6.20 = $9,300/year x 4.111 (present worth of a uniform series of payment for six years) =	38,232.30
Present worth of a major overhaul three years from now = $4,000 x .7118 (time/value factor) =	2,847.20
Present worth of the salvage at the end of six years = $1,500 x 0.5066 (time/value factor) =	+ 759.90
The Total Present Worth of the Tractor	$61,839.40

If we consider the uniform annual costs of the machine, then (at 12% interest) the following happens:

The uniform annual cost of the initial investment ($20,000) x .24323 (capital recovery factor) =	$ 4,864.60
The uniform maintenance and operating costs =	9,300.00
The uniform cost of motor repair in the third year is the present worth times the capital recovery factor, $2,847 x .24323 =	692.52
The equivalent uniform cost of the salvage, $1,500 x .12323 (sinking fund factor) =	+ 184.85
Total Equivalent Uniform Annual Costs	$15,041.97

This is the same as if the total present worth was multiplied by the capital recovery factor: $61,839.40 x .24323 = $15,041.20. If the machine is used 1,500 hours per year, then the hourly base operating cost is approximately $10 per hour.

Another benefit of life cycle costing is having the ability to compare the equivalent uniform costs between two different machines. This comparison can help with the decision to rent or purchase.

Life cycle costs are not always determined easily. The initial investment and the operating costs can be estimated, and maintenance costs can be determined from past experience with similar machines; but anticipating a motor overhaul precisely or knowing the projected salvage price is difficult. Interest rates and time factors are critical in determining life cycle costs. By varying the time intervals and/or the interest rate when comparing the alternatives, a good investment might appear poor, or vice versa. It is therefore essential that realistic, accurate rates be used.

Chapter 7

USING MEANS' BUILDING CONSTRUCTION COST DATA

Chapter 7
USING MEANS' BUILDING CONSTRUCTION COST DATA

Users of Means *Building Construction Cost Data* are chiefly interested in obtaining quick, reasonable, average prices for building construction items. This is the primary purpose of the annual book – to eliminate guesswork when pricing unknowns. Many persons use the cost data, whether for bids or verification of quotations or budgets, without being fully aware of how the prices are obtained and derived. Without this knowledge, this vast resource is not being used to fullest advantage. In addition to the basic cost data, the book also contains a wealth of information to aid the estimator, the contractor, the designer and the owner to better plan and manage building construction projects. Productivity data is provided in order to assist with scheduling. National labor rates are analyzed. Tables and charts for location and time adjustments are included and help the estimator to tailor the prices to a specific location. And ultimately, the book is a list of line items for over 20,000 individual components of construction. This information, outlined in the Uniform Construction Index (UCI) division format, provides an invaluable checklist to the construction professional to assure that all required items are included in a project.

Format & Data

The major portion of *Building Construction Cost Data* is the Unit Price section. This is the primary source of unit cost data and is organized according to the 16 divisions of the UCI. This index was developed by representatives of all parties concerned with the building construction industry and has been adopted by the American Institute of Architects (AIA), the Associated General Contractors of America, Inc. (AGC) and the Construction Specifications Institute, Inc. (CSI).

Uniform Construction Index (UCI) Divisions:

Division 1 – General Requirements
Division 2 – Site Work
Division 3 – Concrete
Division 4 – Masonry

Division 5 – Metals
Division 6 – Wood & Plastics
Division 7 – Moisture-Thermal Control
Division 8 – Doors, Windows & Glass
Division 9 – Finishes
Division 10 – Specialties
Division 11 – Equipment
Division 12 – Furnishings
Division 13 – Special Construction
Division 14 – Conveying Systems
Division 15 – Mechanical
Division 16 – Electrical

In addition to the sixteen UCI divisions of the Unit Price section, Division 17, Square Foot and Cubic Foot Costs, presents consolidated data from over ten thousand five hundred actual reported construction projects and provides information based on total project costs as well as costs for major components. Division 18, Repair and Remodeling, presents cost data for many construction items commonly encountered in the maintenance and renovation of existing structures. Division 19, the City Cost Indexes, represents the compilation of construction data for 162 major U.S. and Canadian cities. A cost factor is given for each city, relative to the national average. The final section of the book, the Circle Reference Number section, provides supporting cost, design and reference information for the Unit Price section. Individual materials and construction methods are presented in depth and detail under Circle Reference Number headings.

The prices as presented in *Building Construction Cost Data* are national averages. Material and equipment costs are developed through annual contact with manufacturers, dealers, distributors and contractors throughout the United States. Means' staff of engineers is constantly updating prices and keeping abreast of changes and fluctuations within the industry. Labor rates are the national average of each trade as determined from union agreements from thirty major U.S. cities. Throughout the calendar year, as new wage agreements are negotiated, labor costs should be factored accordingly.

There are various factors and assumptions on which the costs, as presented in *Building Construction Cost Data*, have been based:

Quality – The costs are based on methods, materials and workmanship in accordance with U.S. Government standards and represent good, sound construction practice.

Overtime – The costs as presented, include *no* allowance for overtime. If overtime or premium time is anticipated, labor costs must be factored accordingly.

Productivity – The daily output figures are based on an eight hour workday, during daylight hours. The chart in Figure 6.8 shows that as the number of hours worked per day (over eight) increases, and as the days per week (over five) increase, production efficiency decreases. (See Chapter 6.)

Size of Project – Costs in *Building Construction Cost Data* are based on commercial and industrial buildings which cost $500,000 and up. Large residential projects are also included.

Local Factors — Weather conditions, season of the year, local union restrictions, and unusual building code requirements can all have a significant impact on construction costs. The availability of a skilled labor force, sufficient materials and even adequate energy and utilities will also affect costs. These factors vary in impact and are not dependent upon location. They must be reviewed for each project in every area.

In the presentation of prices in *Building Construction Cost Data*, certain rounding rules are employed to make the numbers easy to use without significantly affecting accuracy. The rules are used consistently and are as follows:

Prices		Rounded to nearest
From	To	
$ 0.01	$ 5.00	0.01
5.01	20.00	0.05
20.01	100.00	1.00
100.01	1,000.00	5.00
1,000.01	10,000.00	25.00
10,000.01	50,000.00	100.00
50,000.01	up	500.00

Unit Price Section

The Unit Price section of *Building Construction Cost Data* contains a great deal of information in addition to the unit cost for each construction component. Figure 7.1 is a typical page, showing costs for brick veneer. Note that prices are included for more than ten types of brick and ten bonding patterns and course types. In addition, each type and bond is priced per thousand brick as well as per square foot of wall area. The information and cost data is broken down and itemized in this way to provide not only for the most detailed pricing possible, but also to accommodate different methods of quantity takeoff and estimating.

Within each individual line item, there is a description of the construction component, information regarding typical crews designated to perform the work, and the daily output of each crew. Costs are presented bare, or unburdened, as well as with markups for overhead and profit. Figure 7.2 is a graphic representation of how to use the Unit Price section as presented in *Building Construction Cost Data*.

Line Numbers

Every construction item in the Means unit price cost data books has a unique line number. This line number acts as an address so that each item can be quickly located and/or referenced. The numbering system is based on the UCI classification by division. In Figure 7.2, note the bold number in reverse type, "3.1". This number represents the major UCI subdivision, in this case Formwork, of the major UCI Division 3 — Concrete. All 16 UCI divisions are organized in this manner. Within each subdivision, the data is broken down into major classifications. These

4.2 **Brick Masonry**		CREW	DAILY OUTPUT	UNIT	BARE COSTS			TOTAL INCL O&P
					MAT.	INST.	TOTAL	
030	Common face brick	B-9	1,200	S.F.	.15	.67	.82	1.09
040	Wire cut face brick	"	900	"	.15	.89	1.04	1.40
54-001	**STEPS** With select common at $205 per M	D-1	.30	M	243	975	1,218	1,650
56-001	**VENEER** 4" thick, sel. common, 8" x 2-2/3" x 4" @ $205/M (6.75/S.F.)	D-2	1.55	M	263	535	798	1,050
005	Standard 8" x 2-2/3" x 4", running bond, red face, $225 per M		1.50		285	550	835	1,100
010 (61)	Buff or gray face, brick at $260 per M (6.75/S.F.)		1.50		320	550	870	1,150
015	Full header every 6th course (7.88/S.F.)		1.45		320	570	890	1,175
020 (62)	English, full header every 2nd course (10.13/S.F.)		1.40		320	590	910	1,200
025	Flemish, alternate header every course (9.00/S.F.)		1.35		320	615	935	1,225
030 (59)	Flemish, alt. header every 6th course (7.13/S.F.)		1.45		320	570	890	1,175
032	Full headers throughout (13.50/S.F.)		1.40		320	590	910	1,200
034	Rowlock course (13.50 per S.F.)		1.35		320	615	935	1,225
036	Rowlock stretcher (4.50 per S.F.)		1.40		320	590	910	1,200
038	Soldier course (6.75 per S.F.)		1.35		320	615	935	1,225
040	Sailor course (4.50 per S.F.)		1.30		320	635	955	1,250
045	Glazed face, 8" x 2-2/3" x 4" $750 per M, running bond		1.40		825	590	1,415	1,750
047	Full header every 6th course (7.88 per S.F.)		1.35		825	615	1,440	1,775
050	Jumbo 12" x 4" x 6" running bond, $900 per M (3.00 per S.F.)		1.30		1,056	635	1,691	2,075
060	Norman 12" x 2-2/3" x 4" run. bond, $395 per M (4.50 per S.F.)		1.45		482	570	1,052	1,350
065	Norwegian 12" x 3-1/5" x 4" at $455 per M (3.75 per S.F.)		1.40		553	590	1,143	1,450
070	Economy 8" x 4" x 4" at $380 per M (4.50 per S.F.)		1.40		464	590	1,054	1,350
075	Engineer 8" x 3-1/5" x 4" at $265 per M (5.63 per S.F.)		1.45		332	570	902	1,175
080	Roman 12" x 2" x 4" at $470 per M (6.00 per S.F.)		1.50		549	550	1,099	1,400
085	SCR 12" x 2-2/3" x 6" at $555 per M (4.50 per S.F.)		1.40		668	590	1,258	1,575
090	Utility 12" x 4" x 4" at $650 per M (3.00 per S.F.)		1.35		766	615	1,381	1,725
092	8" x 8" x 4" at $930 per M (2.25 per S.F.)		.99		1,069	835	1,904	2,375
094	8" x 16" x 4" at $1820 per M (1.13 per S.F.)	▼	.51		2,057	1,625	3,682	4,575
101	For battered walls, add				30%			
102	For corbels, add				60%			
103	For curved walls, add				30%			
104	For pits and trenches, deduct			▼	20%			
105	Std., sel. common, 8" x 2-2/3" x 4" $205 per M (6.75 per S.F.)	D-2	230	S.F.	1.80	3.60	5.40	7.10
150	Standard 8" x 2-2/3" x 4", running bond, red face, @ $225 per M		220		1.95	3.76	5.71	7.50
155	Buff or gray face, brick at $260 per M (6.75 per S.F.)		220		2.15	3.76	5.91	7.75
160	Full header every 6th course (7.88 per S.F.)		185		2.50	4.48	6.98	9.15
165	English, full header every 2nd course (10.13 per S.F.)		140		3.25	5.90	9.15	12
170	Flemish, alter. header every course (9.00 per S.F.)		150		2.90	5.50	8.40	11.05
180	Flemish, alt. header every 6th course (7.13/S.F.)		205		2.30	4.04	6.34	8.30
182	Full headers throughout (13.50 per S.F.)		105		4.30	7.90	12.20	16
184	Rowlock course (13.50 per S.F.)		100		4.30	8.30	12.60	16.55
186	Rowlock stretcher (4.50 per S.F.)		310		1.45	2.67	4.12	5.40
188	Soldier course (6.75 per S.F.)		200		2.15	4.14	6.29	8.25
190	Sailor course (4.50 per S.F.)		290		1.45	2.86	4.31	5.65
195	Glazed face, brick at $750 per M, running bond		210		5.60	3.94	9.54	11.80
197	Full header every 6th course (7.88 per S.F.)		170		6.50	4.87	11.37	14.10
200	Jumbo 12" x 4" x 6" running bond, @ $900 per M (3.00 per S.F.)		435		3.15	1.90	5.05	6.20
205	Norman, 12" x 2-2/3" x 4" running bond, @ $395/M (4.50/S.F.)		320		2.15	2.59	4.74	6.05
210	Norwegian 12" x 3-1/5" x 4" at $455/M (3.75 per S.F.)		375		2.05	2.21	4.26	5.40
220	Economy 8" x 4" x 4" $380 per M (4.50 per S.F.)		310		2.10	2.67	4.77	6.10
230	Engineer 8" x 3-1/5" x 4" at $265 per M (5.63 per S.F.)		260		1.85	3.18	5.03	6.60
240	Roman 12" x 2" x 4" at $470 per M (6.00 per S.F.)		250		3.30	3.31	6.61	8.35
250	SCR 12" x 2-2/3" x 6" at $555 per M (4.50 per S.F.)		310		3	2.67	5.67	7.10
260	Utility 12" x 4" x 4" at $650 per M (3.00 per S.F.)		450		2.30	1.84	4.14	5.15
262	8" x 8" x 4" at $930 per M (2.25 per S.F.)		440		2.40	1.88	4.28	5.35
264	8" x 16" x 4" at $1820 per M (1.13 per S.F.)	▼	455		2.35	1.82	4.17	5.20
270	For cavity wall construction, add				15%			
280	For stacked bond, add				10%			
290	For interior veneer construction, add			▼	15%			

Figure 7.1

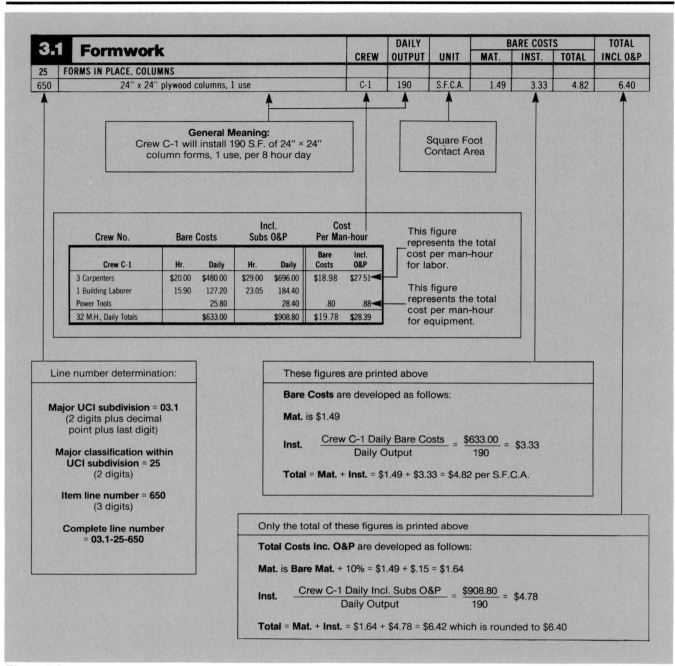

3.1 **Formwork**	CREW	DAILY OUTPUT	UNIT	BARE COSTS			TOTAL INCL O&P
				MAT.	INST.	TOTAL	
25 FORMS IN PLACE, COLUMNS							
650 24" x 24" plywood columns, 1 use	C-1	190	S.F.C.A.	1.49	3.33	4.82	6.40

General Meaning:
Crew C-1 will install 190 S.F. of 24" × 24" column forms, 1 use, per 8 hour day

Square Foot Contact Area

Crew C-1	Bare Costs		Incl. Subs O&P		Cost Per Man-hour	
	Hr.	Daily	Hr.	Daily	Bare Costs	Incl. O&P
3 Carpenters	$20.00	$480.00	$29.00	$696.00	$18.98	$27.51
1 Building Laborer	15.90	127.20	23.05	184.40		
Power Tools		25.80		28.40	.80	.88
32 M.H., Daily Totals		$633.00		$908.80	$19.78	$28.39

This figure represents the total cost per man-hour for labor.

This figure represents the total cost per man-hour for equipment.

Line number determination:

Major UCI subdivision = 03.1
(2 digits plus decimal point plus last digit)

Major classification within UCI subdivision = 25
(2 digits)

Item line number = 650
(3 digits)

Complete line number = 03.1-25-650

These figures are printed above

Bare Costs are developed as follows:

Mat. is $1.49

Inst. $\dfrac{\text{Crew C-1 Daily Bare Costs}}{\text{Daily Output}} = \dfrac{\$633.00}{190} = \$3.33$

Total = **Mat.** + **Inst.** = $1.49 + $3.33 = $4.82 per S.F.C.A.

Only the total of these figures is printed above

Total Costs Inc. O&P are developed as follows:

Mat. is **Bare Mat.** + 10% = $1.49 + $.15 = $1.64

Inst. $\dfrac{\text{Crew C-1 Daily Incl. Subs O&P}}{\text{Daily Output}} = \dfrac{\$908.80}{190} = \$4.78$

Total = **Mat.** + **Inst.** = $1.64 + $4.78 = $6.42 which is rounded to $6.40

Figure 7.2

major classifications are listed alphabetically and are designated by bold type for both numbers and descriptions. Each item, or line, is further defined by an individual number. As shown in Figure 7.2, the full line number for each item consists of: a major UCI subdivision number – a major classification number – an item line number. Each full line number describes a unique construction element. For example, in Figure 7.1, the line number for Norman brick veneer, running bond (per square foot) is 4.2-56-205.

Line Description

Each line has a text description of the item for which costs are listed. The description may be self-contained and all inclusive as is line 4.2-56-001 in Figure 7.1. If indented, the complete description for a line is dependent upon information provided above. All indented items are delineations (by size, color, material, etc.) or breakdowns of previously described items. An index is provided in the back of *Building Construction Cost Data* to aid in locating particular items.

Crew

For each construction element, (each line item), a minimum typical crew is designated as appropriate to perform the work. The crew may include one or more trades, foremen, craftsmen and helpers, and any equipment required for proper installation of the described item. If an individual trade installs the item using only hand tools, the smallest efficient number of tradesmen will be indicated (1 Carp, 2 Carp, etc.). Abbreviations for trades are shown in Figure 7.3. If more than one trade is required to install the item and/or if powered equipment is needed, a crew number will be designated (B-5, D-3, etc.). A complete listing of crews is presented in the Foreword pages of *Building Construction Cost Data* (see Figure 7.4). Each crew breakdown contains the following components:

1. Number and type of workers designated.
2. Number, size, and type of any equipment required.
3. Hourly labor costs listed two ways: bare (base rate including fringe benefits) and including installing contractor's overhead and profit (billing rate). See Figure 7.3.
4. Daily equipment costs, based on the weekly equipment rental cost divided by 5, plus the hourly operating cost, times 8 hours. This cost is listed two ways: as a bare cost and with a 10% percent markup to cover handling and management costs.
5. Labor and equipment are broken down further: cost per man-hour for labor, and cost per man-hour for the equipment.
6. The total daily labor man-hours for the crew.
7. The total bare costs per day for the crew, including equipment.
8. The total daily cost of the crew including the installing contractor's overhead and profit.

The total daily cost of the craftsmen involved or the total daily cost of the crew indicated is used to calculate the unit installation cost for each item (for both bare costs and cost including overhead and profit).

Abbr.	Trade	Base Rate Incl. Fringes		Workers' Comp. Ins.	Average Fixed Overhead	Subs Overhead	Subs Profit	Subs Total Overhead & Profit		Rate with Subs O & P	
		Hourly	Daily					%	Amount	Hourly	Daily
Skwk	Skilled Workers Average (35 trades)	$20.50	$164.00	9.3%	13.8%	12.8%	10%	45.9%	$ 9.40	$29.90	$239.20
	Helpers Average (5 trades)	15.55	124.40	9.8		13.0		46.6	7.25	22.80	182.40
	Foremen Average, Inside (50¢ over trade)	21.00	168.00	9.3		12.8		45.9	9.65	30.65	245.20
	Foremen Average, Outside ($2.00 over trade)	22.50	180.00	9.3		12.8		45.9	10.35	32.85	262.80
Clab	Common Building Laborers	15.90	127.20	10.1		11.0		44.9	7.15	23.05	184.40
Asbe	Asbestos Workers	22.75	182.00	7.7		16.0		47.5	10.80	33.55	268.40
Boil	Boilermakers	22.75	182.00	6.6		16.0		46.4	10.55	33.30	266.40
Bric	Bricklayers	20.50	164.00	7.6		11.0		42.4	8.70	29.20	233.60
Brhe	Bricklayer Helpers	16.00	128.00	7.6		11.0		42.4	6.80	22.80	182.40
Carp	Carpenters	20.00	160.00	10.1		11.0		44.9	9.00	29.00	232.00
Cefi	Cement Finishers	19.20	153.60	5.9		11.0		40.7	7.80	27.00	216.00
Elec	Electricians	22.40	179.20	4.0		16.0		43.8	9.80	32.20	257.60
Elev	Elevator Constructors	22.65	181.20	5.5		16.0		45.3	10.25	32.90	263.20
Eqhv	Equipment Operators, Crane or Shovel	21.05	168.40	7.2		14.0		45.0	9.45	30.50	244.00
Eqmd	Equipment Operators, Medium Equipment	20.60	164.80	7.2		14.0		45.0	9.25	29.85	238.80
Eqlt	Equipment Operators, Light Equipment	19.45	155.60	7.2		14.0		45.0	8.75	28.20	225.60
Eqol	Equipment Operators, Oilers	17.50	140.00	7.2		14.0		45.0	7.90	25.40	203.20
Eqmm	Equipment Operators, Master Mechanics	21.80	174.40	7.2		14.0		45.0	9.80	31.60	252.80
Glaz	Glaziers	20.15	161.20	7.9		11.0		42.7	8.60	28.75	230.00
Lath	Lathers	20.10	160.80	6.3		11.0		41.1	8.25	28.35	226.80
Marb	Marble Setters	20.10	160.80	7.6		11.0		42.4	8.50	28.60	228.80
Mill	Millwrights	20.75	166.00	6.6		11.0		41.4	8.60	29.35	234.80
Mstz	Mosaic and Terrazzo Workers	19.90	159.20	5.4		11.0		40.2	8.00	27.90	223.20
Pord	Painters, Ordinary	19.25	154.00	7.7		11.0		42.5	8.20	27.45	219.60
Psst	Painters, Structural Steel	20.00	160.00	27.0		11.0		61.8	12.35	32.35	258.80
Pape	Paper Hangers	19.50	156.00	7.7		11.0		42.5	8.30	27.80	222.40
Pile	Pile Drivers	20.10	160.80	17.0		16.0		56.8	11.40	31.50	252.00
Plas	Plasterers	19.90	159.20	7.7		11.0		42.5	8.45	28.35	226.80
Plah	Plasterer Helpers	16.50	132.00	7.7		11.0		42.5	7.00	23.50	188.00
Plum	Plumbers	22.55	180.40	4.8		16.0		44.6	10.05	32.60	260.80
Rodm	Rodmen (Reinforcing)	21.75	174.00	16.8		14.0		54.6	11.90	33.65	269.20
Rofc	Roofers, Composition	18.80	150.40	18.2		11.0		53.0	9.95	28.75	230.00
Rots	Roofers, Tile & Slate	18.95	151.60	18.2		11.0		53.0	10.05	29.00	232.00
Rohe	Roofer Helpers (Composition)	13.75	110.00	18.2		11.0		53.0	7.30	21.05	168.40
Shee	Sheet Metal Workers	22.70	181.60	6.3		16.0		46.1	10.45	33.15	265.20
Spri	Sprinkler Installers	23.25	186.00	5.5		16.0		45.3	10.55	33.80	270.40
Stpi	Steamfitters or Pipefitters	22.75	182.00	4.8		16.0		44.6	10.15	32.90	263.20
Ston	Stone Masons	20.30	162.40	7.6		11.0		42.4	8.60	28.90	231.20
Sswk	Structural Steel Workers	21.70	173.60	19.3		14.0		57.1	12.40	34.10	272.80
Tilf	Tile Layers (Floor)	19.75	158.00	5.4		11.0		40.2	7.95	27.70	221.60
Tilh	Tile Layer Helpers	15.60	124.80	5.4		11.0		40.2	6.30	21.90	175.20
Trlt	Truck Drivers, Light	16.35	130.80	8.6		11.0		43.4	7.10	23.45	187.60
Trhv	Truck Drivers, Heavy	16.60	132.80	8.6		11.0		43.4	7.20	23.80	190.40
Sswl	Welders, Structural Steel	21.70	173.60	19.3		14.0		57.1	12.40	34.10	272.80
Wrck	*Wrecking	15.90	127.20	20.7	▼	11.0	▼	55.5	8.80	24.70	197.60

*Not included in Averages.

Figure 7.3

CREWS

Crew B-15

Crew No.	Bare Costs		Incl. Subs O & P		Cost Per Man-hour	
	Hr.	Daily	Hr.	Daily	Bare Costs	Incl. O&P
1 Equipment Oper. (med)	$20.60	$164.80	$29.85	$238.80	$17.64	$25.42
.5 Building Laborer	15.90	63.60	23.05	92.20		
2 Truck Drivers (heavy)	16.60	265.60	23.80	380.80		
2 Dump Trucks, 16 Ton		559.20		615.10		
1 Dozer, 200 H.P.		634.80		698.30	42.64	46.90
28 M.H., Daily Totals		$1688.00		$2025.20	$60.28	$72.32

Crew B-16

Crew No.	Hr.	Daily	Hr.	Daily	Bare Costs	Incl. O&P
1 Labor Foreman (outside)	$17.90	$143.20	$25.95	$207.60	$16.57	$23.96
2 Building Laborers	15.90	254.40	23.05	368.80		
1 Truck Driver (heavy)	16.60	132.80	23.80	190.40		
1 Dump Truck, 16 Ton		279.60		307.55	8.73	9.61
32 M.H., Daily Totals		$810.00		$1074.35	$25.30	$33.57

Crew B-17

Crew No.	Hr.	Daily	Hr.	Daily	Bare Costs	Incl. O&P
2 Building Laborers	$15.90	$254.40	$23.05	$368.80	$16.96	$24.52
1 Equip. Oper. (light)	19.45	155.60	28.20	225.60		
1 Truck Driver (heavy)	16.60	132.80	23.80	190.40		
1 Backhoe Loader, 48 H.P.		156.00		171.60		
1 Dump Truck, 12 Ton		220.20		242.20	11.75	12.93
32 M.H., Daily Totals		$919.00		$1198.60	$28.71	$37.45

Crew B-18

Crew No.	Hr.	Daily	Hr.	Daily	Bare Costs	Incl. O&P
1 Labor Foreman (outside)	$17.90	$143.20	$25.95	$207.60	$16.56	$24.01
2 Building Laborers	15.90	254.40	23.05	368.80		
1 Vibrating Compactor		39.85		43.85	1.66	1.82
24 M.H., Daily Totals		$437.45		$620.25	$18.22	$25.83

Crew B-19

Crew No.	Hr.	Daily	Hr.	Daily	Bare Costs	Incl. O&P
1 Pile Driver Foreman	$22.10	$176.80	$34.65	$277.20	$20.26	$30.88
4 Pile Drivers	20.10	643.20	31.50	1008.00		
2 Equip. Oper. (crane)	21.05	336.80	30.50	488.00		
1 Equip. Oper. Oiler	17.50	140.00	25.40	203.20		
1 Crane, 40 Ton & Access.		483.40		531.75		
60 L.F. Leads, 15K Ft. Lbs.		48.00		52.80		
1 Hammer, 15K Ft. Lbs.		200.60		220.65		
1 Air Compr., 600 C.F.M.		242.80		267.10		
2-50 Ft. Air Hoses, 3" Dia.		19.10		21.00	15.52	17.08
64 M.H., Daily Totals		$2290.70		$3069.70	$35.78	$47.96

Crew B-20

Crew No.	Hr.	Daily	Hr.	Daily	Bare Costs	Incl. O&P
1 Plumber Foreman (out)	$24.55	$196.40	$35.50	$284.00	$21.00	$30.38
1 Plumber	22.55	180.40	32.60	260.80		
1 Building Laborer	15.90	127.20	23.05	184.40		
24 M.H., Daily Totals		$504.00		$729.20	$21.00	$30.38

Crew B-21

Crew No.	Hr.	Daily	Hr.	Daily	Bare Costs	Incl. O&P
1 Plumber Foreman (out)	$24.55	$196.40	$35.50	$284.00	$21.00	$30.40
1 Plumber	22.55	180.40	32.60	260.80		
1 Building Laborer	15.90	127.20	23.05	184.40		
.5 Equip. Oper. (crane)	21.05	84.20	30.50	122.00		
.5 S.P. Crane, 5 Ton		90.10		99.10	3.21	3.53
28 M.H., Daily Totals		$678.30		$950.30	$24.21	$33.93

Crew B-22

Crew No.	Hr.	Daily	Hr.	Daily	Bare Costs	Incl. O&P
1 Plumber Foreman (out)	$24.55	$196.40	$35.50	$284.00	$21.01	$30.40
1 Plumber	22.55	180.40	32.60	260.80		
1 Building Laborer	15.90	127.20	23.05	184.40		
.75 Equip. Oper. (crane)	21.05	126.30	30.50	183.00		
.75 S.P. Crane, 5 Ton		135.15		148.65	4.50	4.95
30 M.H., Daily Totals		$765.45		$1060.85	$25.51	$35.35

Crew B-23

Crew No.	Hr.	Daily	Hr.	Daily	Bare Costs	Incl. O&P
1 Labor Foreman (outside)	$17.90	$143.20	$25.95	$207.60	$16.30	$23.63
4 Building Laborers	15.90	508.80	23.05	737.60		
Truck & Drill Rig		146.60		161.25		
Appropriate Fixtures		67.20		73.90	5.34	5.87
40 M.H., Daily Totals		$865.80		$1180.35	$21.64	$29.50

Crew B-24

Crew No.	Hr.	Daily	Hr.	Daily	Bare Costs	Incl. O&P
1 Cement Finisher	$19.20	$153.60	$27.00	$216.00	$18.36	$26.35
1 Building Laborer	15.90	127.20	23.05	184.40		
1 Carpenter	20.00	160.00	29.00	232.00		
24 M.H., Daily Totals		$440.80		$632.40	$18.36	$26.35

Crew B-25

Crew No.	Hr.	Daily	Hr.	Daily	Bare Costs	Incl. O&P
1 Labor Foreman (outside)	$17.90	$143.20	$25.95	$207.60	$17.04	$24.70
7 Building Laborers	15.90	890.40	23.05	1290.80		
2 Equip. Oper. (med.)	20.60	329.60	29.85	477.60		
1 Paving Machine		544.40		598.85		
1 Tandem Roller, 10 Ton		175.20		192.70	8.99	9.89
80 M.H., Daily Totals		$2082.80		$2767.55	$26.03	$34.59

Crew B-26

Crew No.	Hr.	Daily	Hr.	Daily	Bare Costs	Incl. O&P
1 Labor Foreman (outside)	$17.90	$143.20	$25.95	$207.60	$17.76	$25.87
6 Building Laborers	15.90	763.20	23.05	1106.40		
2 Equip. Oper. (med.)	20.60	329.60	29.85	477.60		
1 Rodman (reinf.)	21.75	174.00	33.65	269.20		
1 Cement Finisher	19.20	153.60	27.00	216.00		
1 Grader, 30,000 Lbs.		422.40		464.65		
1 Paving Mach. & Equip.		1125.00		1237.50	17.58	19.34
88 M.H., Daily Totals		$3111.00		$3978.95	$35.34	$45.21

Crew B-27

Crew No.	Hr.	Daily	Hr.	Daily	Bare Costs	Incl. O&P
1 Labor Foreman (outside)	$17.90	$143.20	$25.95	$207.60	$16.40	$23.77
3 Building Laborers	15.90	381.60	23.05	553.20		
1 Berm Machine		81.70		89.85	2.55	2.80
32 M.H., Daily Totals		$606.50		$850.65	$18.95	$26.57

Crew B-28

Crew No.	Hr.	Daily	Hr.	Daily	Bare Costs	Incl. O&P
2 Carpenters	$20.00	$320.00	$29.00	$464.00	$18.63	$27.01
1 Building Laborer	15.90	127.20	23.05	184.40		
24 M.H., Daily Totals		$447.20		$648.40	$18.63	$27.01

Crew B-29

Crew No.	Hr.	Daily	Hr.	Daily	Bare Costs	Incl. O&P
1 Labor Foreman (outside)	$17.90	$143.20	$25.95	$207.60	$17.15	$24.86
4 Building Laborers	15.90	508.80	23.05	737.60		
1 Equip. Oper. (crane)	21.05	168.40	30.50	244.00		
1 Equip. Oper. Oiler	17.50	140.00	25.40	203.20		
1 Gradall, 3 Ton, 1/2 C.Y.		440.40		484.45	7.86	8.65
56 M.H., Daily Totals		$1400.80		$1876.85	$25.01	$33.51

Figure 7.4

The crew designation does not mean that this is the only crew that can perform the work. Crew size and content have been developed and chosen based on practical experience and feed back from contractors and represent a labor and equipment make-up commonly found in the industry. The most appropriate crew for a given task is best determined based on particular project requirements. Unit costs may vary if crew sizes or content are significantly changed.

Figure 7.5 is a page from Division 1.5 of *Building Construction Cost Data*. This type of page lists the equipment costs used in the presentation and calculation of the crew costs and unit price data. Rental costs are shown as daily, weekly, and monthly rates. The Hourly Operating Cost represents the cost of fuel, lubrication and routine maintenance. The column on the right in Figure 7.5 is the Crew's Equipment Cost. These figures represent the costs as included in the bare daily crew costs and are calculated as follows:

Line number:	1.5-05-191 (Figure 7.5)
Equipment:	Grader, self-propelled, 30,000 lb.
Rent per Week:	$1,450.00
Hourly Operating Cost:	$16.55

$$\frac{\text{Weekly rental}}{\text{5 days per week}} + (\text{Hourly Oper. Cost x 8 hrs/day}) = \text{Crews Equipment Cost}$$

$$\frac{\$1,450}{5} + (\$16.55 \times 8) = \$422.40$$

The Crews' Equipment Cost is basically the daily cost of equipment. This figure is based on rental by the week. Note how the equipment costs in the example above are used in developing the crew cost for Crew B-26 in Figure 7.4. The daily equipment costs, including overhead and profit, contain a 10% fee added to the bare costs to cover the handling and overhead associated with use of the equipment.

The daily output represents the number of units that the designated minimum crew will install in one 8 hour day. (See "Units" below.) These figures have been determined from construction experience under actual working conditions. With a designation of the appropriate crew and determination of the daily output, the unit costs for installation are easily calculated:

$$\frac{\text{Daily Crew Cost (\$/day)}}{\text{Daily Output (units/day)}} = \text{Unit Installation Cost (\$/unit)}$$

The man-hours per unit can also be easily determined using the data provided. A man-hour is the equivalent of one worker working for one hour, and is a relative indicator of productivity. To calculate man-hours per unit:

$$\frac{\text{Total Daily Crew Man-hours}}{\text{Daily Output}} = \frac{\text{Man-Hours/Day}}{\text{Units/Day}} = \text{Man-Hours per Unit}$$

The resulting units of productivity can be very useful as an aid for scheduling. Manpower allocations are more readily determined and time durations can be calculated based on crew size.

1.5	Contractor Equipment	UNIT	HOURLY OPER. COST	RENT PER DAY	RENT PER WEEK	RENT PER MONTH	CREWS EQUIPMENT COST
05-001	EARTHWORK EQUIPMENT RENTAL Without operators unless						
002	noted by*						
004	(13) Aggregate Spreader, push type 8' to 12' wide	Ea.	.65	79	230	690	51.20
005	Augers for truck or trailer mounting, vertical drilling						
006	4" to 36" diam., 54 H.P., gas, 10' spindle travel	Ea.	6.70	155	465	1,475	146.60
007	14' spindle travel		7	185	550	1,650	166
008	Auger, horizontal boring machine, 12" to 36" diameter, 45 H.P.		6.15	595	1,775	5,375	404.20
009	12" to 48" diameter, 65 H.P.		8.45	625	2,075	6,100	482.60
010	(17) Backhoe, diesel hydraulic, crawler mounted, 1/2 C.Y. capacity		6.50	495*	1,050	3,425	262
012	5/8 C.Y. capacity		7.40	520*	1,075	3,525	274.20
014	3/4 C.Y. capacity		10.65	590*	1,275	5,000	340.20
015	1 C.Y. capacity		13.60	920*	1,675	4,900	443.80
020	1-1/2 C.Y. capacity		17.45	990*	2,200	6,375	579.60
030	2 C.Y. capacity		27	1,200*	2,925	8,825	801
032	2-1/2 C.Y. capacity		42	1,475*	4,150	11,800	1,166
034	3-1/2 C.Y. capacity		49	1,775*	5,100	15,200	1,412
035	Gradall type, truck mounted, 3 ton @ 15' radius, 5/8 C.Y.		17.55	870*	1,500	4,550	440.40
037	1 C.Y. capacity		23	1,050*	2,225	6,625	629
040	Backhoe-loader, wheel type, 40 to 45 H.P., 5/8 C.Y. capacity		4.70	335*	400	1,250	117.60
045	45 H.P. to 60 H.P., 3/4 C.Y. capacity		5.75	405*	550	1,700	156
046	80 H.P., 1-1/4 C.Y. capacity		8.65	465*	825	2,325	234.20
050	Brush chipper, gas engine, 6" cutter head, 35 H.P.		3.13	125	395	1,150	104.05
055	12" cutter head, 130 H.P.		6.25	165	435	1,275	137
060	15" cutter head, 165 H.P.		8	200	490	1,500	162
075	Bucket, clamshell, general purpose, 3/8 C.Y.		.42	35	105	305	24.35
080	1/2 C.Y.		.58	40	125	380	29.65
085	3/4 C.Y.		.65	52	150	460	35.20
090	1 C.Y.		.77	54	170	500	40.15
095	1-1/2 C.Y.		1.10	70	210	625	50.80
100	2 C.Y.		1.20	85	280	855	65.60
101	(17) Bucket, dragline, medium duty, 1/2 C.Y.		.37	26	67	200	16.35
102	3/4 C.Y.		.43	30	90	280	21.45
103	1 C.Y.		.50	36	110	320	26
104	1-1/2 C.Y.		.58	44	135	385	31.65
105	2 C.Y.		.70	58	175	520	40.60
107	3 C.Y.		1.01	90	255	750	59.10
120	Compactor, roller, 2 drum, 2000 lb., operator walking		2.45	93	280	835	75.60
125	Rammer compactor, gas, 1000 lb. blow		1.02	52	150	450	38.15
130	Vibratory plate, gas, 13" plate, 1000 lb. blow		.54	41	120	355	28.30
135	24" plate, 5000 lb. blow		.73	50	170	495	39.85
137	Curb builder, 14 H.P., gas, single screw		2.85	88	265	800	75.80
139	Double screw	▼	2.59	100	305	925	81.70
175	Extractor, piling, see lines 250 to 275						
180							
186	Grader, self-propelled, 25,000 lb.	Ea.	11.85	405	1,225	4,325	339.80
191	30,000 lb.		16.55	485	1,450	5,100	422.40
192	40,000 lb.		22	635	1,900	6,300	556
193	55,000 lb.		28.10	950	2,850	9,100	794.80
195	Hammer, pavement demo., hyd., gas, self-prop., 1000 to 1250 lb.		6.18	265	815	2,450	212.45
200	1300 to 1500 lb.		6.65	290	865	2,600	226.20
205	(13) Pile driving hammer, steam or air, 4150 ft.-lb. @ 225 BPM		3.83	130	390	1,150	108.65
210	8750 ft.-lb. @ 145 BPM		5.14	200	605	1,650	162.10
215	15,000 ft.-lb. @ 60 BPM		5.95	285	765	1,975	200.60
220	24,450 ft.-lb. @ 111 BPM	▼	7.25	365	1,125	2,900	283
225	Leads, 15,000 ft.-lb. hammers	L.F.				12	.80
230	24,450 ft.-lb. hammers and heavier	"				13	.85
235	Diesel type hammer, 22,400 ft.-lb.	Ea.	8.40	435	1,275	3,025	322.20
240	41,300 ft.-lb.		12.55	615	2,125	4,950	525.40
245	141,000 ft.-lb.		21	1,050	3,150	9,550	798
250	Vib. elec. hammer/ext., 200 KW diesel generator, 34 H.P.	▼	13.45	580	1,750	5,250	457.60

Figure 7.5

Unit

The unit column (see Figures 7.1 and 7.2) defines the component for which the costs have been calculated. It is this "unit" on which Unit Price Estimating is based. The units as used represent standard estimating and quantity takeoff procedures. However, the estimator should always check to be sure that the units taken off are the same as those priced. Note in Figure 7.1 that the same items are priced based on two very different units — per thousand brick and per square foot. A list of standard abbreviations is included at the back of *Building Construction Cost Data*.

Bare Costs

The three columns listed under "Bare Costs" — "Material", "Installation" and "Total", represent the actual cost of construction items to the contractor. In other words, bare costs are those which *do not* include the overhead and profit of the installing contractor, whether a subcontractor or a general contracting company using its own crews.

Material: Material costs are based on the national average contractor purchase price delivered to the job site. Delivered costs are assumed to be within a 20 mile radius of metropolitan areas. No sales tax is included in the material prices because of variations from state to state.

The prices are based on large quantities that would normally be purchased for projects costing $500,000 and up. Prices for small quantities must be adjusted accordingly. If more current costs for materials are available for the appropriate location, it is recommended that adjustments be made to the unit costs to reflect any cost difference.

Installation: The unit cost for installation of an item is calculated as shown above (see "Daily Output"). The total daily cost of the designated crew is divided by the number of units that the crew will install in one day. The resulting unit price for installation includes both labor and equipment costs.

The labor rates used to determine the bare installation costs are shown for 35 standard trades in Figure 7.3, under the column "Base Rate Including Fringes". This rate includes a worker's actual hourly wage plus employer-paid benefits (health insurance, vacation, pension, etc.). The labor rates used are *national average* union rates based on trade union agreements (as of January 1 of the current year) from 30 major cities in the United States. As new wage agreements are negotiated within a calendar year, labor costs should be adjusted. The determination of the equipment portion of installation costs is discussed above. (See "Crews".)

Total Bare Costs: This column simply represents the arithmetic sum of the bare material and installation costs. This total is the average cost to the contractor for the particular item of construction, supplied and installed, or "in place". No overhead and/or profit is included.

Total Including Overhead and Profit

The prices in the "Total Including Overhead and Profit" column might also be called the "billing rate". These prices are, on the average, what the installing contractor would charge for the particular item of work. The term "installing contractor" can refer to either a subcontractor or a general contractor. In effect, this rate reflects the amount the subcontractor would charge to the general contractor or what the general contractor would charge the owner for work performed by the general contractor's own employees. The general contractor normally adds a percentage to subcontractor prices (commonly 10%) for supervision and management.

The "Total Including Overhead and Profit" costs are determined by adding the following two calculations:

1. Bare materials – increased by 10% for handling. See Figure 7.2.
2. Bare daily crew costs – increased to include overhead and profit, then divided by the daily output. See Figures 7.2 and 7.4.

In order to increase crew cost to include overhead and profit, labor and equipment costs are treated separately. 10% is added to the bare equipment cost for handling, management, etc. Labor costs are increased, depending upon trade by percentages for overhead and profit (as shown in Figure 7.3). The resulting rates are listed in the right hand columns of Figure 7.3. Note that the percentage increase for overhead and profit for the average skilled worker is 45.9% of the base rate. The following items are included in the increase for overhead and profit, as shown in Figure 7.3:

Workers' Compensation and Employer's Liability:
Workers' Compensation and Employer's Liability Insurance rates vary from state to state and are tied into the construction trade safety records in that particular state. Rates also vary by trade according to the hazard involved. (See Figures 7.6 and 7.7.) The proper authorities will most likely keep the contractor well informed of the rates and obligations.

State and Federal Unemployment Insurance:
The employer's tax rate is adjusted by a merit-rating system according to the number of former employees applying for benefits. Contractors who find it possible to offer a maximum of steady employment can enjoy a reduction in the unemployment tax rate.

Employer-Paid Social Security (FICA):
The tax rate is adjusted annually by the federal government. It is a percentage of an employee's salary up to a maximum annual contribution.

Builder's Risk and Public Liability:
These insurance rates vary according to the trades involved and the state in which the work is done.

Overhead: The column listed as "Sub's Overhead" provides percentages to be added for office or operating overhead. This is the cost of doing business. The percentages are presented as national averages by trade as shown in Figure 7.3. Note that the operating overhead costs are applied to *labor only* in *Building Construction Cost Data*. A detailed discussion of operating, or office overhead and its application is included in Chapter 4.

Profit: This percentage is the fee added by the contractor to offer both a return on investment and an allowance to cover the risk involved in the type of construction being bid. The profit percentage may vary from 4% on large, straightforward projects to as much as 25% on smaller, high-risk jobs. Profit percentages are directly affected by economic conditions, the expected number of bidders, and the estimated risk involved in the project. For estimating purposes, *Building Construction Cost Data* assumes 10% as a reasonable average profit factor.

Workers' Compensation Rates (National Averages by Trade and Building Type)

Trade	Insurance Rate (% of Labor Cost)		% of Building Cost			% of Labor Cost		
	Range	Average	Office Bldgs.	Schools & Apts.	Mfg.	Office Bldgs.	Schools & Apts.	Mfg.
Excavation, Grading, etc.	2.1% to 27.8%	7.2%	4.8%	4.9%	4.5%	.35%	.35%	.32%
Piles & Foundations	4.0 to 47.6	17.0	7.1	5.2	8.7	1.21	.88	1.48
Concrete	2.3 to 27.1	9.2	5.0	14.8	3.7	.46	1.36	.34
Masonry	1.6 to 18.7	7.6	6.9	7.5	1.9	.52	.57	.14
Structural Steel	3.1 to 42.9	19.3	10.7	3.9	17.6	2.07	.75	3.40
Misc. & Ornamental Metals	1.3 to 15.7	6.8	2.8	4.0	3.6	.19	.27	.24
Carpentry & Millwork	2.9 to 54.1	10.1	3.7	4.0	0.5	.37	.40	.05
Metal or Composition Siding	2.7 to 23.3	7.8	2.3	0.3	4.3	.18	.02	.34
Roofing	3.7 to 52.7	18.2	2.3	2.6	3.1	.42	.47	.56
Doors & Hardware	2.0 to 15.9	5.9	0.9	1.4	0.4	.05	.08	.02
Sash & Glazing	3.0 to 33.3	7.9	3.5	4.0	1.0	.28	.32	.08
Lath & Plaster	2.3 to 22.9	7.7	3.3	6.9	0.8	.25	.53	.06
Tile, Marble & Floors	1.1 to 18.7	5.4	2.6	3.0	0.5	.14	.16	.03
Acoustical Ceilings	1.6 to 15.4	6.3	2.4	0.2	0.3	.15	.01	.02
Painting	2.6 to 20.0	7.7	1.5	1.6	1.6	.12	.12	.12
Interior Partitions	2.9 to 54.1	10.1	3.9	4.3	4.4	.39	.43	.44
Miscellaneous Items	1.2 to 92.4	9.6	5.2	3.7	9.7	.50	.36	.93
Elevators	1.4 to 15.6	5.5	2.1	1.1	2.2	.12	.06	.12
Sprinklers	1.4 to 16.8	5.5	0.5	—	2.0	.03	—	.11
Plumbing	1.3 to 12.5	4.8	4.9	7.2	5.2	.24	.35	.25
Heat., Vent., Air Conditioning	1.8 to 14.5	6.3	13.5	11.0	12.9	.85	.69	.81
Electrical	1.0 to 13.1	4.0	10.1	8.4	11.1	.40	.34	.44
Total	1.0% to 92.4%	—	100.0%	100.0%	100.0%	9.29%	8.52%	10.30%
			Overall Weighted Average				9.37%	

Figure 7.6

Workers' Compensation Rates. Average Rates by States.

State	Weighted Average	State	Weighted Average	State	Weighted Average
Alabama	6.4%	Kentucky	5.7%	North Dakota	6.9%
Alaska	12.4	Louisiana	6.4	Ohio	7.0
Arizona	10.5	Maine	14.3	Oklahoma	8.1
Arkansas	6.4	Maryland	14.7	Oregon	21.5
California	11.5	Massachusetts	12.5	Pennsylvania	10.2
Colorado	10.9	Michigan	11.3	Rhode Island	12.2
Connecticut	15.0	Minnesota	13.6	South Carolina	7.4
Delaware	9.7	Mississippi	5.4	South Dakota	6.1
District of Columbia	16.5	Missouri	5.2	Tennessee	4.8
Florida	11.2	Montana	12.0	Texas	6.0
Georgia	5.4	Nebraska	6.1	Utah	5.3
Hawaii	25.1	Nevada	10.6	Vermont	6.1
Idaho	8.1	New Hampshire	13.3	Virginia	7.3
Illinois	11.4	New Jersey	6.6	Washington	6.8
Indiana	2.5	New Mexico	14.4	West Virginia	8.7
Iowa	6.3	New York	8.9	Wisconsin	6.5
Kansas	6.3	North Carolina	4.7	Wyoming	5.4

Figure 7.7

Square Foot and Cubic Foot Costs

Division 17 in *Building Construction Cost Data* has been developed to facilitate the preparation of rapid preliminary budget estimates. The cost figures in this division are derived from more than 10,500 actual building projects contained in the R.S. Means data bank of construction costs and include the contractor's overhead and profit. The prices shown *do not* include architectural fees or land costs. Costs for new projects are added to the files each year, while projects over ten years old are discarded. For this reason, certain costs may not show a uniform, annual progression. In no case are all subdivisions of a project listed.

These projects were located throughout the United States and reflect differences in square foot and cubic foot costs due to differences in both labor and material costs, plus differences in the owners' requirements. For instance, a bank in a large city would have different features and costs than one in a rural area. This is true of all the different types of buildings analyzed. All individual cost items were computed and tabulated separately. Thus, the sum of the median figures for Plumbing, H.V.A.C. and Electrical will not normally add up to the total Mechanical and Electrical costs arrived at by separate analysis and tabulation of the projects.

The data and prices presented (as shown in Figure 7.8) are listed as square foot or cubic foot costs and as a percentage of total costs. Each category tabulates the data in a similar manner. The median, or middle figure, is listed. This means that 50% of all projects had lower costs, and 50% had higher costs than the median figure. Figures in the "¼" column indicate that 25% of the projects had lower costs and 75% had higher costs.

Similarly, figures in the "¾" column indicate that 75% had lower costs and 25% of the projects had higher costs.

The costs and figures represent all projects and do not take into account project size. As a rule, larger buildings (of the same type and relative location) will cost less to build per square foot than similar buildings of a smaller size. This cost difference is due to economies of scale as well as a lower exterior envelope-to-floor area ratio. A conversion is necessary to adjust project costs based on size relative to the norm. Figure 7.9 lists typical sizes (by square foot) and typical ranges of sizes for different building types.

Figure 7.10 is an Area Conversion Scale that can be used to adjust costs based on project size. For example, a proposed mid-rise office building is to be 34,000 square feet. From Figure 7.9, the typical size is 52,000 square feet. A size factor is calculated:

$$\frac{\text{Proposed Building Area}}{\text{Typical Building Area}} = \frac{34,000 \text{ S.F.}}{52,000 \text{ S.F.}} = 0.65$$

The size factor, applied to the Area Conversion Scale, indicates a cost multiplier of 1.06.

$$\text{Cost Multiplier} \times \text{Median Cost} = \text{Converted Cost}$$
$$1.06 \quad \times \quad \$57.15 \quad = \quad \$60.58$$

A rough budget cost for the proposed building based on national averages is $60.58 per square foot.

There are two stages of project development when square foot cost estimates are most useful. The first is during the conceptual stage when

17.1 S.F., C.F. and % of Total Costs	UNIT	UNIT COSTS			% OF TOTAL		
		1/4	MEDIAN	3/4	1/4	MEDIAN	3/4
52-001 JAILS	S.F.	101	113	132			
002 Total project costs	C.F.	7.45	9.25	11.60			
180 Equipment	S.F.	3.87	10.25	17.15	3.80%	8.90%	14.80%
272 Plumbing		5.90	10.15	12.25	7%	8.30%	12%
277 Heating, ventilating, air conditioning		5.90	10.70	15.50	6.30%	9.40%	12.10%
290 Electrical		8.60	11.35	14.35	7.80%	9.80%	12.40%
310 Total: Mechanical & Electrical	↓	22.15	31.80	41.25	23.20%	29.60%	35.30%
53-001 LIBRARIES	S.F.	56.80	69.55	86.75			
002 Total project costs	C.F.	3.94	4.77	5.95			
050 Masonry	S.F.	3.14	5.70	9.40	4%	6.50%	9.40%
114 Roofing		2.05	2.59	3.70	1.90%	3.30%	3.50%
158 Painting		1.08	1.54	3.12	.90%	1.90%	3%
180 Equipment		.69	1.75	3.42	1.40%	2.70%	4.80%
272 Plumbing		2.35	3.24	4.32	3.60%	4.50%	5.80%
277 Heating, ventilating, air conditioning		5.75	8.15	10.60	8.70%	11%	13.20%
290 Electrical		5.80	7.10	9.45	8.40%	10.90%	12.10%
310 Total: Mechanical & Electrical	↓	12.25	17.15	24.25	19.40%	25.50%	29.60%
55-001 MEDICAL CLINICS	↓	54.40	67.05	83.20			
002 Total project costs	C.F.	4.03	5.31	7.05			
180 Equipment	S.F.	1.44	2.81	4.64	1.90%	4.30%	6.80%
272 Plumbing		3.75	5.15	7.10	6.10%	8.40%	10.20%
277 Heating, ventilating, air conditioning		4.56	5.95	8.65	6.70%	9%	11.70%
290 Electrical		5.15	6.60	8.60	8.10%	9.90%	12%
310 Total: Mechanical & Electrical	↓	11.85	15.20	21.30	19%	24.20%	30.10%
350 See also division 11.1-37							
57-001 MEDICAL OFFICES	S.F.	50.25	63.30	76.20			
002 Total project costs	C.F.	3.85	5.10	6.80			
180 Equipment	S.F.	1.74	3.38	4.78	3.40%	5.90%	7.10%
272 Plumbing		3.08	4.57	6.30	5.70%	6.90%	9.40%
277 Heating, ventilating, air conditioning		3.65	5.40	6.90	6.50%	8%	10.40%
290 Electrical		4.26	6.15	8	7.60%	9.80%	11.70%
310 Total: Mechanical & Electrical	↓	9.80	13.75	18.25	17.20%	22.40%	27.40%
59-001 MOTELS	S.F.	47.85	49.70	72.80			
002 Total project costs	C.F.	2.94	5.55	6.75			
272 Plumbing	S.F.	2.22	4.03	6.85	3.80%	8.90%	12.60%
277 Heating, ventilating, air conditioning		1.75	3.01	3.21	4.10%	6.20%	8.20%
290 Electrical		2.62	4.75	7.10	4.70%	9.50%	10.90%
310 Total: Mechanical & Electrical	↓	8.35	14.05	16.40	17.30%	27.70%	33.30%
500							
900 Per rental unit, total cost	Unit	13,500	22,700	32,300			
950 Total: Mechanical & Electrical	"	3,750	5,025	5,525			
60-001 NURSING HOMES	S.F.	51.55	66.80	82.40			
002 Total project costs	C.F.	4.09	5.25	7			
180 Equipment	S.F.	1.61	2.09	3.27	2%	3.60%	6%
272 Plumbing		4.48	5.45	8.15	8.30%	10.30%	14.10%
277 Heating, ventilating, air conditioning		4.80	6.95	8.15	10.60%	11.70%	11.80%
290 Electrical		5.15	6.50	8	9.70%	11%	12.50%
310 Total: Mechanical & Electrical	↓	11.75	16.05	23.15	22%	28.10%	33.20%
320							
900 Per bed or person, total cost	Bed	20,100	25,700	32,200			
61-001 OFFICES Low-Rise (1 to 4 story)	S.F.	41.25	53.35	70.15			
002 Total project costs	C.F.	3	4.26	5.70			
010 Sitework	S.F.	3.04	5	7.85	5.30%	9.20%	13.40%
050 Masonry		1.67	3.28	6.26	3%	5.90%	8.50%
180 Equipment		.58	.99	2.64	1.40%	1.70%	4.40%
272 Plumbing	↓	1.58	2.38	3.41	3.60%	4.50%	6.10%

Figure 7.8

94

few, if any details are available. At this time, square foot costs are useful for ballpark budget purposes. As soon as details become available in the project design, the square foot approach should be discontinued and the project priced more accurately. The second is after the estimate is completed. Square foot costs can be used for verification and as a check against gross errors.

When using the figures in Division 17, it is recommended that the median cost column be consulted for preliminary figures if no additional information is available. When costs have been modified to account for project size and have been converted for location (see City Cost Indexes), the median numbers (as shown in Figure 7.8) should provide a fairly accurate base figure. This figure should then be adjusted according to the estimator's experience, local economic conditions, code requirements and the owner's particular requirements. There is no need to factor the percentage figures, as these should remain relatively constant from city to city.

Square Foot Base Size						
Building Type	Median Cost Per S.F.	Typical Size Gross S.F.	Typical Range Gross S.F.	Building Type	Median Cost Per S.F.	Typical Size Gross S.F.	Typical Range Gross S.F.
Apartments, Low Rise	$ 38.90	21,000	9,700 - 37,200	Jails	$113.00	13,700	7,500 - 28,000
Apartments, Mid Rise	49.00	50,000	32,000 - 100,000	Libraries	69.55	12,000	7,000 - 31,000
Apartments, High Rise	54.35	310,000	100,000 - 650,000	Medical Clinics	67.05	7,200	4,200 - 15,700
Auditoriums	65.35	25,000	7,600 - 39,000	Medical Offices	63.30	6,000	4,000 - 15,000
Auto Sales	41.35	20,000	10,800 - 28,600	Motels	49.70	27,000	15,800 - 51,000
Banks	90.25	4,200	2,500 - 7,500	Nursing Homes	66.80	23,000	15,000 - 37,000
Churches	59.75	9,000	5,300 - 13,200	Offices, Low Rise	53.35	8,600	4,700 - 19,000
Clubs, Country	58.00	6,500	4,500 - 15,000	Offices, Mid Rise	57.15	52,000	31,300 - 83,100
Clubs, Social	57.10	10,000	6,000 - 13,500	Offices, High Rise	70.60	260,000	151,000 - 468,000
Clubs, YMCA	61.30	28,300	12,800 - 39,400	Police Stations	88.45	10,500	4,000 - 19,000
Colleges (Class)	79.10	50,000	23,500 - 98,500	Post Offices	66.80	12,400	6,800 - 30,000
Colleges (Science Lab)	92.45	45,600	16,600 - 80,000	Power Plants	440.00	7,500	1,000 - 20,000
College (Student Union)	85.20	33,400	16,000 - 85,000	Religious Education	49.45	9,000	6,000 - 12,000
Community Center	61.85	9,400	5,300 - 16,700	Research	86.95	19,000	6,300 - 45,000
Court Houses	82.60	32,400	17,800 - 106,000	Restaurants	78.40	4,400	2,800 - 6,000
Dept. Stores	36.50	90,000	44,000 - 122,000	Retail Stores	38.30	7,200	4,000 - 17,600
Dormitories, Low Rise	58.85	24,500	13,400 - 40,000	Schools, Elementary	58.15	41,000	24,500 - 55,000
Dormitories, Mid Rise	75.90	55,600	36,100 - 90,000	Schools, Jr. High	57.95	92,000	52,000 - 119,000
Factories	31.20	26,400	12,900 - 50,000	Schools, Sr.High	57.00	101,000	50,500 - 175,000
Fire Stations	63.55	5,800	4,000 - 8,700	Schools, Vocational	55.05	37,000	20,500 - 82,000
Fraternity Houses	56.35	12,500	8,200 - 14,800	Sports Arenas	45.15	15,000	5,000 - 40,000
Funeral Homes	56.45	7,800	4,500 - 11,000	Supermarkets	37.75	20,000	12,000 - 30,000
Garages, Commercial	42.60	9,300	5,000 - 13,600	Swimming Pools	65.15	13,000	7,800 - 22,000
Garages, Municipal	45.25	8,300	4,500 - 12,600	Telephone Exchange	99.65	4,500	1,200 - 10,600
Garages, Parking	19.45	163,000	76,400 - 225,300	Terminals, Bus	43.90	11,400	6,300 - 16,500
Gymnasiums	55.00	19,200	11,600 - 41,000	Theaters	53.25	10,500	8,800 - 17,500
Hospitals	111.00	55,000	27,200 - 125,000	Town Halls	63.70	10,800	4,800 - 23,400
House (Elderly)	54.90	37,000	21,000 - 66,000	Warehouses	25.40	25,000	8,000 - 72,000
Housing (Public)	46.10	36,000	14,400 - 74,400	Warehouse & Office	27.75	25,000	8,000 - 72,000
Ice Rinks	43.90	29,000	27,200 - 33,600				

Figure 7.9

Repair & Remodeling

Cost figures in *Building Construction Cost Data* are based on new construction utilizing the most cost-effective combination of labor, equipment and material. The work is scheduled in the proper sequence to allow the various trades to accomplish their tasks in an efficient manner. Division 18 contains unit prices for construction items associated with repair and remodeling work. For expanded coverage, see Means' *Repair and Remodeling Cost Data*.

There are many factors unique to repair and remodeling that can affect project costs. The economy of scale associated with new construction often has no influence on the cost of repair and remodeling. Small quantities of components may have to be custom fabricated at great expense. Work schedule coordination between trades frequently becomes

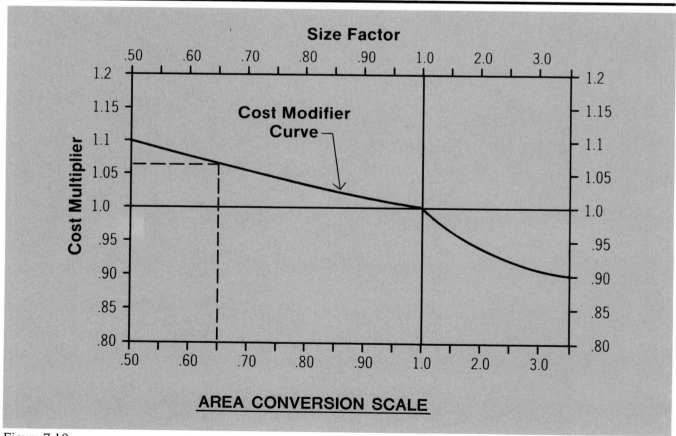

Figure 7.10

difficult; work area restrictions can lead to subcontractor quotations with start-up and shutdown costs in excess of the cost of the actual work involved. Some of the more prominent factors affecting repair and remodeling projects are listed below:

1. A large amount of cutting and patching may be required to match the existing construction. It is often more economical to remove entire walls rather than create many new door and window openings. This sort of trade-off has to be carefully analyzed. Matching "existing conditions" may be impossible because certain materials may no longer be manufactured, and substitutions can be expensive. Piping and ductwork runs may not be as simple as they are in the case of new construction. Wiring may have to be snaked through existing walls and floors.

2. Dust and noise protection of adjoining non-construction areas can involve a substantial number of special precautions and may alter normal construction methods.

3. The use of certain equipment may be curtailed as a result of the physical limitations of the project; workmen may be forced to use small equipment or hand tools.

4. Material handling becomes more costly due to the confines of an enclosed building. For multi-story construction, low capacity elevators and stairwells may be the only access to the upper floors.

5. Both existing and completed finish work will need to be protected in order to prevent damage during ensuing work.

6. Work may have to be done on other than normal shifts – around an existing production facility that has to stay in operation throughout the repair and remodeling. Costs for overtime work may be incurred as a result.

7. There may be an increased requirement for shoring and bracing to support the building while structural changes are being made, or to allow for the temporary storage of construction materials on above-grade floors.

These factors and their consequences, can significantly increase the costs for repair and remodeling work as compared with new construction. R.S. Means has developed a method to quantify these factors by adding percentages to the costs of work that is affected. These suggested percentages are shown in Figure 7.11 as minimums and maximums. The estimator must use sound judgement and experience when applying these factors. The effects of each of these factors should be considered in the planning, bidding and construction phases in order to minimize the potential increased costs associated with repair and remodeling projects.

There are other considerations to be anticipated in estimating for repair and remodeling. Weather protection may be required for existing structures, and during the installation of new windows or heating systems. Pedestrian protection is often required in urban areas. On small projects and because of local conditions, it may be necessary to pay a tradesman for a minimum of four hours for a task that actually requires less time. Unit prices should be used with caution in situations when these kinds of minimum charges may be incurred.

All of the above factors can be anticipated and the basic costs developed before a repair and remodeling project begins. It is the hidden problems, the unknowns, that pose the greatest challenge to the estimator and cause the most anxiety. These problems are often discovered during demolition and may be impossible to anticipate. Projects may be delayed due to these unexpected conditions, and these delays ultimately increase construction costs. Other parts of the project, and thus their cost, are also affected. Only experience, good judgement and a thorough knowledge of the existing structure can help to reduce the number of unknowns and their potential effects.

City Cost Indexes

The unit prices in *Building Construction Cost Data* are national averages. When they are to be applied to a particular location, these prices must be adjusted to local conditions. R.S. Means has developed the City Cost Indexes for just that purpose. Division 19 of *Building Construction Cost Data* contains tables of indexes for 162 U.S. and Canadian cities based on a 30 major city average of 100. The figures are broken down into material and installation for the 16 UCI divisions, as shown in Figure 7.12. Please note that for each city there is a weighted average for the material, installation and total indexes. This average is based on the relative contribution of each division to the construction process as a whole. The information in Figure 7.13 does not represent any one building type but instead, all building types as a whole. The figures may be used as a general guide to determine how much time should be spent on each portion of an estimate. When doing an estimate, more time should be spent on the divisions that have a higher percent contribution to the project. Caution should be exercised when using set percentages for projects that have unusually high or low division contributions.

17-001	FACTORS To be added to construction costs for particular job requirements								
010	of repair and remodeling projects								
050	**1** Cut & patch to match existing construction, add, minimum			Costs	2%	3%			
055	Maximum				5%	9%			
080	**2** Dust protection, add, minimum				1%	2%			
085	Maximum				4%	11%			
110	**3** Equipment usage curtailment, add, minimum				1%	1%			
115	Maximum				3%	10%			
140	**4** Material handling & storage limitation, add, minimum				1%	1%			
145	Maximum				6%	7%			
170	**5** Protection of existing work, add, minimum				2%	2%			
175	Maximum				5%	7%			
200	**6** Shift work requirements, add, minimum					5%			
205	Maximum					30%			
230	**7** Temporary shoring and bracing, add, minimum				2%	5%			
235	Maximum				5%	12%			

Figure 7.11

ALABAMA / ALASKA / ARIZONA

DIVISION	BIRMINGHAM MAT.	INST.	TOTAL	HUNTSVILLE MAT.	INST.	TOTAL	MOBILE MAT.	INST.	TOTAL	MONTGOMERY MAT.	INST.	TOTAL	ANCHORAGE MAT.	INST.	TOTAL	PHOENIX MAT.	INST.	TOTAL
2 SITE WORK	96.7	90.8	94.1	115.6	92.1	104.9	118.4	87.0	104.2	88.2	89.9	88.9	154.7	129.1	143.1	88.2	96.6	92.0
3.1 FORMWORK	90.4	72.2	76.2	92.4	73.7	77.8	97.0	74.6	79.5	102.2	72.9	79.3	114.1	145.8	138.8	109.1	92.7	96.3
3.2 REINFORCING	94.6	76.8	87.0	95.8	73.5	86.4	83.0	73.1	78.8	83.0	76.8	80.3	117.8	138.8	126.7	113.3	100.3	107.8
3.3 CAST IN PLACE CONC.	89.4	91.8	90.9	102.0	93.5	96.8	100.1	93.1	95.7	101.3	92.9	96.1	226.0	112.5	155.4	109.1	93.7	99.5
3 CONCRETE	90.7	82.8	85.6	98.7	84.0	89.2	95.7	84.1	88.2	97.5	83.7	88.5	179.7	127.8	146.2	110.0	93.9	99.6
4 MASONRY	79.9	75.0	76.1	87.3	73.6	76.7	92.4	79.7	82.7	86.1	72.3	75.5	139.4	148.4	146.3	93.0	89.7	90.5
5 METALS	96.0	82.4	91.1	100.5	80.3	93.2	93.8	80.6	89.0	94.7	82.3	90.2	116.7	129.8	121.4	98.9	97.7	98.5
6 WOOD & PLASTICS	91.5	73.4	81.4	104.6	73.9	87.4	92.0	77.4	83.8	101.2	73.2	85.5	117.8	145.2	133.2	100.8	92.2	96.0
7 MOISTURE PROTECTION	84.5	68.8	79.6	92.3	70.0	85.3	87.1	70.8	82.0	88.3	69.3	82.3	102.5	146.8	116.4	92.4	87.7	90.9
8 DOORS, WINDOWS, GLASS	91.2	73.8	82.1	101.6	73.6	86.9	99.2	75.5	86.8	98.5	73.1	85.2	129.6	145.4	137.9	103.4	88.6	95.6
9.1 LATH & PLASTER	96.2	69.7	76.0	86.4	73.9	76.8	92.0	81.4	83.9	108.5	75.0	82.9	120.4	146.0	139.9	90.6	92.2	91.8
9.2 DRYWALL	100.5	72.9	87.4	110.4	73.5	92.9	92.4	78.1	85.6	100.6	73.7	87.9	122.0	146.9	133.8	90.2	91.2	90.7
9.5 ACOUSTICAL WORK	98.8	73.0	84.7	101.2	73.6	86.1	94.2	76.9	84.7	94.2	72.3	82.2	125.5	146.9	137.2	103.5	91.3	96.9
9.6 FLOORING	111.9	78.1	102.9	94.0	73.6	88.6	113.9	81.9	105.4	99.9	72.3	92.6	117.2	146.9	125.1	92.8	92.8	92.8
9.8 PAINTING	107.0	72.2	79.0	110.6	73.5	80.8	121.5	77.8	86.4	119.8	72.2	81.6	123.1	146.8	142.2	94.9	89.0	90.2
9 FINISHES	103.5	72.8	86.9	105.4	73.6	88.2	100.3	78.4	88.5	102.1	73.1	86.4	121.3	146.8	135.1	92.3	90.6	91.4
10-14 TOTAL DIV. 10-14	100.0	76.0	92.7	100.0	73.6	92.0	100.0	76.1	92.7	100.0	72.3	91.6	100.0	146.9	114.1	100.0	99.5	99.8
15 MECHANICAL	96.4	77.3	86.5	99.7	76.5	87.7	97.5	77.4	87.1	99.2	73.3	85.8	107.7	146.6	127.9	98.8	83.8	91.0
16 ELECTRICAL	94.0	77.3	82.1	91.9	77.1	81.4	89.7	78.2	81.5	90.7	72.2	77.5	110.8	146.8	136.5	105.1	89.4	93.9
1-16 WEIGHTED AVERAGE	94.3	78.0	85.4	99.7	77.8	87.7	97.3	79.6	87.6	96.1	76.2	85.2	125.3	141.3	134.1	99.2	90.6	94.5

ARIZONA / ARKANSAS / CALIFORNIA

DIVISION	TUCSON MAT.	INST.	TOTAL	FORT SMITH MAT.	INST.	TOTAL	LITTLE ROCK MAT.	INST.	TOTAL	ANAHEIM MAT.	INST.	TOTAL	BAKERSFIELD MAT.	INST.	TOTAL	FRESNO MAT.	INST.	TOTAL
2 SITE WORK	106.6	96.9	102.2	96.7	93.0	95.0	103.3	95.6	99.8	101.1	112.6	106.3	93.2	113.6	102.4	91.7	120.5	104.7
3.1 FORMWORK	102.1	92.5	94.6	102.6	72.8	79.4	95.6	75.3	79.8	94.9	130.7	122.8	113.7	130.7	127.0	99.6	122.1	117.1
3.2 REINFORCING	95.1	100.3	97.3	124.6	72.3	102.4	117.8	74.8	99.6	99.4	128.5	111.7	96.1	128.5	109.8	106.5	128.5	115.8
3.3 CAST IN PLACE CONC.	105.7	98.3	101.1	90.6	92.8	92.0	98.5	93.8	95.6	109.5	109.3	109.4	103.4	109.5	107.2	93.1	107.2	101.9
3 CONCRETE	102.7	96.2	98.5	100.5	83.2	89.3	102.2	84.9	91.0	104.3	119.3	114.0	103.9	119.5	114.0	97.4	114.0	108.7
4 MASONRY	90.2	89.7	89.8	93.6	72.4	77.3	93.7	74.9	79.2	106.5	125.2	120.9	99.6	117.3	113.2	111.1	119.6	117.7
5 METALS	91.0	99.3	94.0	97.0	79.7	90.7	106.6	81.5	97.5	99.4	121.5	107.4	99.8	121.8	107.7	95.2	121.7	104.8
6 WOOD & PLASTICS	107.3	91.6	98.5	106.7	73.3	88.0	94.3	75.7	83.9	95.7	128.0	113.8	96.4	128.0	114.1	96.9	118.6	109.1
7 MOISTURE PROTECTION	106.8	76.8	97.3	84.7	72.4	80.8	84.2	74.9	81.3	108.2	131.4	115.5	84.7	116.8	94.8	107.7	110.5	108.6
8 DOORS, WINDOWS, GLASS	88.7	88.6	88.7	93.5	72.4	82.4	95.9	74.9	84.8	94.0	127.2	111.4	100.6	124.3	113.0	101.6	121.3	111.9
9.1 LATH & PLASTER	107.6	89.9	94.1	92.9	73.1	77.8	98.5	75.5	81.0	97.1	131.7	123.5	96.8	115.6	111.2	101.8	123.9	118.6
9.2 DRYWALL	87.1	91.2	89.1	95.2	72.4	84.4	114.8	74.9	95.8	97.5	129.0	112.4	98.3	123.9	110.5	98.7	121.5	109.5
9.5 ACOUSTICAL WORK	114.9	91.3	102.0	84.5	72.4	77.9	84.5	74.9	79.2	82.2	129.0	107.8	89.7	129.0	111.2	97.5	119.7	109.6
9.6 FLOORING	109.8	92.8	105.3	89.1	72.4	84.7	88.3	74.9	84.7	117.5	125.5	119.6	112.0	118.9	113.8	88.3	119.7	96.6
9.8 PAINTING	96.5	88.7	90.3	111.0	72.3	80.0	104.8	65.8	73.5	108.3	125.3	122.0	120.2	116.5	117.3	100.8	105.7	106.2
9 FINISHES	95.9	90.4	92.9	94.5	72.4	82.6	105.0	71.7	87.0	101.9	127.7	115.8	102.9	120.9	112.6	97.3	115.8	107.3
10-14 TOTAL DIV. 10-14	100.0	98.8	99.6	100.0	72.4	91.6	100.0	74.9	92.4	100.0	125.7	107.7	100.0	122.8	106.9	100.0	143.9	113.2
15 MECHANICAL	98.8	83.8	91.0	97.5	72.5	84.5	97.0	73.1	84.6	96.7	125.7	111.8	94.9	116.6	106.1	92.4	125.2	109.4
16 ELECTRICAL	102.3	88.7	92.6	99.2	75.5	82.3	93.4	76.2	81.1	98.7	125.3	117.7	106.1	116.5	113.5	109.7	119.6	116.8
1-16 WEIGHTED AVERAGE	98.9	90.7	94.4	96.7	76.4	85.5	98.7	77.8	87.2	100.6	123.9	113.4	98.5	118.8	109.6	98.6	120.3	110.5

CALIFORNIA

DIVISION	LOS ANGELES MAT.	INST.	TOTAL	OXNARD MAT.	INST.	TOTAL	RIVERSIDE MAT.	INST.	TOTAL	SACRAMENTO MAT.	INST.	TOTAL	SAN DIEGO MAT.	INST.	TOTAL	SAN FRANCISCO MAT.	INST.	TOTAL
2 SITE WORK	95.2	114.9	104.1	98.0	104.3	100.9	95.2	111.4	102.5	83.1	105.8	93.4	98.5	108.3	102.9	103.1	113.9	108.0
3.1 FORMWORK	112.8	131.1	127.1	90.0	131.0	122.0	102.5	130.7	124.5	100.9	127.1	121.4	105.8	128.5	123.5	104.9	134.6	128.1
3.2 REINFORCING	62.7	128.5	90.6	99.4	128.5	111.7	124.6	128.5	126.2	99.4	128.5	111.7	145.3	128.5	138.2	123.5	128.5	125.6
3.3 CAST IN PLACE CONC.	92.4	112.3	104.8	102.5	110.0	107.2	102.5	109.6	107.0	116.1	106.4	110.1	103.8	104.1	104.0	101.6	116.3	110.7
3 CONCRETE	90.0	121.1	110.1	99.3	119.8	112.6	107.3	119.5	115.2	109.3	116.4	113.9	113.3	115.8	114.9	107.1	124.5	118.3
4 MASONRY	110.4	125.2	121.8	98.5	125.4	119.1	102.9	124.8	119.7	101.4	125.9	120.3	109.1	113.3	112.4	130.9	138.0	136.3
5 METALS	101.7	122.5	109.2	105.6	121.8	111.5	99.5	121.6	107.5	111.4	121.7	115.1	99.2	120.5	106.9	104.4	124.8	111.8
6 WOOD & PLASTICS	100.6	129.1	116.6	92.6	128.5	112.8	98.5	128.0	115.0	78.4	125.0	104.6	93.9	125.3	111.5	95.0	134.2	117.0
7 MOISTURE PROTECTION	103.9	131.8	112.6	89.8	131.4	102.9	90.3	127.5	102.0	85.3	122.0	96.9	94.6	119.6	102.5	101.0	129.2	109.9
8 DOORS, WINDOWS, GLASS	101.6	127.2	115.1	103.1	127.2	115.8	103.7	127.2	116.1	92.3	126.5	110.2	107.5	120.6	114.4	113.2	133.5	123.8
9.1 LATH & PLASTER	96.3	131.7	123.3	97.5	126.6	119.7	97.5	125.7	119.0	98.8	123.1	117.4	103.2	114.8	112.0	101.7	144.7	134.5
9.2 DRYWALL	90.0	129.0	108.5	98.8	127.4	112.4	94.8	129.0	111.0	97.2	123.6	109.7	106.0	124.1	114.6	81.7	136.0	107.4
9.5 ACOUSTICAL WORK	98.4	129.0	115.1	88.4	129.0	110.6	88.4	129.0	110.6	86.6	126.0	108.1	100.5	126.3	114.6	100.5	135.8	119.8
9.6 FLOORING	96.6	125.5	104.2	95.2	125.5	103.2	95.2	125.5	103.2	85.7	126.0	96.3	98.0	117.5	103.2	106.1	138.1	114.6
9.8 PAINTING	85.6	126.9	118.8	92.3	125.1	118.7	100.5	124.5	119.8	112.4	126.0	123.3	92.1	128.5	121.3	100.6	140.5	132.6
9 FINISHES	91.9	128.2	111.5	96.5	126.6	112.7	95.0	127.0	112.3	95.3	124.8	111.2	102.3	124.8	114.4	91.1	138.2	116.5
10-14 TOTAL DIV. 10-14	100.0	126.1	107.8	100.0	125.7	107.7	100.0	125.5	107.7	100.0	146.0	113.9	100.0	124.2	107.3	100.0	150.5	115.2
15 MECHANICAL	97.4	126.2	112.3	98.7	125.9	112.8	96.5	126.6	112.1	98.2	126.4	112.8	102.9	125.0	114.4	100.8	160.0	131.5
16 ELECTRICAL	101.8	133.2	124.2	98.7	125.1	117.5	98.2	124.5	117.0	109.7	125.9	121.3	106.1	113.8	111.6	110.7	152.7	140.6
1-16 WEIGHTED AVERAGE	98.1	125.6	113.2	98.8	123.6	112.4	99.0	123.8	112.6	99.2	123.6	112.5	103.4	118.5	111.7	104.0	139.3	123.3

Figure 7.12

In addition to adjusting costs in *Building Construction Cost Data* for particular locations, the City Cost Index can also be used to adjust costs from one city to another. For example, the price of a particular building type is known for City A. In order to budget the costs of the same building type in City B, the following calculation can be made:

$$\frac{\text{City B Index}}{\text{City A Index}} \quad x \quad \text{City A Cost} \quad = \quad \text{City B Cost}$$

While City Cost Indexes provide a means to adjust prices for location, the Historical Cost Index, as shown in Figure 7.14, provides a means to adjust for time. Using the same principle as above, a time adjustment factor can be calculated:

$$\frac{\text{Index for Year X}}{\text{Index for Year Y}} \quad = \quad \text{Time Adjustment Factor}$$

This time adjustment factor can be used to determine what the budget costs would be for a particular building type in Year X, based on costs for a similar building type known from Year Y. Used in conjunction, the two indexes allow for cost adjustments from one city during a given year to

Component Contribution by UCI Division

No.	Division	%	No.	Division	%	No.	Division	%
1.5	CONTRACTOR EQUIP.*	6.8%	5.1	Structural Metals	2.2%	9.1	Lath & Plaster	0.4%
2.3	Earthwork	1.7	5.2	Metal Joists & Deck	1.5	9.2	Drywall	4.7
2.4	Caissons & Pilings	0.7	5.4	Misc. & Ornamental Metals	2.6	9.3	Tile & Terrazzo	1.1
2.5	Site Utilities	0.6	5	METALS	6.4	9.5	Acoustical Work	0.8
2.6	Roads & Walks	0.8	6.1	Rough Carpentry	1.6	9.6	Flooring	1.4
2.7	Site Improvements	0.1	6.2	Finish Carpentry	0.1	9.8	Painting	2.2
2.8	Landscaping	1.2	6	WOOD & PLASTICS	1.8	9	FINISHES	10.5
2	SITEWORK	5.1	7.1	Water & Dampproofing	0.7		DIVISIONS 10-14	8.3
3.1	Formwork	5.8	7.2	Insulation	0.6	15.1	Plumbing	5.0
3.2	Reinforcing	2.4	7.3	Shingles	0.3	15.5	Fire Protection	2.5
3.3	Cast in Place Concrete	9.8	7.4	Roofing & Siding	3.3	15.6	Heating	7.2
3.4	Precast Concrete	0.3	7.6	Sheet Metal Work	0.2	15.7	Air Condit. & Vent.	4.4
3.5	Cementitious Decks	0.1	7	MOISTURE PROTECTION	5.0	15	MECHANICAL	19.0
3	CONCRETE	18.5	8.1	Doors & Frames	1.5	16	ELECTRICAL	9.5
4.1	Mortar & Accessories	0.3	8.6	Windows	2.5		TOTAL	100.0%
4.2	Brick Masonry	2.7	8.8	Glass & Glazing	1.8			
4.3	Block & Tile Work	6.6	8	DOORS, WINDOWS, GLASS	5.8			
4.4	Stone	0.4						
4	MASONRY	10.0						

*Percentage for contractor equipment is spread among divisions and included above for information only.

Figure 7.13

another city in another year (the present or otherwise). For example, an office building built in San Francisco in 1974, originally cost $1,000,000. How much will a similar building cost in Phoenix in l986? Adjustment factors are developed as shown above using data from Figures 7.12 and 7.14:

$$\frac{\text{Phoenix index}}{\text{San Francisco index}} = \frac{94.5}{123.3} = 0.77$$

$$\frac{\text{1986 index}}{\text{1974 index}} = \frac{192.0}{94.7} = 2.03$$

Original cost x location adjustment x time adjustment = Proposed new cost

$1,000,000 x 0.77 x 2.03 = $1,563,000

Circle Reference Numbers

Throughout the Unit Price pages of *Building Construction Cost Data*, certain line items contain circle reference numbers (see Figure 7.15) which refer the reader to expanded data and information in the back of the book. The Circle Reference Number section contains over seventy pages with 143 tables, charts, definitions and costs, all of which corroborate the unit price data. The development of many unit costs is explained and detailed in this section. This information can be very helpful to the estimator, particularly when more information is needed about materials and considerations that have gone into a unit price line item. Figure 7.16 is an example of the development of cost (see Figure 7.15 for the line item that references Circle Reference Number 49).

Year	"Quarterly City Cost Index" Jan. 1, 1975 = 100		Current Index Based on Jan. 1, 1986 = 100		Year	"Quarterly City Cost Index" Jan. 1, 1975 = 100	Current Index Based on Jan. 1, 1986 = 100		Year	"Quarterly City Cost Index" Jan. 1, 1975 = 100	Current Index Based on Jan. 1, 1986 = 100	
	Est.	Actual	Est.	Actual		Actual	Est.	Actual		Actual	Est.	Actual
Oct. 1986					July 1973	86.3	44.9		July 1957	42.2	22.0	
July 1986					1972	79.7	41.5		1956	40.4	21.0	
April 1986					1971	73.5	38.3		1955	38.1	19.8	
Jan. 1986	192.0		100.0	100.0	1970	65.8	34.3		1954	36.7	19.1	
July 1985		189.1	98.5		1969	61.6	32.1		1953	36.2	18.9	
1984		187.6	97.7		1968	56.9	29.6		1952	35.3	18.4	
1983		183.5	95.6		1967	53.9	28.1		1951	34.4	17.9	
1982		174.3	90.8		1966	51.9	27.0		1950	31.4	16.4	
1981		160.2	83.4		1965	49.7	25.9		1949	30.4	15.8	
1980		144.0	75.0		1964	48.6	25.3		1948	30.4	15.8	
1979		132.3	68.9		1963	47.3	24.6		1947	27.6	14.4	
1978		122.4	63.8		1962	46.2	24.1		1946	23.2	12.1	
1977		113.3	59.0		1961	45.4	23.6		1945	20.2	10.5	
1976		107.3	55.9		1960	45.0	23.4		1944	19.3	10.1	
1975		102.6	53.4		1959	44.2	23.0		1943	18.6	9.7	
1974		94.7	49.3		1958	43.0	22.4		1942	18.0	9.4	

Figure 7.14

3.3 Cast in Place Concrete	CREW	DAILY OUTPUT	UNIT	BARE COSTS			TOTAL INCL O&P
				MAT.	INST.	TOTAL	
130 Non-metallic, 55 lb. bags, natural (grey), minimum			Lb.	.30		.30	.33M
131 Maximum				.40		.40	.44M
132 Non-metallic, colors, mininum				.35		.35	.38M
134 Maximum				.45		.45	.49M
140 Non-metallic, non-slip, 100 lb. bags, minimum				.35		.35	.38M
142 Maximum			↓	.45		.45	.49M
150 Solution type, 300 to 400 S.F. per gallon			Gal.	4.80		4.80	5.30M
151							
155 Release agent, for tilt slabs			Gal.	7.50		7.50	8.25M
157 For forms, average				5		5	5.50M
160 Sealer, hardener and dustproofer, clear, 450 S.F., minimum				7		7	7.70M
162 Maximum				16.50		16.50	18.15M
170 Colors (300-400 S.F. per gallon)			↓	15		15	16.50M
171							
180 Set accelerator for below freezing, 1 to 1-1/2 gal. per C.Y.			Gal.	4.20		4.20	4.62M
190 Set retarder, 2 to 4 fl. oz. per bag of cement			"	12.80		12.80	14.10M
200 Waterproofing, integral 1 lb. per bag of cement			Lb.	.72		.72	.79M
210 Powdered metallic, 40 lbs. per 100 S.F., minimum				.77		.77	.84M
212 Maximum			↓	1		1	1.10M
220 Water reducing admixture, average			Gal.	7.75		7.75	8.50M
10-001 (45) CONCRETE, FIELD MIX FOB forms 2250 psi			C.Y.	44.60		44.60	49M
002 3000 psi				47.45		47.45	52M
12-001 (43) CONCRETE, READY MIX Regular weight, 2000 psi				45.55		45.55	50M
010 2500 psi				47.25		47.25	52M
015 (42) 3000 psi				48.90		48.90	54M
020 3500 psi				50.55		50.55	56M
025 3750 psi				51.50		51.50	57M
030 4000 psi				52.20		52.20	57M
035 4500 psi				54.15		54.15	60M
040 5000 psi				55.15		55.15	61M
100 For high early strength cement, add				10%			
101 For structural lightweight with regular sand, add				27%			
200 For all lightweight aggregate, add			↓	50%			
300 For integral colors, 2500 psi, 5 bag mix							
310 Red, yellow or brown, 1.8 lb. per bag, add			C.Y.	12.60		12.60	13.85M
320 9.4 lb. per bag, add				66		66	73M
340 Black, 1.8 lb. per bag, add				13.10		13.10	14.40M
350 7.5 lb. per bag, add				55		55	61M
370 Green, 1.8 lb. per bag, add				27		27	30M
380 7.5 lb. per bag, add			↓	115		115	125M
14-001 CONCRETE IN PLACE Including forms (4 uses), reinforcing							
005 steel, including finishing unless otherwise indicated							
010 (35) Average for concrete framed building,							
011 including finishing	C-17B	15.75	C.Y.	98	120	218	280
013 (47) Average for substructure only, simple design, incl. finishing	↓	29.07	↓	69	65	134	170
015 Average for superstructure only, including finishing	↓	13.42	↓	105	140	245	315
020 (50) Base, granolithic, 1" x 5" high, straight	C-10	175	L.F.	.12	2.81	2.93	4.01
022 Cove	"	140	"	.12	3.51	3.63	4.98
030 Beams, 5 kip per L.F., 10' span	C-17A	6.28	C.Y.	168	285	453	595
035 25' span		7.40		135	240	375	495
050 (122) Chimney foundations, minimum		26.70		89	67	156	195
051 Maximum		19.70		102	91	193	240
070 (49) Columns, square, 12" x 12", minimum reinforcing		4.60		180	390	570	755
072 Average reinforcing	↓	4.10		255	435	690	910
074 Maximum reinforcing	C-17B	3.84		380	495	875	1,125
080 16" x 16", minimum reinforcing	C-17A	6.25		160	285	445	585
082 Average reinforcing	"	4.93		250	360	610	795
084 Maximum reinforcing	C-17B	4.34		420	435	855	1,075
090 24" x 24", minimum reinforcing	C-17A	9.08		140	195	335	435
092 Average reinforcing	"	6.90	↓	210	260	470	605

Figure 7.15

CIRCLE REFERENCE NUMBERS

(49) Average C.Y. of Concrete (cont.)

Columns, Square Square Tied	(Line 082) 16" Square				(Line 092) 24" Square			
	Material		**Installation**		**Material**		**Installation**	
4000 psi concrete	1 C.Y.	$ 52.20	1 C.Y.	$ 43.05	1 C.Y.	$ 52.20	1 C.Y.	$ 32.15
Formwork, 4 uses	81 S.F. @ 49¢	39.70	81 S.F. @ $2.69	217.90	54 S.F. @ 50¢	27.00	54 S.F. @ $2.66	143.65
Reinforcing steel, avg.	634# @ 25¢	158.85	634# @ 16¢	101.45	524# @ 25¢	131.20	524# @ 16¢	83.10
Total per C.Y.		$250.75		$362.40		$210.40		$258.90

Note: Reinforcing of 16" and 24" square columns can vary from 144 lb. to 972 lb. per C.Y.

Columns, Round Tied Reinforced	(Line 122) 16" Diameter				(Line 142) 24" Diameter			
	Material		**Installation**		**Material**		**Installation**	
4000 psi concrete	1 C.Y.	$ 52.20	1 C.Y.	$ 33.50	1 C.Y.	$ 52.20	1 C.Y.	$ 24.20
Formwork, fiber forms	19 L.F. @ $4.75	90.25	19 L.F. @ $4.52	85.90	9 L.F. @ $9.20	82.80	9 L.F. @ $4.87	43.85
Reinforcing steel, avg.	606# @ 25¢	151.50	600# @ 16¢	96.00	600# @ 25¢	150.00	600# @ 15¢	90.00
Ties	70# @ 23¢	16.10	70# @ 23¢	16.15	18# @ 26¢	4.70	18# @ 23¢	4.15
Total per C.Y.		$310.05		$231.55		$289.70		$162.20

Note: Reinforcing of 16" and 24" diameter columns can vary from 160 lb. to 1150 lb. per C.Y.

Flat Plate	(Line 210) 100 psf, 15' Span				(Line 215) 100 psf, 25' Span			
	Material		**Installation**		**Material**		**Installation**	
4000 psi concrete	1 C.Y.	$ 52.20	1 C.Y.	$ 53.70	1 C.Y.	$52.20	1 C.Y.	$40.50
Formwork, 4 uses	59 S.F. @ 48¢	28.30	59 S.F. @ $1.78	105.00	32 S.F. @ 49¢	15.70	32 S.F. @ $1.79	57.30
Reinforcing steel	126# @ 26¢	32.75	126# @ 12¢	15.10	112# @ 26¢	29.10	112# @ 12¢	13.45
Total per C.Y.		$113.25		$173.80		$97.00		$111.25

Flat Slab	(Line 190) 100 psf, 20' Span				(Line 195) 100 psf, 30' Span			
	Material		**Installation**		**Material**		**Installation**	
4000 psi concrete	1 C.Y.	$52.20	1 C.Y.	$39.10	1 C.Y.	$52.20	1 C.Y.	$34.50
Formwork, 4 uses	42 S.F. @ 68¢	28.55	42 S.F. @ $1.91	80.20	28 S.F. @ 68¢	19.05	28 S.F. @ $1.91	53.50
Reinforcing steel	120# @ 26¢	31.20	120# @ 12¢	14.40	131# @ 26¢	34.05	131# @ 12¢	15.70
Total per C.Y.		$111.95		$133.70		$105.30		$103.70

Grade Wall, 8' High	(Line 420) 8" Thick				(Line 430) 15" Thick			
	Material		**Installation**		**Material**		**Installation**	
3000 psi concrete	1 C.Y.	$48.90	1 C.Y.	$ 13.40	1 C.Y.	$48.90	1 C.Y.	$ 8.50
Formwork, 4 uses	81 S.F. @ 50¢	40.50	81 S.F. @ $1.94	157.15	41 S.F. @ 50¢	20.50	41 S.F. @ $1.94	79.55
Reinforcing steel	44# @ 26¢	11.45	44# @ 12¢	5.30	44# @ 26¢	14.05	44# @ 12¢	6.50
Total per C.Y.		$100.85		$175.85		$83.45		$94.55

Metal Pan Joists, 30" One Way	(Line 250) 100 psf, 15' Span				(Line 255) 100 psf, 25' Span			
	Material		**Installation**		**Material**		**Installation**	
4000 psi concrete	1 C.Y.	$ 52.20	1 C.Y.	$ 44.85	1 C.Y.	$ 52.20	1 C.Y.	$ 29.30
Formwork, 4 uses	49 S.F. @ 73¢	35.75	49 S.F. @ $2.03	99.45	40 S.F. @ $1.08	43.20	40 S.F. @ $2.83	113.20
Reinforcing steel	47# @ 26¢	12.20	47# @ 12¢	5.65	81# @ 26¢	21.05	81# @ 12¢	9.70
30" metal pans	44 S.F. @ 23¢	10.10	44 S.F. @ 26¢	11.45	37 S.F. @ 23¢	8.50	37 S.F. @ 26¢	9.60
Total per C.Y.		$110.25		$161.40		$124.95		$161.80

Pile Caps	(Line 590) Under 5 C.Y.				(Line 595) Over 10 C.Y.			
	Material		**Installation**		**Material**		**Installation**	
3000 psi concrete	1.05 C.Y.	$51.35	1.05 C.Y.	$10.75	1.05 C.Y.	$51.35	1.05 C.Y.	$ 5.75
Formwork, 4 uses	16 S.F. @ 44¢	7.05	16 S.F. @ $1.65	26.40	8.5 S.F. @ 44¢	3.75	8.5 S.F. @ $1.65	14.00
Reinforcing steel	44# @ 26¢	11.45	44# @ 12¢	5.30	54# @ 26¢	14.05	54# @ 12¢	6.50
Total per C.Y.		$69.85		$42.25		$69.15		$26.25

Slab on Grade	(Line 465) 4" Thick				(Line 470) 6" Thick			
	Material		**Installation**		**Material**		**Installation**	
3500 psi concrete	1.05 C.Y.	$53.10	1.05 C.Y.	$8.85	1.05 C.Y.	$53.10	1.05 C.Y.	$5.95
Formwork, 4 uses	9.2 L.F. @ 16¢	1.45	9.2 L.F. @ $1.06	9.75	6 L.F. @ 16¢	.95	6 L.F. @ $1.06	6.35
W.W. Fabric	81 S.F. @ 7.65¢	6.20	81 S.F. @ 9.95¢	8.05	54 S.F. @ 7.65¢	4.15	54 S.F. @ 9.95¢	5.40
Total per C.Y.		$60.75		$26.65		$58.20		$17.70

Figure 7.16

Chapter 8
ESTIMATING BY UCI DIVISION

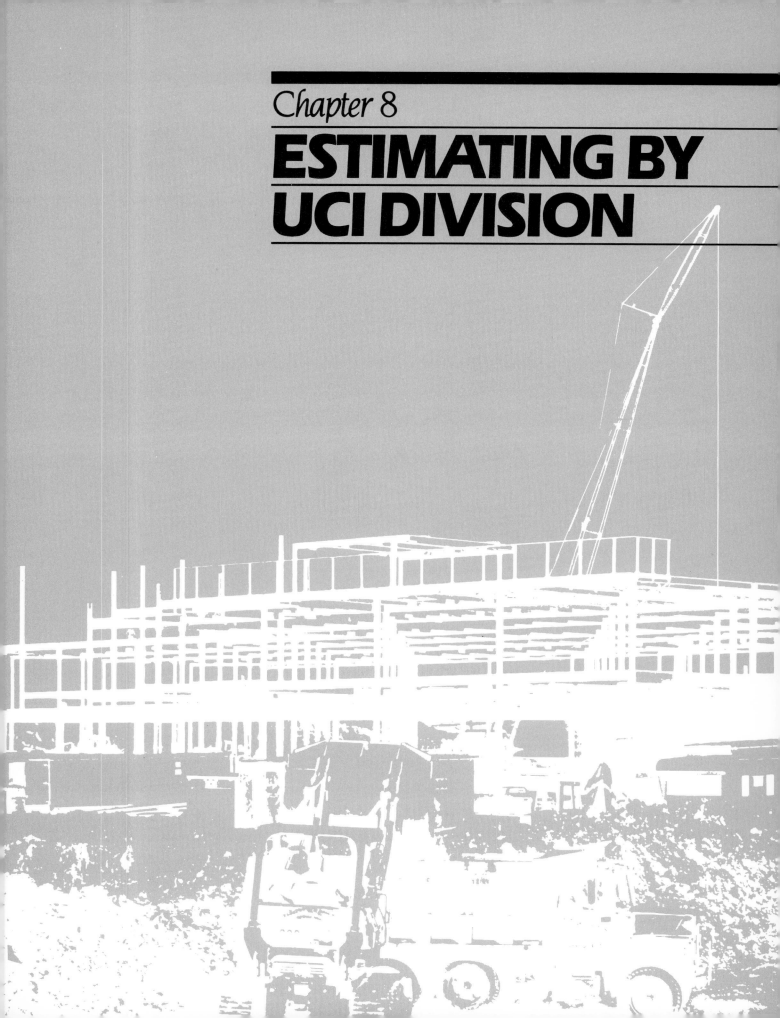

Chapter 8
ESTIMATING BY UCI DIVISION

There are two basic approaches to performing a Unit Price estimate. One is to proceed with the estimate, the quantity takeoff and pricing in a sequence similar to the order in which a building is constructed. Using this method, concrete for footings is priced very early in the estimate, after excavation but before backfill. The concrete used for upper level floor slabs is estimated much later, after structural steel. This is the approach taken for a Systems estimate. The advantage to this method is that experienced estimators can visualize the construction process while proceeding with the estimate. As a result, omissions are less likely. The basic disadvantage of this system is that it is not easy to determine and track costs for each division (or subcontract). Costs for a particular trade may be spread throughout the estimate.

The second approach to unit price estimating is by UCI division. Most architectural specifications today are written according to this format, using the sixteen UCI divisions. Trades and subcontracts are generally limited to work within one division (e.g., Mechanical, or Masonry). It makes sense, therefore that the estimate should also be organized in the UCI format. Using this method, the estimator may have to be more careful to include all required work. Nevertheless, the advantages outweigh potential drawbacks. Most specifications contain references to related work for all divisions. These references serve as an aid to assure completeness, but the estimator for the general contractor still has the responsibility of making sure that subcontractors include all that is specified and required for the appropriate portions of the project. The estimator must also decide what work will be subcontracted and what will be performed by the work force of the general contractor. These decisions can have a significant effect on the final cost of a project. Traditionally, work has been done at a lower cost using the general contractor's own labor force. With the specialization of trades, however, subcontractors can often perform work faster, and thus at a lower cost.

Cost accounting and control is another area affected by the choice of estimating approach. Whichever method is chosen should be used consistently, from estimating — to field reporting — to final analysis. The first approach, estimating in the sequence of construction, brings the same challenge to cost accounting as it does to estimating — the difficulty of keeping similar items grouped together as the work of single trades.

The second method of estimating and cost accounting, by UCI division, may take longer when it comes to compiling all costs for each division (e.g., until all concrete or site work is complete). However, each trade will be separated and the records will be in accordance with the specifications. Since material purchases and scheduling of manpower and subcontractors are based on the construction sequence, these items should be derived from the project schedule. This schedule is established after and formulated from the unit price estimate, and is the basis of project coordination.

Most project specifications contain a list of alternates which must be included with a submitted bid. These alternates become a series of mini-estimates within the total project estimate. Each alternate may include deductions of some items from the project, originally specified, as well as the addition of other items. Often mistakenly regarded as incidentals, alternates are often left until the project estimate is complete. In order to efficiently determine alternate costs, without performing a completely new estimate for each, the project estimate must be organized with the alternates in mind. If items are to be deducted as part of an alternate, they must be separated in the project estimate. Similarly, when measuring for quantities, pertinent dimensions and quantities for the "adds" of an alternate should be listed separately. If forethought is used, alternates can be estimated quickly and accurately.

The following discussions and the sample estimate are presented by UCI division for the reasons mentioned above. Ultimately, the choice of method is not crucial as long as all items are included and all costs accounted.

Sample Estimate: Project Description

The project for the sample estimate is a three story office building with a basement parking garage. The 2.6 acre site is located in a suburban area with good access and sufficient material storage area. The proposed building is composite steel frame with an aluminum panel and glass curtain wall system. Plans for the building are shown in Figures 8.1 to 8.15. These plans are provided for illustrative purposes only and represent the major features of the building. In actuality, such a building would require many more sheets of drawings with more plans, details, sections and elevations. Also included would be a full set of specifications. For the purposes of the example, however, these figures provide sufficient information. The quantities as given in the sample estimate represent realistic conditions. Assumptions have also been made for items not shown in Figures 8.1 to 8.15 that would normally be included in the plans and specifications of a project of this type.

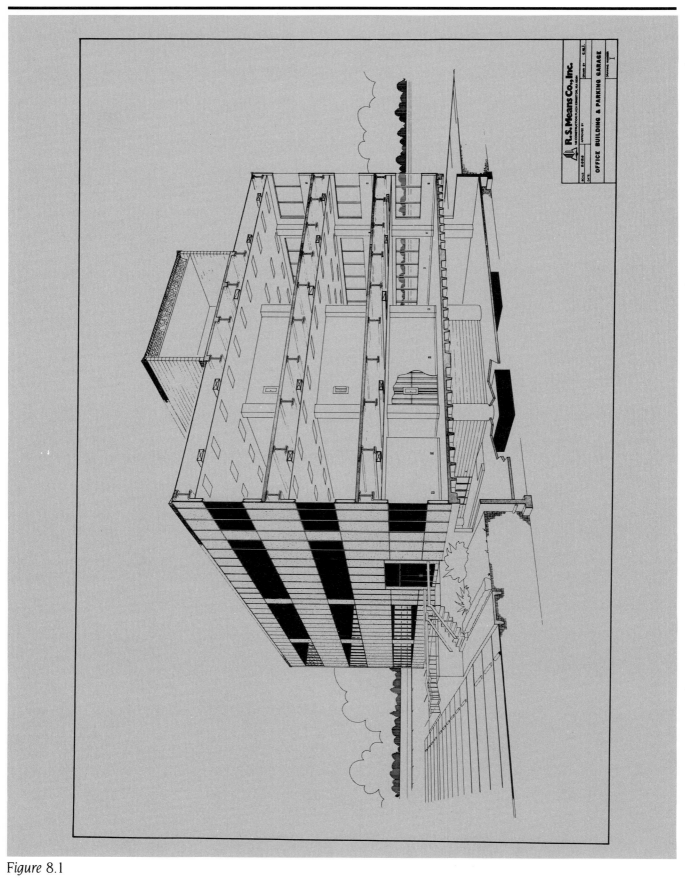

Figure 8.1

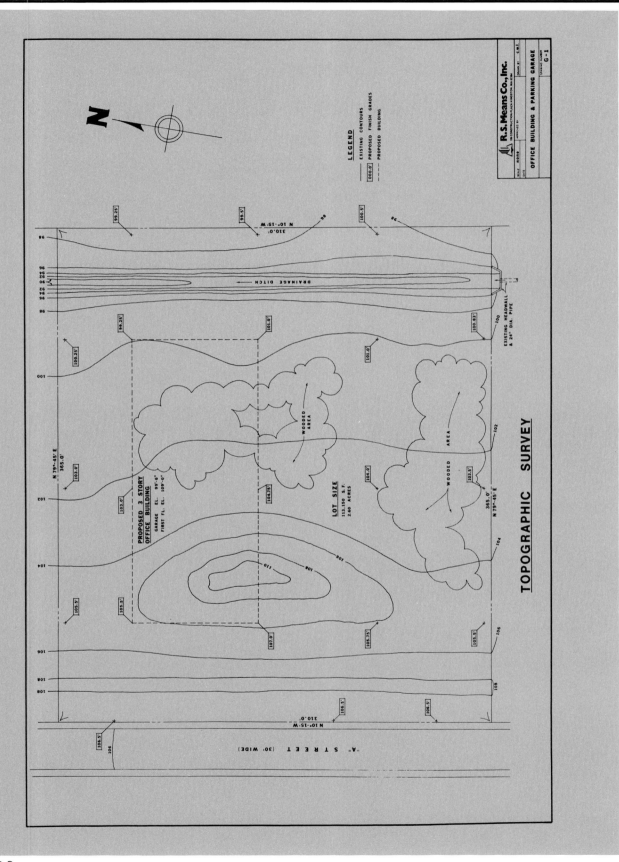

Figure 8.2

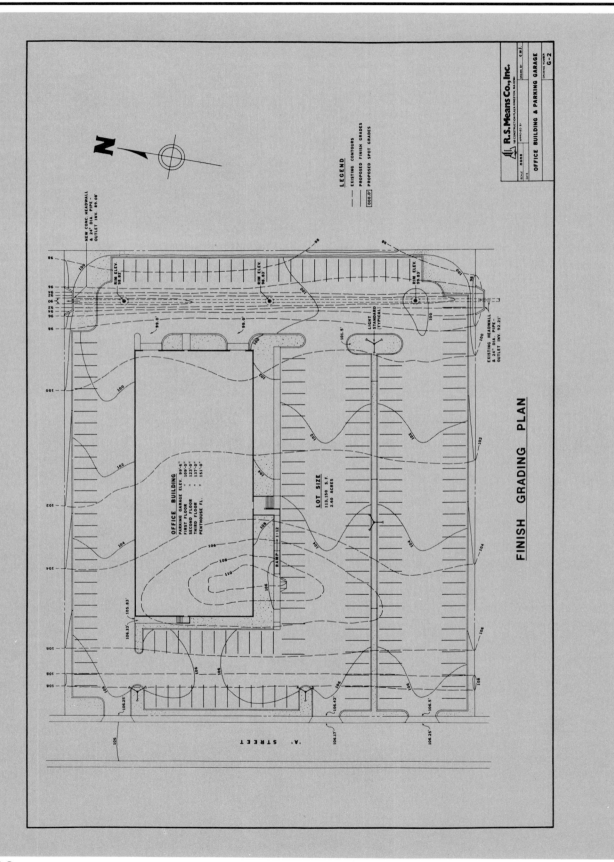

Figure 8.3

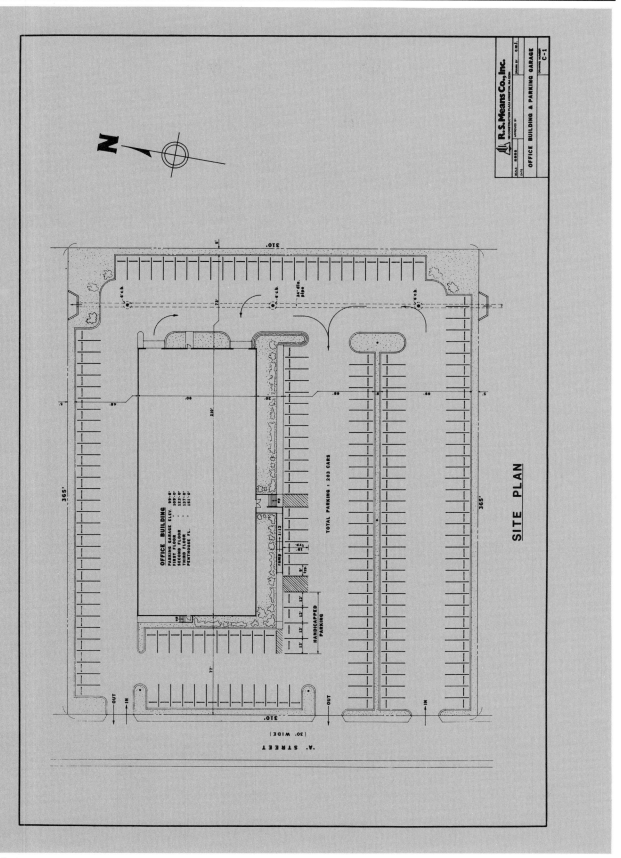

Figure 8.4

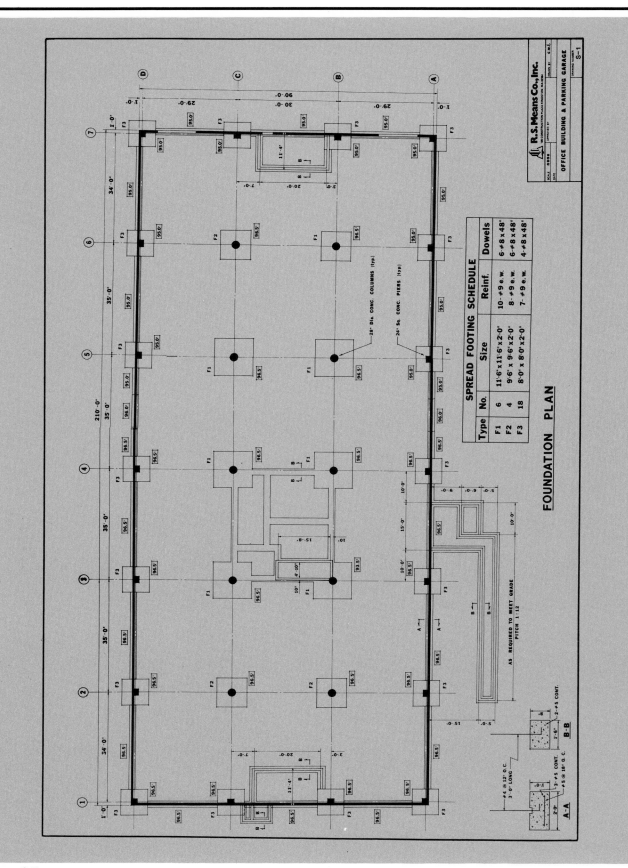

Figure 8.5

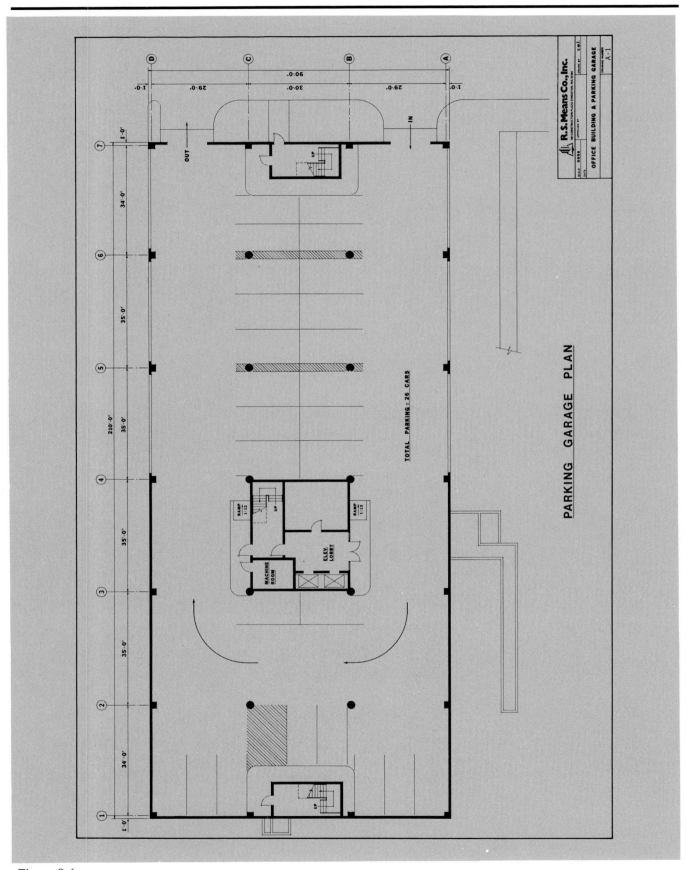

Figure 8.6

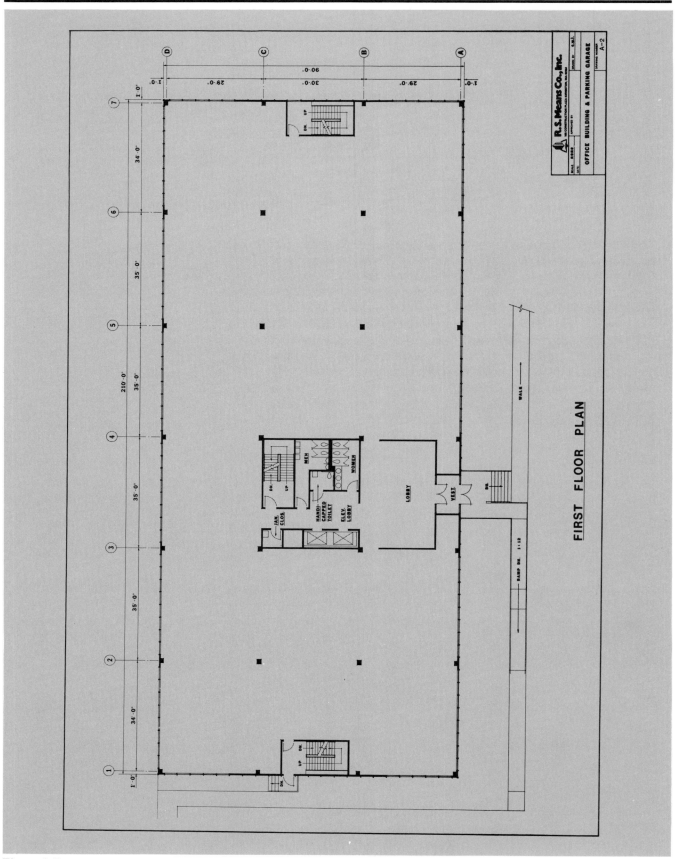

FIRST FLOOR PLAN

Figure 8.7

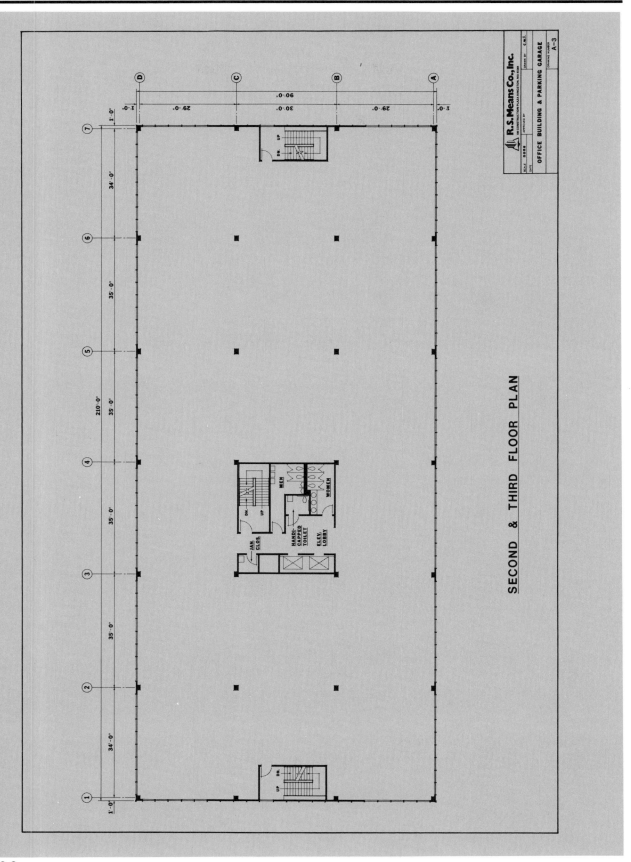

SECOND & THIRD FLOOR PLAN

Figure 8.8

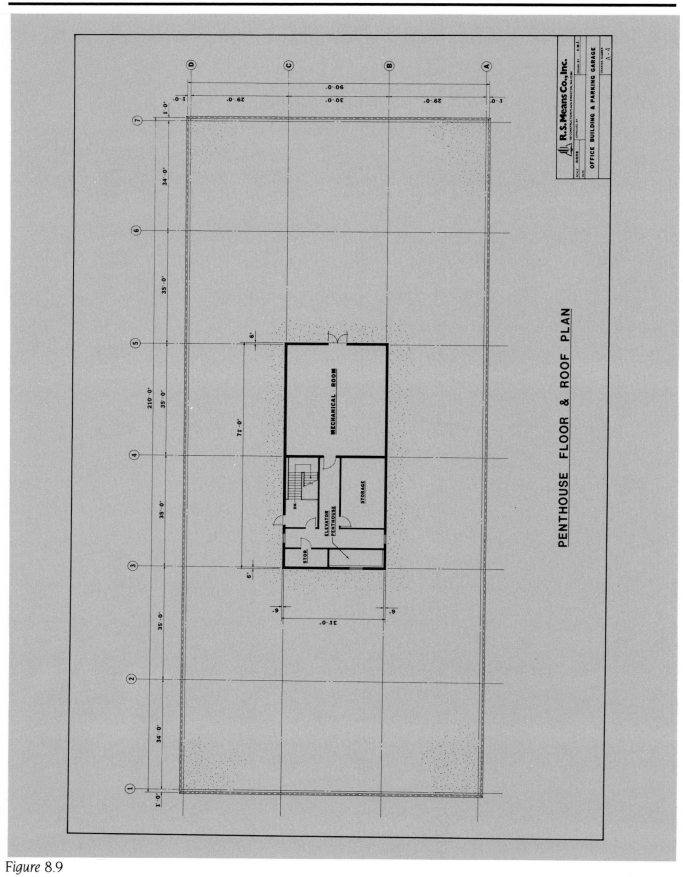

PENTHOUSE FLOOR & ROOF PLAN

Figure 8.9

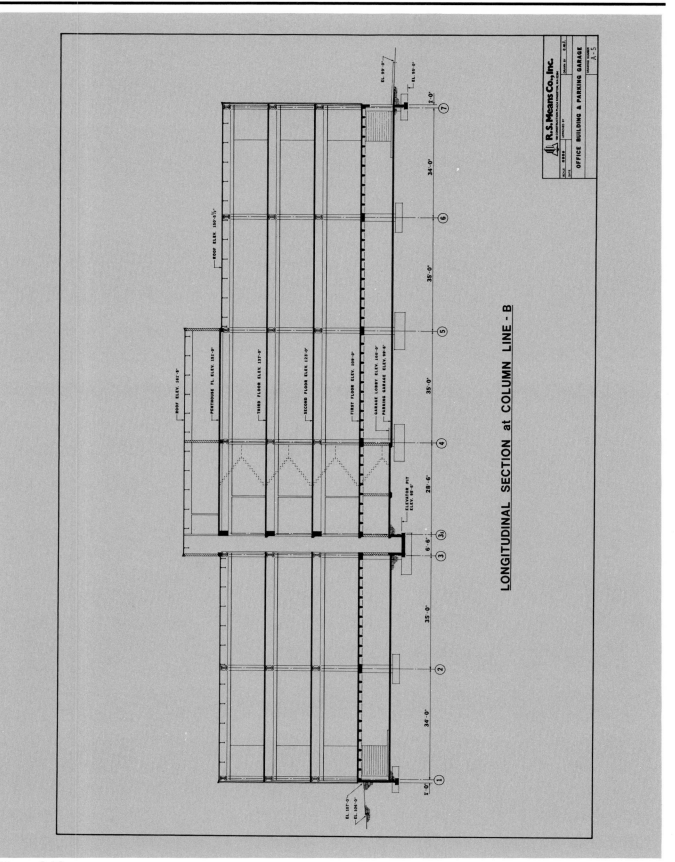

LONGITUDINAL SECTION at COLUMN LINE - B

Figure 8.10

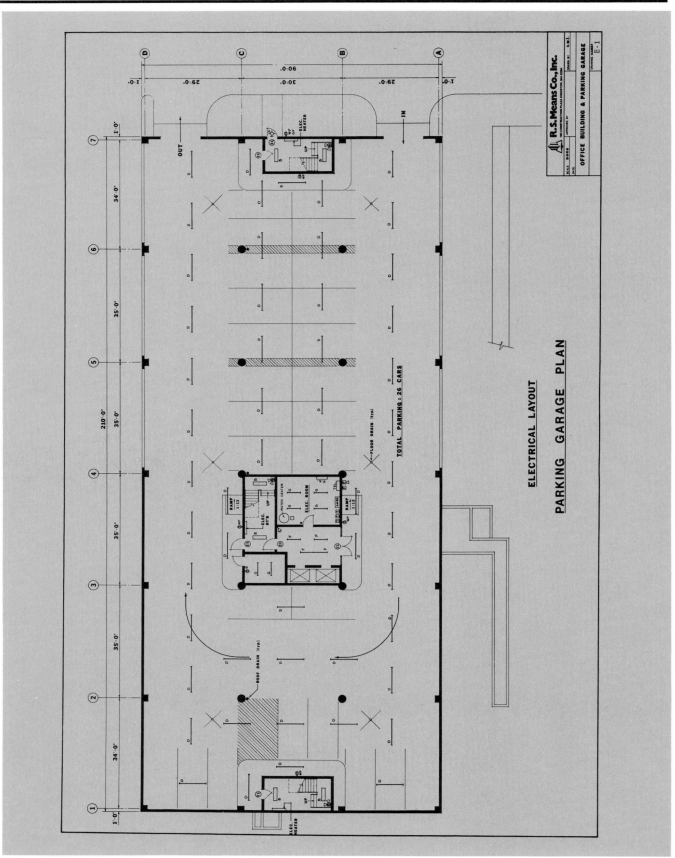

ELECTRICAL LAYOUT

PARKING GARAGE PLAN

Figure 8.11

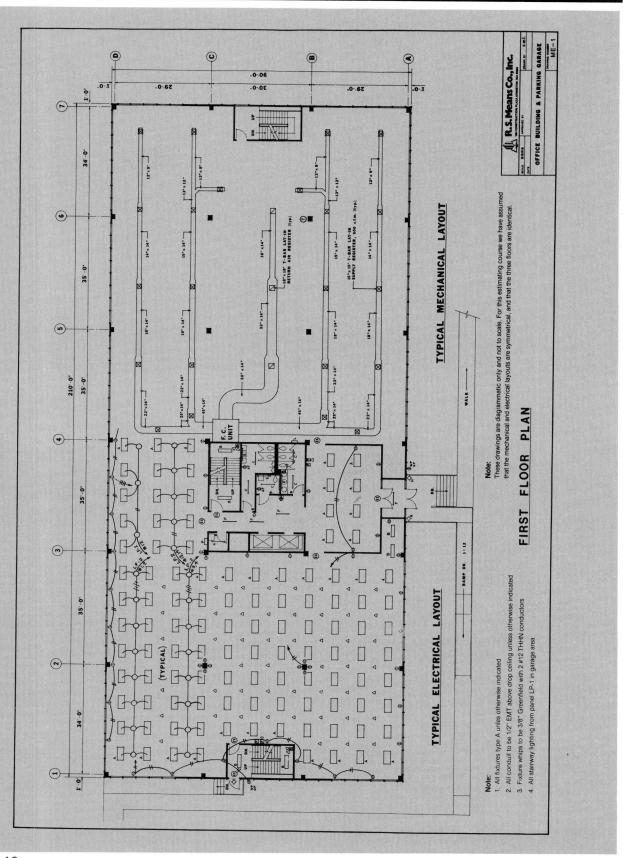

Figure 8.12

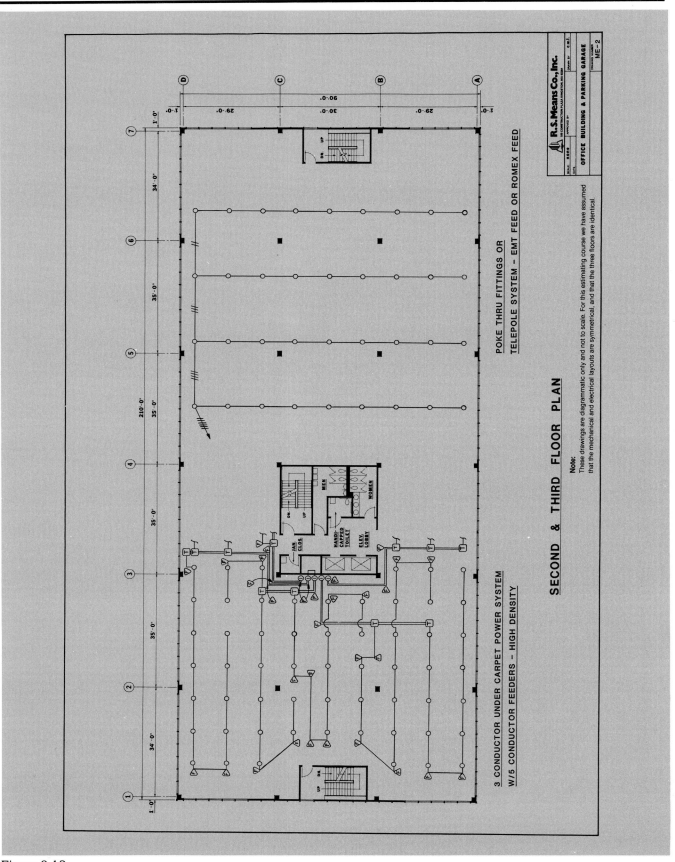

Figure 8.13

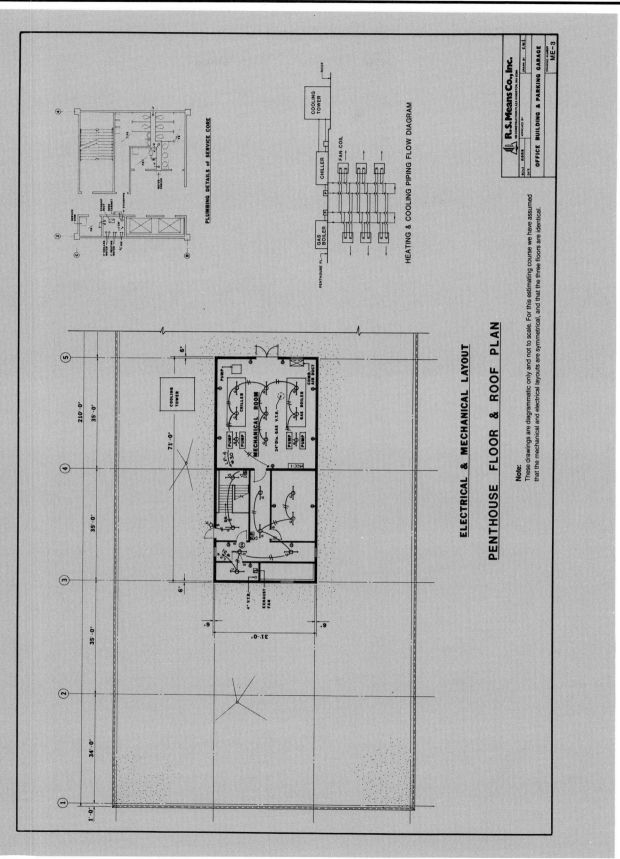

ELECTRICAL & MECHANICAL LAYOUT

PENTHOUSE FLOOR & ROOF PLAN

Note:
These drawings are diagrammatic only and not to scale. For this estimating course we have assumed that the mechanical and electrical layouts are symmetrical, and that the three floors are identical.

PLUMBING DETAILS of SERVICE CORE

HEATING & COOLING PIPING FLOW DIAGRAM

R.S. Means Co., inc.
OFFICE BUILDING & PARKING GARAGE
ME-3

Figure 8.14

121

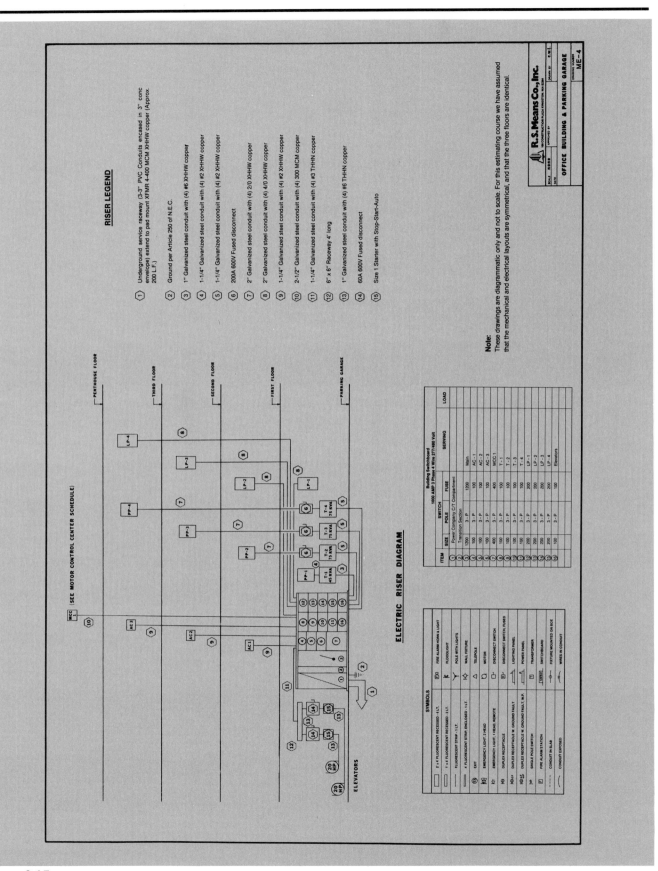

Figure 8.15

Division 1:
General Requirements

When estimating by UCI division, the estimator must be careful to include all items which, while not attributable to one trade or to the physical construction of the building, are nevertheless required to successfully complete the project. These items are included in the General Requirements section. Often referred to as the "General Conditions" or "Project Overhead", they are usually set forth in the first part of the specifications. Some requirements may not be directly specified even though they are required to perform the work. Standardized sets of General Conditions have been developed by various segments of the construction industry, such as those by the American Institute of Architects, the Consulting Engineers Council/U.S., National Society of Professional Engineers, and others. These standardized documents usually include:

- Definitions
- Contract document descriptions
- Contractor's rights and responsibilities
- Architect-engineer's authority and responsibilities
- Owner's rights and responsibilities
- Variation from contract provisions
- Payment requirements and restrictions
- Requirements for the performance of the work
- Insurance and bond requirements
- Job conditions and operation

Since these documents are generic, additions, deletions and modifications unique to specific projects are often included in Supplementary General Conditions.

Estimated costs for Division 1 are often recorded on a standardized form or checklist similar to the Project Overhead Summary shown in Figures 8.16 and 8.17. Such pre-printed forms or checklists are helpful to be sure that all requirements are included and priced. Many of the costs are dependent upon work in other divisions or on the total cost and/or time duration of the job. Project overhead costs should be determined throughout the estimating process and finalized when all other divisions have been estimated and a preliminary schedule established.

The following are brief discussions of various items that may be included as project overhead. The goal is to develop an approach to the estimate which will assure that all project requirements are included.

Personnel

Job site personnel may be included as either project overhead or office overhead, often depending upon the size of the project and the contractor's accounting methods. For example, if a project is large enough to require a full-time superintendent, then all costs for that person (time related) may be charged completely as project overhead. If the superintendent is responsible for a number of smaller jobs, then the expense may be either included in office overhead, or proportioned for each job. The same principles may apply to the salaries of field engineers, project managers, and time keepers.

If there is no full-time field engineer on the project, then costs may be incurred for establishing grades and setting stakes, building layout, producing as-built drawings, shop drawings or maintenance records.

MEANS PROJECT OVERHEAD SUMMARY

SHEET NO.						
PROJECT				ESTIMATE NO.		
LOCATION		ARCHITECT		DATE		
QUANTITIES BY:	PRICES BY:	EXTENSIONS BY:		CHECKED BY:		

DESCRIPTION	QUANTITY	UNIT	MATERIAL/EQUIPMENT		LABOR		TOTAL COST	
			UNIT	TOTAL	UNIT	TOTAL	UNIT	TOTAL
Job Organization: Superintendent								
Project Manager								
Timekeeper & Material Clerk								
Clerical								
Safety, Watchman & First Aid								
Travel Expense: Superintendent								
Project Manager								
Engineering: Layout								
Inspection/Quantities								
Drawings								
CPM Schedule								
Testing: Soil								
Materials								
Structural								
Equipment: Cranes								
Concrete Pump, Conveyor, Etc.								
Elevators, Hoists								
Freight & Hauling								
Loading, Unloading, Erecting, Etc.								
Maintenance								
Pumping								
Scaffolding								
Small Power Equipment/Tools								
Field Offices: Job Office								
Architect/Owner's Office								
Temporary Telephones								
Utilities								
Temporary Toilets								
Storage Areas & Sheds								
Temporary Utilities: Heat								
Light & Power								
Water								
PAGE TOTALS								

Figure 8.16

DESCRIPTION	QUANTITY	UNIT	MATERIAL/EQUIPMENT		LABOR		TOTAL COST	
			UNIT	TOTAL	UNIT	TOTAL	UNIT	TOTAL
Total Brought Forward								
Winter Protection: Temp. Heat/Protection								
Snow Plowing								
Thawing Materials								
Temporary Roads								
Signs & Barricades: Site Sign								
Temporary Fences								
Temporary Stairs, Ladders & Floors								
Photographs								
Clean Up								
Dumpster								
Final Clean Up								
Punch List								
Permits: Building								
Misc.								
Insurance: Builders Risk								
Owner's Protective Liability								
Umbrella								
Unemployment Ins. & Social Security								
Taxes								
City Sales Tax								
State Sales Tax								
Bonds								
Performance								
Material & Equipment								
Main Office Expense								
Special Items								
TOTALS:								

Figure 8.17

With regard to surveying and layout of the building and roads, it is important to determine who is the responsible party – the owner, general contractor or appropriate subcontractor. This responsibility should be established, if not done so in the contract documents, so that costs may be properly allocated.

Depending upon the size of the project, a carpenter and/or a laborer may be assigned to the job on a full-time basis for miscellaneous work. In such cases, workers are directly responsible to the job superintendent for various tasks; the costs of this work would not be attributable to any specific division and would most appropriately be included as project overhead.

Equipment

As discussed in Chapter 4, equipment costs may be recorded as project overhead or included in each appropriate division. Some equipment, however, will be used by more than one trade; examples are personnel or material hoists and cranes. The allocation of costs in these cases should be according to company practice.

Testing

Various tests may be required by the owner, local building officials or as specified in the contract documents. Depending upon the stage of design development and the role of the contractor, soil borings and/or percolation tests may be required. Usually this type of testing is the responsibility of the designer or engineer, paid for directly by the owner. Most testing during construction is required to verify conformance of the materials and methods to the requirements of the specifications. The most common testing is as follows:

Soil compaction: Soil compaction is usually specified as a percentage of maximum density. Strict compaction methods are required under slabs on grade and at backfill of foundation walls and footings. Testing may be required every day (or possibly every lift). Soil samples may have to be lab tested for cohesiveness, permeability and/or water content. Watering may be required to achieve the specified compaction.

Concrete: Concrete tests may be required at two stages: slump tests during placement and compression tests after a specified curing time. Slump tests, indicating relative water and cement content, may be required for each truck load, after placement of a certain number of cubic yards, each day or per building section. Compression tests are performed on samples placed in cylinders usually after 7 and 28 days of curing time. The cylinders are tested by outside laboratories. If the concrete samples fail to meet design specifications, core drilling of in-place building samples for further testing may be required.

Miscellaneous Testing: Other testing may be necessary based on the type of construction and owner or architect/engineer requirements. Core samples of asphalt paving are often required to verify specified thickness. Steel connection and weld testing may be specified for critical structural points. Masonry absorption tests may be also required.

The costs of testing installed materials may be included – in different ways – as project overhead. One method is separately itemizing the costs for each individual test; or, a fixed allowance can be made based on the size and type of project. Budget costs derived from this second method are shown in Figure 8.18. A third approach is to include a percentage of total project costs.

1.1	Overhead	CREW	DAILY OUTPUT	UNIT	BARE COSTS			TOTAL INCL O&P
					MAT.	INST.	TOTAL	
480	Roads, gravel fill, no surfacing, 4" gravel thickness	B-14	715	S.Y.	.60	1.35	1.95	2.54
490	8" gravel thickness	"	615	"	1.14	1.57	2.71	3.44
520	Sidewalks, 2" x 12" planks, 2 uses	1 Carp	350	S.F.	.36	.46	.82	1.06
522	Exterior plywood, 2 uses, 1/2" thick		750		.19	.21	.40	.52
523	5/8" thick		650		.25	.25	.50	.63
525	3/4" thick	↓	600		.34	.27	.61	.76
526	Signs, hi-intensity reflectorized, no posts, buy			↓	8.40		8.40	9.25M
527	Stair tread protection, 2" x 12" planks, 1 use	1 Carp	75	Tread	.94	2.13	3.07	4.13
529	Exterior plywood, 1/2" thick, 1 use		65		.43	2.46	2.89	4.04
530	3/4" thick, 1 use	↓	60	↓	.78	2.67	3.45	4.72
550	Storage vans, trailer mounted, 16' x 8', buy	2 Skwk	1.80	Ea.	2,200	180	2,380	2,675
552	Rent per month				75		75	83M
555	28' x 10', buy	2 Skwk	1.40		2,600	235	2,835	3,200
557	Rent per month			↓	80		80	88M
560	Surveyor stakes, hardwood, 1" x 1" x 48" long			C	25		25	28M
562	2" x 2" x 18" long				25		25	28M
564	2" x 2" x 24" long				29		29	32M
566	2" x 4" x 24" long			↓	40		40	44M
580	Toilet, portable, see Division 1.5-15-641							
60-001	TESTING For concrete building costing $1,000,000, minimum			Project				5,000
002	Maximum							50,000
005	Steel building, minimum							5,000
007	Maximum							10,000
010	For building costing, $10,000,000, minimum							35,000
015	Maximum			↓				50,000
020	Asphalt testing, compressive strength Marshall stability, set of 3			Ea.				100
022	Density, set of 3							39
025	Extraction, individual tests on sample							80
030	Penetration							25
035	Mix design, 5 specimens							640
036	Additional specimen							80
040	Specific gravity							31
042	Swell test							62
045	Water effect and cohesion, set of 6							154
047	Water effect and plastic flow							62
060	Concrete testing, aggregates, abrasion							62
065	Absorption							26
080	Petrographic analysis							450
090	Specific gravity							25
100	Sieve analysis, washed							67
105	Unwashed							36
120	Sulfate soundness							68
130	Weight per cubic foot							16
150	Cement, physical tests							255
160	Chemical tests							309
180	Compressive strength, cylinders, delivered to lab							9
190	Picked up by lab, minimum							8
195	Average							10
200	Maximum							19
220	Compressive strength, cores (not incl. drilling)			↓				26
225	Core drilling, 4" diameter (plus technician)			Inch				15
226	Technician for core drilling			Hr.				33
230	Patching core holes			Ea.				21
240	Drying shrinkage at 28 days							245
250	Flexural test beams							32
260	Mix design, one batch mix							155
265	Added trial batches							104
280	Modulus of elasticity							124
290	Tensile test, cylinders			↓				52

Figure 8.18

Temporary Services

Required temporary services may or may not be included in the specifications. A typical statement in the specifications is: "Contractor shall supply all material, labor, equipment, tools, utilities and other items and services required for the proper and timely performance of the work and completion of the project." As far as the owner and designer are concerned, such a statement eliminates a great deal of ambiguity. To the estimator, this means many items that must be estimated. Temporary utilities, such as heat, light, power and water are a major consideration. The estimator must not only account for anticipated monthly (or time related) costs, but should also be sure that installation and removal costs are included, whether by the appropriate subcontractor or the general contractor.

The time of year may also have an impact on the cost of temporary services. Snow removal costs must be anticipated in climates where such conditions are likely. If construction begins during a wet season, or there is a high ground water table, then dewatering may be necessary. Usually the boring logs give the contractor a feel for the probable ground water elevation. Logs should be examined for the time of year in which the borings were taken. If high infiltration rates are expected, wellpoints may be required. The pumping allowance is usually priced from an analysis of the expected duration and volume of water. This information dictates pump size, labor to install, and power to operate the pumps. This can be an expensive item, since the pumps may have to operate 168 hours per week during certain phases of construction.

An office trailer and/or storage trailers or containers are usually required and included in the specifications. Even if these items are owned by the contractor, costs should still be allocated to the job as part of project overhead. Telephone, utility and temporary toilet facilities are other costs in this category.

Depending upon the location and local environment, some security services may be required. In addition to security personnel or guard dogs, fences, gates, special lighting and alarms may also be needed. A guard shack with heat, power and telephone, can be an expensive temporary cost.

Temporary Construction

Temporary construction may also involve many items which are not specified in the construction documents. Temporary partitions, doors, fences and barricades may be required to delineate or isolate portions of the building or site. In addition to these items, railings, catwalks or safety nets may also be necessary for the protection of workers. Depending upon the project size, an OSHA representative may visit the site to assure that all such safety precautions are being observed.

Ramps, temporary stairs and ladders are often necessary during construction for access between floors. When the permanent stairs are installed, temporary wood fillers are needed in metal pan treads until the concrete fill is placed. Workers will almost always use a new, permanent elevator for access throughout the building. While this use is almost always restricted, precautionary measures must be taken to protect the doors and cab. Invariably, some damage occurs. Protection of any and all finished surfaces throughout the course of the project must be priced and included in the estimate.

Job Cleanup

An amount should always be carried in the estimate for cleanup of the grounds and the building, both during the construction process and upon completion. The cleanup can be broken down into three basic categories, and these can be estimated separately:

- Continuous (daily or otherwise) cleaning of the building and site.
- Rubbish handling and removal.
- Final cleanup.

Costs for continuous cleaning can be included as an allowance, or estimated by required man-hours. Rubbish handling should include barrels, a trash chute if necessary, dumpster rental and disposal fees. These fees vary depending upon the project, and a permit may also be required. Costs for final cleanup should be based upon past projects and may include subcontract costs for items such as the cleaning of windows and waxing of floors. Included in the costs for final cleanup may be an allowance for repair of minor damage to finished work.

Miscellaneous General Conditions

Many other items must be taken into account when costs are being determined for project overhead. Among the major considerations are:

1. *Scaffolding or Swing Staging* — It is important to determine who is responsible for rental, erection and dismantling of scaffolding. If a subcontractor is responsible, it may be necessary to leave the scaffolding in place long enough for use by other trades. Scaffolding is priced by the section or per hundred square feet.

2. *Small Tools* — An allowance, based on past experience, should be carried for small tools. This allowance should cover hand tools as well as small power tools for use by workers on the general contractor's payroll. Small tools have a habit of "walking" and a certain amount of replacement is necessary. Special tools like magnetic drills may be required for specific tasks.

3. *Permits* — Various types of permits may be required depending upon local codes and regulations. Following are some examples:

   a. General building permit
   b. Subtrade permits (mechanical, electrical, etc.)
   c. Street use permit
   d. Sidewalk use permit
   e. Permit to allow work on Sundays
   f. Rubbish burning permit (if allowed)
   g. Blasting permit

   Both the necessity of the permit and the responsibility for acquiring it must be determined. If the work is being done in an unfamiliar location, local building officials should be consulted regarding unusual or unknown requirements.

4. *Insurance* — Insurance coverage for each project and locality — above and beyond normal, required operating insurance — should be reviewed to assure that coverage is adequate. The contract documents will often specify certain required policy limits. The need for specific policies or riders should be anticipated (for example, fire or XCU — explosion collapse, underground).

Other items commonly included in project overhead are: photographs, job signs, sample panels and materials for owner/architect approval, and an allowance for replacement of broken glass. For some materials, such as imported goods or custom fabricated items, both shipping costs and off site storage fees can be expected. An allowance should be included for anticipated costs pertaining to punchlist items. These costs are likely to be based on past experience.

Some project overhead costs can be calculated at the beginning of the estimate. Others will be included as the estimating process proceeds. Still other costs are estimated last since they are dependent upon the total cost and duration of the project. Because many of the overhead items are not directly specified, the estimator must use experience and visualize the construction process to assure that all requirements are met. It is not important when or where these items are included, but that they *are* included. One contractor may list certain costs as project overhead, while another contractor would allocate the same costs (and responsibility) to a subcontractor. Either way, the costs are recorded in the estimate.

Sample Estimate: Division 1

At this initial stage of the estimating process, it is best to list as many as possible the items that are considered overhead. From a thorough review of the construction documents, especially the General and Supplementary Conditions, the estimator should be aware of both the specified requirements and those which are implied but not directly stated. Items are added to the list throughout the estimate. Pricing occurs at the end because a majority of the costs are time related or dependent upon total project cost.

The allocation of work and equipment to be included in the particular subtrades should be decided at this time. For example, the estimator must decide if the temporary fence is to be installed by the general contractor's personnel or if the work is to be subcontracted. Responsibility for establishing grades and building layout could be given to an employed field engineer, an outside engineering firm, or to the appropriate subcontractors. These choices should be made at the beginning of the estimate. Figures 8.19 and 8.20 are the Project Overhead Summary for the three-story office building. All items known at this point are listed. Additions to the list and appropriate pricing will occur later in the estimate. Note that certain lump sum (LS) items have been included. Prices for these items (insurance, for example) can be determined either from historical costs or from telephone quotations.

MEANS PROJECT OVERHEAD SUMMARY

PROJECT Office Building

LOCATION	ARCHITECT	DATE 1986

QUANTITIES BY: EBW	PRICES BY: RSM	EXTENSIONS BY: SLM	CHECKED BY: JDM

DESCRIPTION	QUANTITY	UNIT	MATERIAL/EQUIPMENT UNIT	MATERIAL/EQUIPMENT TOTAL	LABOR UNIT	LABOR TOTAL	TOTAL COST UNIT	TOTAL COST TOTAL
Job Organization: Superintendent 1.1-22-105		WK.			910			
Project Manager								
Timekeeper & Material Clerk 1.1-22-120		WK.			495			
Clerical								
Safety, Watchman & First Aid								
Travel Expense: Superintendent								
Project Manager								
Engineering: Layout 1.1-50-120		Day			420			
Inspection/Quantities								
Drawings								
CPM Schedule								
Testing: Soil								
Materials	1	LS		7500				
Structural								
Equipment: Cranes								
Concrete Pump, Conveyor, Etc.								
Elevators, Hoists	By Division							
Freight & Hauling								
Loading, Unloading, Erecting, Etc.								
Maintenance								
Pumping								
Scaffolding								
Small Power Equipment/Tools 1.1-48-001	0.5	%						
Field Offices: Job Office Trailer 1.1-58- 428 446		Mo.	202					
Architect/Owner's Office								
Temporary Telephones								
Utilities		Mo.	200					
Temporary Toilets								
Storage Areas & Sheds 1.1- 58-557		Mo.	80					
Temporary Utilities: Heat								
Light & Power 1.1-58- 350 355	567	CSF						
~~Water~~ Power 1.1-58- 370 375		Mo.						
PAGE TOTALS								

Figure 8.19

| DESCRIPTION | QUANTITY | UNIT | MATERIAL/EQUIPMENT | | | | LABOR | | | | TOTAL COST | | | |
			UNIT	TOTAL			UNIT	TOTAL			UNIT	TOTAL		
Total Brought Forward														
Winter Protection: Temp. Heat/Protection 1.1-58-330	567	CSF	14.16				18.75							
Snow Plowing														
Thawing Materials														
Temporary Roads 1.1-58-480	750	SY	.60				1.35							
Signs & Barricades: Site Sign	1	LS		7 5 0										
Temporary Fences 1.1-58-255	1350	LF	1.51				3.16							
Temporary Stairs, Ladders & Floors														
Photographs By Owner														
Clean Up Continuous-One Laborer		wk.					636							
Dumpster 2.1-43-060		wk.	150											
Final Clean Up 1.1-04-010	56.7	MSF	1.58				26							
Punch List	0.2	%												
Permits: Building 1.1-36-001/010	1	%												
Misc.														
Insurance: Builders Risk Additional Rider	1	LS		7 0 0										
Owner's Protective Liability														
Umbrella														
Unemployment Ins. & Social Security														
Taxes														
City Sales Tax														
State Sales Tax														
Bonds														
Performance														
Material & Equipment														
Main Office Expense														
Special Items														
TOTALS:														

Figure 8.20

Division 2: Site Work

Prior to quantity takeoff, pricing, or even the site visit, the estimator must read the specifications carefully and examine the plans thoroughly. By knowing – before the site visit – what to expect and what work is required, the estimator is less likely to overlook features and should be able to save time by avoiding a second site visit. In addition to being familiar with project requirements, the estimator might also find a Job Site Analysis form helpful (as in Figures 2.3 and 2.4) to assure that all items are included.

For the other divisions in new building construction, the plans and specifications include almost all of the data required for complete and proper estimating and construction. Site work, however, is similar to remodeling or renovation work. Certain existing conditions and "unknowns" may not be shown on the plans. It is the responsibility of the estimator to discover these conditions and to include appropriate costs in the estimate.

The first step in preparing the site work estimate is to determine areas and limits from the plans (to be checked in the field) for:

- Limits of the total parcel
- Limits of the work area
- Areas of tree removal and clearing
- Stripping of topsoil
- Cut and fill
- Building and utility excavation
- Roads and walks
- Paving
- Landscaping

There are three basic methods to determine area from a plan. The first is with a planimeter – a device which, when rolled along a designated perimeter, will measure area. The resulting measurement must then be converted to the scale of the drawing. Trigonometry can also be used to determine area. It is applied to the distances and bearings supplied by a survey. Sines and cosines are used to calculate coordinates, which are in turn used to calculate area. The planimeter may be used only if the drawing is to scale and the scale is known. The trigonometric method may be used on a drawing not to scale, but only if survey data is available. Both methods are accurate.

A third method, triangulation, is less accurate but can be used in either case. This method involves dividing the area into triangles, squares and rectangles and determining the area of each. Some dimensions must be scaled. An example is shown in Figure 8.21. Triangulation is quick, and depending upon the shape of the site, is accurate to within a few percent.

Soil borings and analyses, if available, should be reviewed prior to the site visit. Test pit and percolation data can also be very useful. Soil type and porosity, any encountered ledge, and the height of the water table, will all have a bearing on the site work estimate.

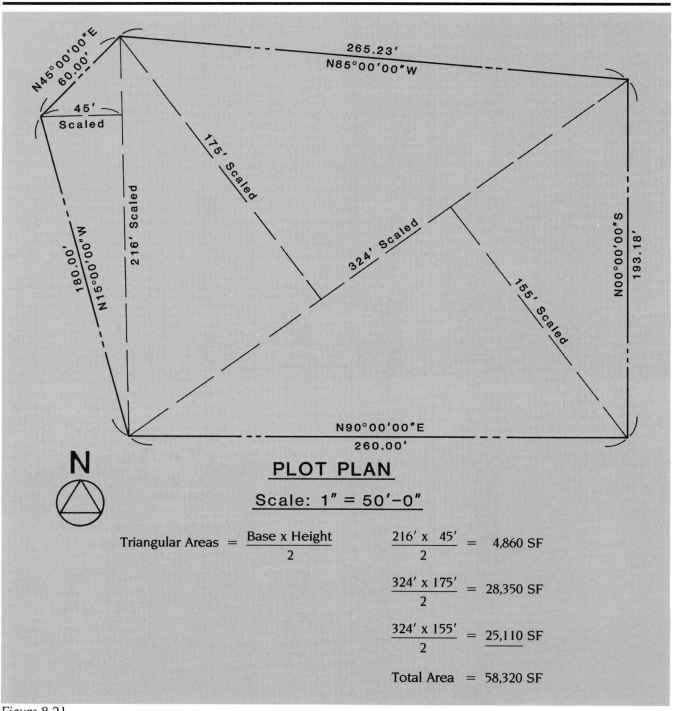

PLOT PLAN

Scale: 1" = 50'-0"

Triangular Areas = $\dfrac{\text{Base x Height}}{2}$

$\dfrac{216' \times 45'}{2} = 4,860$ SF

$\dfrac{324' \times 175'}{2} = 28,350$ SF

$\dfrac{324' \times 155'}{2} = 25,110$ SF

Total Area = 58,320 SF

Figure 8.21

The Site Visit

Once the estimator is familiar with the project requirements, the site visit should be used to confirm and verify information. The initial examination should cover such items as general access, the amount and kind of traffic, location of existing utilities, and site storage. These conditions cannot be quantified, but will all have an impact on site work costs. Boundary lines and stakes should be located, especially if the work area is close to property lines.

The site visit may be conducted according to the sequence in which the site work will be performed: clearing and grubbing, excavation, blasting (if necessary), utilities and drainage, backfill, roads, paving and site improvements.

Estimates for tree removal can be made by actually counting and sizing each tree to be removed. If the site is small or the number of trees few, this may be the easiest (and most accurate) method. If large quantities are involved, a random count method will suffice. The first step is to determine the total acreage to be cleared. Counts of each type and size of vegetation should be made for 16' on either side of a line, 340' long. These counts (at least 3) should be made at random. Each count will reflect relative density for one fourth of an acre. Due to rising lumber costs (especially hardwood) and the growing use of firewood, the estimator may find a company or individual to cut and remove the trees at no cost. The expense of stump and brush removal must still be included.

The estimator should determine a rough soil profile, either from test pits, soil borings, or with a shovel. The depth of loam, or topsoil, is important. The specifications may state whether the topsoil is to be stripped and stockpiled for reuse on the site, or hauled away. If there is no room for topsoil storage on the site so that all is removed (and possibly sold), topsoil may have to be purchased later for the landscaping. Test pits may also be a good indicator of soil stability. Depending upon the site conditions and project requirements, shoring or sheet piling may be required at trenches and excavations.

The estimator should roughly determine the location of building utilities and other excavation areas and should visualize the excavation process. Stockpile areas should be located and a rough determination reached as to proper equipment size and type. The excavation procedure should be based on a key rule of site work — only move the material once. At this stage, the estimator may or may not have an indication as to whether fill will be required or excess hauled away. These questions will be answered during cut and fill calculations. If there is excess fill, haul distance to the dumping area (whether on site or off) will have a bearing not only on cost, but on the selection of equipment. Erosion control measures may be required to prevent soil runoff from stockpiles or excavation areas. If not specified, this possibility should be determined while at the site.

If ledge is evident, either visually or from borings, the estimator should be familiar with local regulations. Where blasting is permitted, items such as mats, overtime work and special permits can be very expensive. Local regulations may require that after exposure by excavation, the ledge be covered (backfilled) before blasting. Because of the fact that subsurface conditions may be unknown, blasting is usually included in the estimate as an allowance per cubic yard. This allowance must include all possibilities.

Existing utilities, whether on-site or off, overhead or underground, should be located and noted or verified on the site plan. The estimator should roughly note locations of the proposed utilities to determine if any problems or conflicts will arise due to existing conditions. For the same reasons, existing drainage conditions should be verified and compared to the proposed drainage.

If the specifications are not clear, the estimator should determine whether or not the excavated material is suitable for backfill. If not, the unsuitable material must be removed and new material purchased and delivered.

Roads, walks, paving, site improvements and landscaping should also be visualized to anticipate any unique conditions or requirements. The quality and detail of the site visit will be reflected in the accuracy and thoroughness of the site work estimate.

Earthwork

Responsibility for layout and staking of the building, grades, utilities and other excavation should be determined prior to estimating. If not, everyone will assume that the other guy is responsible.

There are two basic methods and a third variation of determining cuts and fills for the earthwork portion of a project. The first method is most appropriate for linear excavations (roads and large trenches). It involves determining the cross-sectional area of the excavation at appropriate locations. The area of the cross-sections can be determined by using a planimeter or by the methods shown in Figure 8.22. To calculate volume, two cross-sectional areas are averaged and multiplied by the distance between the sections. The selection and frequency of cross-section locations will have an effect on the calculations. Accuracy is improved if the sections are located so that topography is relatively uniform between each pair. Separate calculations must be made for cuts and for fill.

The second method is to superimpose a grid over the site plan and to determine the existing elevation at each intersection of the grid. The elevations at the four corners of each grid square are averaged. The difference between the proposed elevation and the existing average elevation for each square is calculated (whether cut or fill). All cuts and all fills are added separately to determine excavation quantities. The difference between the two is the amount that must be borrowed or hauled away. A quicker and slightly less accurate variation of this method can also be used. Instead of determining corner elevations and averaging, the estimator can visually determine the average elevations from the relationship of the grid squares to the contours.

A number of factors must be considered when calculating excavation quantities. If all dimensions (elevations and distances) are in feet, then the final cubic foot quantities must be converted to cubic yards. When finish grade elevations are taken from a plan, the estimator must be sure to account for subbases and finish materials (gravel, paving, concrete, topsoil, etc.) which will be on top of the subgrade to reach the final elevations and grades.

Level Cross-Section

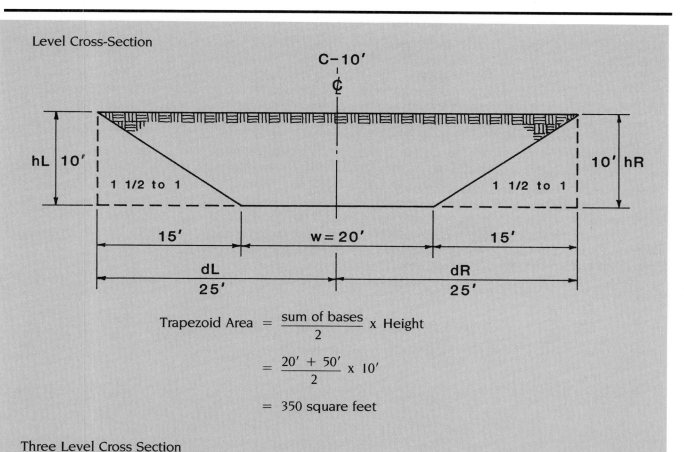

$$\text{Trapezoid Area} = \frac{\text{sum of bases}}{2} \times \text{Height}$$

$$= \frac{20' + 50'}{2} \times 10'$$

$$= 350 \text{ square feet}$$

Three Level Cross Section

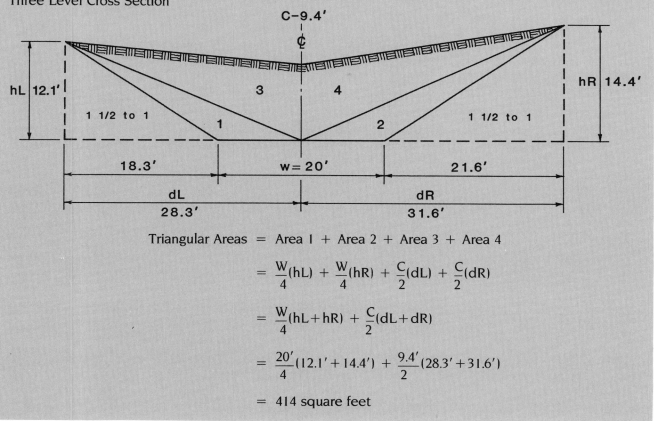

$$\text{Triangular Areas} = \text{Area 1} + \text{Area 2} + \text{Area 3} + \text{Area 4}$$

$$= \frac{W}{4}(hL) + \frac{W}{4}(hR) + \frac{C}{2}(dL) + \frac{C}{2}(dR)$$

$$= \frac{W}{4}(hL+hR) + \frac{C}{2}(dL+dR)$$

$$= \frac{20'}{4}(12.1' + 14.4') + \frac{9.4'}{2}(28.3' + 31.6')$$

$$= 414 \text{ square feet}$$

Figure 8.22

137

Another major factor to consider is the difference between bank volume (material in a natural state), loose volume (after digging), and compacted volume. The relationship of swell and shrinkage is illustrated in Figure 8.23, together with conversion tables. As shown, the volume of materials expands when disturbed or excavated. This same material can most often be compacted to less than the natural bank volume. An example of how these conversion tables are used is shown in the sample estimate. When pricing compaction, the estimator must consider the specified depth of lifts, or layers, which must each be compacted. The specifications should also be checked for required compaction testing.

After figuring bulk excavation, the estimator should take off the quantities for the following types of excavation, paying attention for such items as steps and haunches:

- Perimeter strip footings
- Interior strip footings
- Spread footings
- Utility trenches, meter pits, manholes
- Special items (elevator pits, tunnels, etc.)
- Hand excavation

Caissons and Piles

Caissons, piles and pressure-injected footings are specialty items usually taken off and priced by a subcontractor. The cost of caissons and piles, although priced by the linear foot, is dependent on the number of units to be installed. This is due to the fact that mobilization for the equipment can cost thousands of dollars before the first pile is driven. Typical mobilization costs are shown in Figure 8.24. The mobilization cost will have a lesser effect per unit, as the number of units required increases. When soliciting bids, the estimator should verify that all required costs are included. Pile caps, cutting, testing, and wet conditions will all add to the total cost.

Roads

Temporary roads are an item that may easily be underestimated or overlooked. Under dry conditions, watering, oiling, or calcium chloride treatment may be necessary to prevent dust. Under wet conditions, large quantities of crushed stone and trenching for drainage may be needed. Consideration must be given to the installation of utilities; this procedure may require removal and reconstruction of the temporary road.

As with the building layout, costs must also be included for the layout and grades of roads, curbs and associated utilities. Most specifications will state the requirements for work above rough grade: gravel base, subbase, finish paving courses, etc. Bulk cuts and fills for the roadwork should be determined as part of bulk excavation. Excavation for curbs must also be included. Hand work may be necessary.

Bituminous paving is usually taken off and priced by the square yard, but it is sold by the ton. The average weight of bituminous concrete is 145 pounds per cubic foot. By converting, 1 square yard, 1" thick, weighs approximately 110 pounds. This figure can be used to determine quantities (in tons) for purchase:

Base course: 2" thick, 1,500 SY

1,500 SY X 2" x 110 lbs. = 330,000 lbs. = 165 tons

Finish course: 1" thick, 1,500 SY

1,500 SY X 1" x 110 lbs. = 165,000 lbs. = 82.5 tons

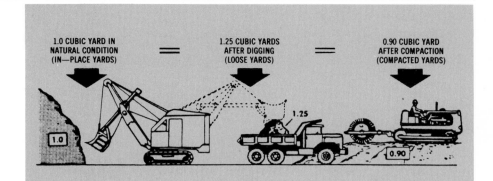

Approximate Material Characteristics*				
Material	Loose (lb/cu yd)	Bank (lb/cu yd)	Swell (%)	Load Factor
Clay, dry	2,100	2,650	26	0.79
Clay, wet	2,700	3,575	32	0.76
Clay and gravel, dry	2,400	2,800	17	0.85
Clay and gravel, wet	2,600	3,100	17	0.85
Earth, dry	2,215	2,850	29	0.78
Earth, moist	2,410	3,080	28	0.78
Earth, wet	2,750	3,380	23	0.81
Gravel, dry	2,780	3,140	13	0.88
Gravel, wet	3,090	3,620	17	0.85
Sand, dry	2,600	2,920	12	0.89
Sand, wet	3,100	3,520	13	0.88
Sand and gravel, dry	2,900	3,250	12	0.89
Sand and gravel, wet	3,400	3,750	10	0.91

*Exact values will vary with grain size, moisture content, compaction, etc. Test to determine exact values for specific soils.

Typical Soil Volume Conversion Factors				
Soil Type	Initial Soil Condition	Bank	Converted to: Loose	Compacted
Clay	Bank	1.00	1.27	0.90
	Loose	0.79	1.00	0.71
	Compacted	1.11	1.41	1.00
Common earth	Bank	1.00	1.25	0.90
	Loose	0.80	1.00	0.72
	Compacted	1.11	1.39	1.00
Rock (blasted)	Bank	1.00	1.50	1.30
	Loose	0.67	1.00	0.87
	Compacted	0.77	1.15	1.00
Sand	Bank	1.00	1.12	0.95
	Loose	0.89	1.00	0.85
	Compacted	1.05	1.18	1.00

Figure 8.23

2.4 Caissons & Piling	CREW	DAILY OUTPUT	UNIT	BARE COSTS			TOTAL INCL O&P
				MAT.	INST.	TOTAL	
250	24" diameter, .116 C.Y./L.F.	B-49	30	V.L.F.	13.90	88	101.90	130
260	30" diameter, .182 C.Y./L.F.		20		22	130	152	200
270	36" diameter, .262 C.Y./L.F.		15		32	175	207	270
280	48" diameter, .465 C.Y./L.F.		10		55	265	320	410
290	60" diameter, .727 C.Y./L.F.		7		87	375	462	595
300	72" diameter, 1.05 C.Y./L.F.		6		130	440	570	725
310	84" diameter, 1.43 C.Y./L.F.		5		170	530	700	890
320	For bell excavation and concrete, add							
322	4' bell diameter, 24" shaft, .444 C.Y.	B-49	10.90	Ea.	38	240	278	365
324	6' bell diameter, 30" shaft, 1.57 C.Y.		3.10		135	850	985	1,275
326	8' bell diameter, 36" shaft, 3.72 C.Y.		1.30		315	2,025	2,340	3,050
328	9' bell diameter, 48" shaft, 4.48 C.Y.		1.10		385	2,400	2,785	3,600
330	10' bell diameter, 60" shaft, 5.24 C.Y.		.90		445	2,925	3,370	4,375
332	12' bell diameter, 72" shaft, 8.74 C.Y.		.60		740	4,400	5,140	6,650
334	14' bell diameter, 84" shaft, 13.6 C.Y.		.40		1,165	6,600	7,765	10,000
360	For rock excavation, sockets, add, minimum		120	C.F.		22	22	29
365	Average		95			28	28	37
370	Maximum		48			55	55	73
390	For 50' to 100' deep, add			V.L.F.	7%	7%		
400	For 100' to 150' deep, add				25%	25%		
410	For 150' to 200' deep, add				30%	30%		
420	For casings left in place, add			Lb.	.50		.50	.55M
430	For other than 50 lb. reinf. per C.Y., add or deduct			"	.51		.51	.56M
440	For steel "I" beam cores, add	B-49	8.30	Ton	500	320	820	975
450	Load and haul excess excavation, 2 miles	B-34B	178	C.Y.		2.32	2.32	2.80
500	Bottom inspection	1 Skwk	1.20	Ea.		135	135	200L
10-001	MOBILIZATION Set up & remove, air compressor, 600 C.F.M.	A-5	3.30			91	91	130
010	1200 C.F.M.	"	2.20			135	135	195
020	Crane, with pile leads and pile hammer, 75 ton	B-8	.50			5,350	5,350	6,675
030	150 ton	"	.31			8,625	8,625	10,800
050	Drill rig, complete to 36", minimum	B-4	1.38			800	800	1,075
060	Up to 84"	"	.92			1,200	1,200	1,625
080	Auxiliary boiler, small	A-5	1.66			180	180	260
090	Large	"	.83			365	365	520
110	Rule of thumb: complete pile driving set up, small	B-19	.45			5,100	5,100	6,825
120	Large	"	.27			8,475	8,475	11,400
15-001	PILES, CONCRETE 200 piles, 60' long							
002	unless specified otherwise, not incl. pile caps or mobilization							
010	Cast in place, thin wall shell pile, straight sided,							
011	not incl. reinforcing, 8" diam., 16 ga., 5.8 lb./L.F.	B-19	700	V.L.F.	3.50	3.27	6.77	8.25
020	10" diameter, 16 ga. corrugated, 7.3 lb./L.F.		650		4.60	3.52	8.12	9.80
030	12" diameter, 16 ga. corrugated, 8.7 lb./L.F.		600		5.85	3.82	9.67	11.55
040	14" diameter, 16 ga. corrugated, 10.0 lb./L.F.		550		7.05	4.16	11.21	13.35
050	16" diameter, 16 ga. corrugated, 11.6 lb./L.F.		500		8.55	4.58	13.13	15.55
080	Cast in place friction pile, 50' long, fluted,							
081	tapered steel, 4000 psi concrete, no reinforcing							
090	12" diameter, 7 ga.	B-19	600	V.L.F.	10.75	3.82	14.57	16.95
100	14" diameter, 7 ga.		560		11.80	4.09	15.89	18.45
110	16" diameter, 7 ga.		520		13.80	4.41	18.21	21
120	18" diameter, 7 ga.		480		16.20	4.77	20.97	24
130	End bearing, fluted, constant diameter,							
132	4000 psi concrete, no reinforcing							
134	12" diameter, 7 ga.	B-19	600	V.L.F.	11.05	3.82	14.87	17.25
136	14" diameter, 7 ga.		560		13.85	4.09	17.94	21
138	16" diameter, 7 ga.		520		15.90	4.41	20.31	23
140	18" diameter, 7 ga.		480		17.35	4.77	22.12	25
150	For reinforcing steel, add			Lb.	.45		.45	.49M
170	For ball or pedestal end, add	B-19	11	C.Y.	62	210	272	345
190	For lengths above 60', concrete, add	"	11	"	62	210	272	345
200	For steel thin shell, pipe only			Lb.	.45		.45	.49M

Figure 8.24

140

Landscaping

If the required topsoil is stockpiled on site, equipment will be needed for hauling and spreading. Likewise if the stockpile is too large or too small, trucks will have to be mobilized for transport. If large trees and shrubs are specified, equipment may be required for digging and placing.

Landscaping, including lawn sprinklers, sod, seeding etc., is usually done by subcontractors. The estimator should make sure that the subcontract includes a certain maintenance period during which all plantings are guaranteed. The required period will be most likely stated in the specifications and should include routine maintenance and replacement of dead plantings.

Sample Estimate: Division 2

Site work quantities may be derived from several different drawings. In this case, data are taken from the topographic survey, the finish grading plan and the site plan. (Figures 8.2, 8.3 and 8.4) For smaller projects, these three plans may be combined as one. The detailed information that would normally be included in a complete set of plans and specifications is not provided for this example. For purposes of this demonstration, quantities as shown reflect realistic conditions and are based on normal construction techniques and materials.

For the site clearing portion of the estimate, areas to be cleared are measured from the topographic survey (Figure 8.2), but verification of area and determination of vegetation type must be done during the site visit. The estimate sheets for Division 2 are shown in Figures 8.25 through 8.29. Note that the units (acres and square yards) used for tree cutting and grubbing are different than those used for light clearing. The estimator should be sure to convert the required units for pricing. For the example, the whole site is to be cleared. The site dimensions are 310' x 365', or 113,150 square feet. Light clearing is priced by the square yard, so the area is converted to 12, 570 square yards. Prices for site clearing are taken from Figure 8.30.

Quantities for bulk excavation are derived using the alternative method as described above and as shown in Figure 8.31. In this example, a grid representing 20' x 20' squares is used. The estimator determines the average elevation change in each square and designates each as a cut (−) or a fill (+). The darkened square within the building is for excavation at the elevator pit. All cuts and fills are totalled separately and converted to cubic yards. An amount to compensate for reduction in volume is added to the total fill yardage before net calculation. This is due to the decrease in volume of earth when compacted (see Figure 8.23). The costs for bulk excavation are taken from Figure 8.32. Compaction is not included and must be added separately.

MEANS CONSOLIDATED ESTIMATE

Division 2

SHEET NO. 1 of 5

PROJECT Office Building | CLASSIFICATION | ESTIMATE NO. 86-1

LOCATION | ARCHITECT | DATE 1986

TAKE OFF BY EBW | QUANTITIES BY EBW | PRICES BY RSM | EXTENSIONS BY SLM | CHECKED JDM

DESCRIPTION	SOURCE/DIMENSIONS			QUANTITY	UNIT	MATERIAL UNIT COST	MATERIAL TOTAL	LABOR UNIT COST	LABOR TOTAL	EQUIPMENT UNIT COST	EQUIPMENT TOTAL	SUBCONTRACT UNIT COST	SUBCONTRACT TOTAL	
Division 2 - Sitework														
Site Clearing														
Med. Trees - Cut	2.1	10	020	.46	Acre			1025	471	920	423			
Grub & Remove Stumps	2.1	10	025	.46	Acre			285	131	760	350			
Light Clearing	2.1	15	030	12570	SY			.08	1006	.17	2137			
Earthwork														
Bulk Excavation	2.3	16	130	5430	CY			.22	1195	.58	3149			
Load Trucks (Loose)	2.3	16	155	3212	CY			.36	1156	.42	1349			
Haul (Loose)	2.3	30	040	3212	CY			.63	2024	1.33	4272			
Compact Fill	2.3	08	030	2860	CY			.63	1802	.81	2317			
Excess Excavation @ Foundation	2.3	16	090	272	CY			.29	79	1.16	316			
Backfill & Compact @ Foundation	2.3	03	130 060	302	CY			2.31	698	1.14	344			
Backfill & Compact @ Elev. Pit	2.3	03	001 060	30	CY			11.22	337	.61	18			
Sub Totals									8899		14675			

Figure 8.25

MEANS CONSOLIDATED ESTIMATE

Division 2
SHEET NO. 2 of 5

PROJECT Office Building — CLASSIFICATION — ESTIMATE NO. 86-1

LOCATION — ARCHITECT — DATE 1986

TAKE OFF BY EBW — QUANTITIES BY EBW — PRICES BY RSM — EXTENSIONS BY SLM — CHECKED JDM

DESCRIPTION	SOURCE/DIMENSIONS			QUANTITY	UNIT	MATERIAL UNIT COST	MATERIAL TOTAL	LABOR UNIT COST	LABOR TOTAL	EQUIPMENT UNIT COST	EQUIPMENT TOTAL	SUBCONTRACT UNIT COST	SUBCONTRACT TOTAL
Division 2: (Cont'd) Earthwork (Cont'd)													
Footing Excavation Spread	2.3	18	004 240	305	CY			1.89	576	1.52	464		
Continuous	2.3	18	004	85	CY			1.46	124	1.17	99		
Backfill @ Footings Incl. Spread Excess	2.3	03	190	390	CY			.25	97	.71	277		
Utility Excavation 24" Drain Exc.	2.3	18	008	230	CY			1.46	336	1.17	269		
Backfill & Compact	2.3	03	060	287	CY			2.12	608	.61	175		
Gas, Water, Sewer	2.3	19	285	240	LF			.21	50	.28	67		
Compaction	2.3	19	320	240	LF			.11	26	.14	34		
Sub Drain Gravel	2.3	20	130	46	CY	8	368	4.38	201				
Floor Slab Gravel 6" Compacted	2.3	20	060	19,000	SF	.15	2850	.11	2090				
Mobilization Dozer, Loader, Backhoe, Compactor	2.3	35		4	Ea.					120	480		
Sub Totals							3218		4108		1865		

Figure 8.26

MEANS CONSOLIDATED ESTIMATE

PROJECT: Office Building
LOCATION:
CLASSIFICATION:
ARCHITECT:

Division 2
SHEET NO. 3 of 5
ESTIMATE NO. 86-1
DATE 1986
CHECKED JDM

TAKE OFF BY: EBW QUANTITIES BY: EBW PRICES BY: RSM EXTENSIONS BY: SLM

DESCRIPTION	SOURCE/DIMENSIONS	QUANTITY	UNIT	MATERIAL UNIT COST	MATERIAL TOTAL	LABOR UNIT COST	LABOR TOTAL	EQUIPMENT UNIT COST	EQUIPMENT TOTAL	SUBCONTRACT UNIT COST	SUBCONTRACT TOTAL
Division 2 : (Cont'd)											
Site Drainage & Utilities											
Catch Basin & Grate	2.5 02 112 210	3	Ea.	445	1335	263	789				
Gas Service 3"	2.5 08 065	80	LF	6.65	532	2.72	218				
Water Service 6"	2.5 30 142	80	LF	5.50	440	4.00	320				
Gate Valve 6"	2.6 30 180	1	Ea.	320	320	100	100				
Sewer 6" PVC	2.5 27 615	80	LF	5.56	445	1.44	115				
Foundation Drain	2.5 29 065	620	LF	1.40	868	.95	589				
Drain Pipe 24" Conc.	2.5 27 168	310	LF	11.50	3565	7.70	2387				
Roads & Walks											
Base Course 9"	2.6 07 020	8530	SY	5	42650	.57	4862				
Paving - Bituminous											
#28/Ton Binder	2.6 10 040	8530	SY	3.05	26016	.91	7762				
#30/Ton Wearing	2.6 10 001	8530	SY	2.45	20898	.63	5374				
Sub Totals					97069		22516				

Figure 8.27

144

MEANS CONSOLIDATED ESTIMATE

Division 2

SHEET NO. 4 of 5

PROJECT Office Building | CLASSIFICATION | ESTIMATE NO. 86-1

LOCATION | ARCHITECT | DATE 1986

TAKE OFF BY EBW | QUANTITIES BY EBW | PRICES BY RSM | EXTENSIONS BY SLM | CHECKED JDM

DESCRIPTION	SOURCE/DIMENSIONS			QUANTITY	UNIT	MATERIAL UNIT COST	MATERIAL TOTAL	LABOR UNIT COST	LABOR TOTAL	EQUIPMENT UNIT COST	EQUIPMENT TOTAL	SUBCONTRACT UNIT COST	SUBCONTRACT TOTAL		
Division 2: (Cont'd)															
Roads & Walks (Cont'd)															
Concrete Curb															
Precast Straight	2.6	22	045	2050	LF	4.70	9635	4	8200						
Precast Radius	2.6	22	060	240	LF	7.10	1704	4.31	1034						
Line Painting															
Stalls	2.6	32	080	203	Stall	.67	136	1.09	221						
Arrows	2.6	32	062	150	SF	.20	30	.41	61						
Precast Bumpers	2.6	35	100	203	Ea.	18	3654	5.45	1106						
Conc. Sidewalks	2.6	40	031	1625	SF	.83	1349	.73	1186						
Conc. Steps	2.6	45	050	95	LF	3.40	323	7.80	741						
from 3.3-14-685															
Sub Totals							16831		12549						

Figure 8.28

MEANS CONSOLIDATED ESTIMATE

PROJECT: Office Building

LOCATION:

CLASSIFICATION:

ARCHITECT:

ESTIMATE NO. 86-1

DATE 1986

CHECKED JDM

TAKE OFF BY: EBW | QUANTITIES BY: EBW | PRICES BY: RSM | EXTENSIONS BY: SLM

SOURCE/DIMENSIONS	DESCRIPTION	QUANTITY	UNIT	MATERIAL UNIT COST	MATERIAL TOTAL	LABOR UNIT COST	LABOR TOTAL	EQUIPMENT UNIT COST	EQUIPMENT TOTAL	SUBCONTRACT UNIT COST	SUBCONTRACT TOTAL
	Division 2: (Cont'd)										
	Lawns & Plantings										
TELEPHONE QUOTE	Landscaping				SUB	CONTRACT					
	Sprinkler	15,700	SF								8400
	Lawn	1745	SY								8971
	Trees & Shrubs (60) (200)										10912
	Sub Total										(28283)
	Sheet 1				3218		8899		14675		
	Sheet 2				97069		41408		1866		
	Sheet 3						22516				
	Sheet 4				16831		12649				
	Sheet 5										28283
	Division 2 Totals				117118		48072		16540		28283

Figure 8.29

2.1	Exploration & Clearing	CREW	DAILY OUTPUT	UNIT	BARE COSTS			TOTAL INCL O&P
					EQUIP.	LABOR	TOTAL	
05-001	**BORINGS** Initial field stake out and determination of elevations	A-6	1	Day		295	295	430L
002								
010	Drawings showing boring details			Total		165	165	240L
020	Report and recommendations from P.E.					365	365	530L
030	Mobilization and demobilization, minimum	B-55	4.80	↓	45	54	99	125
035	For over 100 miles, per added mile		450	Mile	.48	.57	1.05	1.35
060	Auger holes in earth, no samples, 2-1/2" diameter		78.60	L.F.	2.72	3.28	6	7.70
065	4" diameter		67.50		3.17	3.82	6.99	9
080	Cased borings in earth, with samples, 2-1/2" diameter		55.50		3.85	4.65	8.50	10.95
085	4" diameter	↓	32.60		6.55	7.90	14.45	18.65
100	Drilling in rock, "BX" core, no sampling	B-56	34.90		12.15	8.10	20.25	25
105	With casing & sampling		31.70		13.40	8.90	22.30	28
120	"NX" core, no sampling		25.92		16.40	10.90	27.30	34
125	With casing & sampling	↓	25	↓	17	11.30	28.30	35
140	Drill rig and crew with light duty rig	B-55	1	Day	215	260	475	605
145	With heavy duty rig	B-56	1	"	425	285	710	875
10-001	**CLEAR AND GRUB** Light, trees to 6" diam., cut & chip	B-7	1	Acre	735	815	1,550	2,000
015	Grub stumps and remove	B-30	2		570	215	785	935
020	Medium, trees to 10" diam., cut & chip	B-7	.80		920	1,025	1,945	2,500
025	Grub stumps and remove	B-30	1.50		760	285	1,045	1,250
030	Heavy, trees to 16" diam., cut & chip	B-7	.70		1,050	1,175	2,225	2,850
035	Grub stumps and remove	B-30	1.20		950	360	1,310	1,550
040	If burning is allowed, reduce cut & chip			↓				33%
040								
100	Stump removal on site by hydraulic backhoe, 1-1/2 C.Y.							
105	8" to 12" diameter	B-30	33	Ea.	35	13.05	48.05	57
110	14" to 18" diameter		25		46	17.20	63.20	75
115	19" to 24" diameter	↓	16	↓	71	27	98	115
200	Trees, on site using chain saws and chipper,							
205	not incl. stumps, up to 6" diameter	B-7	47	Ea.	15.70	17.40	33.10	42
210	7" to 12" diameter		30		25	27	52	66
215	13" to 18" diameter		23		32	36	68	87
220	19" to 24" diameter	↓	17	↓	43	48	91	115
230	For machine load, 2 mile haul to dump, add			↓		30	30	38L
15-001	**CLEARING** Brush with brush saw & rake	1 Clab	565	S.Y.		.23	.23	.33L
010	By hand	"	280			.45	.45	.66L
030	With dozer, ball and chain, light clearing	B-11A	3,675		.17	.08	.25	.31
040	Medium clearing	"	3,110	↓	.20	.09	.29	.36

					BARE COSTS			
					MAT.	INST.	TOTAL	
20-001	**CORE DRILLING** Reinf. concrete slab up to 6" thick, 1" diameter core	B-89	75	Ea.		12.85	12.85	14.85
015	Each added inch thick, add		600			1.61	1.61	1.86
030	3" diameter core		60			16.10	16.10	18.60
035	Each added inch thick, add		400			2.41	2.41	2.79
050	4" diameter core		45			21	21	25
055	Each added inch thick, add		300			3.22	3.22	3.72
070	6" diameter core		30			32	32	37
075	Each added inch thick, add		200			4.82	4.82	5.60
090	8" diameter core		24			40	40	46
095	Each added inch thick, add		150			6.45	6.45	7.45
110	10" diameter core		18			54	54	62
115	Each added inch thick, add		110			8.75	8.75	10.15
130	12" diameter core		15			64	64	74
135	Each added inch thick, add		90			10.70	10.70	12.40
150	14" diameter core		13			74	74	86
155	Each added inch thick, add		80			12.05	12.05	13.95
170	18" diameter core		10.50			92	92	105
175	Each added inch thick, add	↓	60			16.10	16.10	18.60
176	For horizontal holes, add to above			↓				30%
177	Prestressed hollow core plank, 6" thick							

Figure 8.30

147

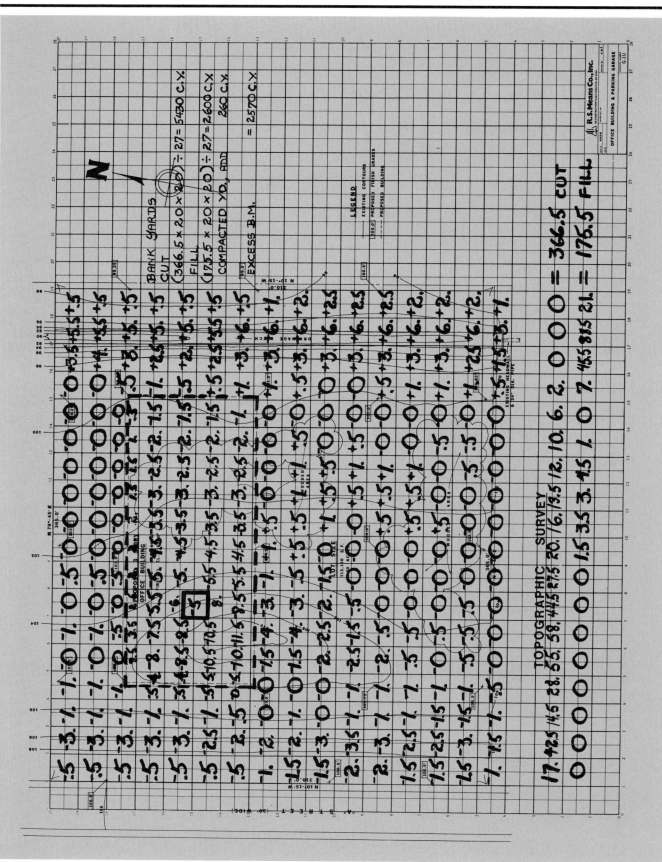

Figure 8.31

148

2.3 Earthwork		CREW	DAILY OUTPUT	UNIT	BARE COSTS EQUIP.	LABOR	TOTAL	TOTAL INCL O&P
100	Hydraulic method, pumped 1000 ft. to shore dump, minimum	B-57	460	C.Y.	1.66	1.87	3.53	4.54
110	Maximum	↓	310		2.46	2.78	5.24	6.75
140	Into scows dumped 20 miles, minimum		425		1.80	2.03	3.83	4.92
150	Maximum	↓	243		3.14	3.55	6.69	8.60
160	For inland rivers in South, deduct			↓	30%	30%		

					BARE COSTS MAT.	INST.	TOTAL	
15-001	**DRILLING AND BLASTING** only, rock, under 1500 C.Y.	B-47	75	C.Y.	1.05	11.45	12.50	15.75
010	Over 1500 C.Y.	"	85		1.05	10.10	11.15	14.05
030	Bulk excavating, can vary greatly, average							14
050	Pits, average			↓				18
070	Drilling only, 2" hole for rock bolts, average	B-47	395	L.F.		2.18	2.18	2.77
080	2-1/2" hole for pre-splitting, average		340	"		2.53	2.53	3.22
130	Deep hole method, up to 1500 C.Y.		50	C.Y.	1.05	17.20	18.25	23
140	Over 1500 C.Y.		66	"	1.05	13.05	14.10	17.75
160	Quarry operations, 2-1/2" to 3-1/2" diameter, up to 1500 C.Y.		350	L.F.		2.46	2.46	3.13
170	Over 1500 C.Y.		425	"		2.02	2.02	2.58
190	Restricted areas, up to 1500 C.Y.		13	C.Y.	1.05	66	67.05	85
200	Over 1500 C.Y.		20		1.05	43	44.05	56
220	Trenches, up to 1500 C.Y.		22		1.05	39	40.05	51
230	Over 1500 C.Y.		26		1.05	33	34.05	43
250	Pier holes, up to 1500 C.Y.		22		1.05	39	40.05	51
260	Over 1500 C.Y.		31		1.05	28	29.05	36
280	Boulders loaded only, not including hauling	↓	85		1.05	10.10	11.15	14.05
290	Drilled, blasted and loaded, not incl. hauling	↓	30	↓	1.05	29	30.05	38
310	Jackhammer operator with compressor	B-9	27.70	Hr.		29	29	40
330	Track mounted air drill with operator and foreman	B-47	14.40	"		60	60	76
350	Blasting caps			Ea.	1.60		1.60	1.76M
370	Explosives			Lb.	1.55		1.55	1.70M
390	Blasting mats, rent, for first day			Ea.	37		37	41M
400	Per added day				21		21	23M
420	Preblast survey for 6 room house, individual lot, minimum	A-6	2.40			125	125	180L
430	Maximum	"	1.35	↓		220	220	320L
450	City block within zone of influence, minimum	A-8	25,200	S.F.		.02	.02	.03L
460	Maximum	"	15,100	"		.04	.04	.05L

					BARE COSTS EQUIP.	LABOR	TOTAL	
16-001	**EXCAVATING, BULK** Medium earth piled or truck							
002	loaded, no trucks or haul included							
005	For mobilization and demobilization, see division 2.3-35							
010	For hauling, see division 2.3-30							
020	Backhoe, hydraulic, crawler mtd., 1 C.Y. cap.=45 C.Y./hr.	B-12A	360	C.Y.	1.23	.86	2.09	2.60
025	1-1/2 C.Y. cap. = 60 C.Y./hr.	B-12B	480		1.21	.64	1.85	2.26
026	2 C.Y. cap. = 75 C.Y./hr.	B-12C	600		1.34	.51	1.85	2.21
030	3-1/2 C.Y. cap. = 150 C.Y./hr.	B-12D	1,200		1.18	.26	1.44	1.67
031	Wheel mounted, 1/2 C.Y. cap. = 20 C.Y./hr.	B-12E	160		1.64	1.93	3.57	4.60
036	3/4 C.Y. cap. = 30 C.Y./hr.	B-12F	240		1.42	1.29	2.71	3.42
050	Clamshell, 1/2 C.Y. cap. = 20 C.Y./hr.	B-12G	160		1.93	1.93	3.86	4.91
055	1 C.Y. cap. = 35 C.Y./hr.	B-12H	280		1.53	1.10	2.63	3.28
070	Dozer, 50' haul, 75 H.P. = 50 C.Y./hr.	B-10L	400		.52	.57	1.09	1.39
075	300 H.P. = 150 C.Y./hr.	B-10M	1,200		.78	.19	.97	1.13
085	150' haul, 75 H.P. = 25 C.Y./hr.	B-10L	200		1.03	1.14	2.17	2.79
090	300 H.P. = 100 C.Y./hr.	B-10M	800		1.16	.29	1.45	1.69
100	Dragline, 3/4 C.Y. cap. = 35 C.Y./hr.	B-12I	280		1.31	1.10	2.41	3.04
105	1-1/2 C.Y. cap. = 65 C.Y./hr.	B-12P	520		.99	.59	1.58	1.95
120	Front end loader, track mtd., 1-1/2 C.Y. cap. = 70 C.Y./hr.	B-10N	560		.49	.41	.90	1.13
125	2-1/2 C.Y. cap. = 95 C.Y./hr.	B-10O	760		.55	.30	.85	1.05
130	3-1/2 C.Y. cap. = 130 C.Y./hr.	B-10P	1,040		.58	.22	.80	.95
135	4-1/2 C.Y. cap. = 160 C.Y./hr.	B-10Q	1,280	↓	.79	.18	.97	1.13

Figure 8.32

Quantities for bulk excavation are based on finish grades. Excess excavation at the foundation to be backfilled must be included as shown in Figure 8.25. Calculations for compaction at the foundation and for loading and hauling excess fill are as follows:

Compaction at foundation:

Excavation (bank CY) = 272 C.Y.

$$\frac{1.0 \text{ Bank C.Y.}}{0.9 \text{ Compacted C.Y.}} \times 272 \text{ C.Y.} = 302 \text{ C.Y. required}$$

Load and haul excess fill:

Excess fill (bank C.Y.) = 2,570 C.Y.

$$\frac{1.25 \text{ Loose C.Y.}}{1.0 \text{ Bank C.Y.}} \times 2,570 \text{ C.Y.} = 3,212 \text{ loose C.Y.}$$

The ratios of bank to loose to compacted earth were derived from Figure 8.23. If the above calculations were not made, almost 700 cubic yards of loading and hauling may not have been included in the estimate. This represents 60-70 truckloads. The calculation for foundation compaction indicates that 302 cubic yards of bank material *when compacted* are required to replace 272 cubic yards of excavated bank material. Only backfill, (and not compaction) is included for the footings, because the costs are primarily for the spreading of excess material. Compaction is included with the foundation backfill and at the floor subbase.

Costs for bituminous paving are taken from Figure 8.33. Note on the estimate sheet that the price per ton for the sample building (Figure 8.27) is different than that in *Building Construction Cost Data*. By simple conversion, prices in *Building Construction Cost Data* can be adjusted to local conditions:

Line no: 2.6-10-001	Wearing Course
National average	$27.30
Local cost (for sample project)	$30.00

$$\frac{\$30.00}{\$27.30} = 1.10$$

Material cost per S.Y. x Conversion factor = Local cost per S.Y.

$2.23 per S.Y. x 1.10 = $2.45 per S.Y.

The landscaping and site improvements for the sample project are to be subcontracted. This relieves the general contractor, not only of the responsibility of pricing, but also of the problems of maintenance and potential plant replacement. The subcontract price, as received by telephone, is shown in Figure 8.34. The estimator must ask the appropriate questions to be sure that all work is included and all requirements met.

2.6 Roads & Walks	CREW	DAILY OUTPUT	UNIT	BARE COSTS MAT.	INST.	TOTAL	TOTAL INCL O&P
02-001 ASPHALT BLOCKS Premolded, 6"x12" x 1-1/4", w/bed & neopr. adhesive	D-1	135	S.F.	2.35	2.16	4.51	5.65
010 3" thick		130		3.40	2.25	5.65	6.95
030 Hexagonal tile, 8" wide, 1-1/4" thick		135		2.60	2.16	4.76	5.95
040 2" thick		130		3.20	2.25	5.45	6.70
050 Square, 8" x 8", 1-1/4" thick		135		2.60	2.16	4.76	5.95
060 2" thick		130		3.20	2.25	5.45	6.70
090 For exposed aggregate (ground finish) add				.50		.50	.55M
091 For colors, add				.30		.30	.33M
05-001 BASE Prepare and roll sub-base, small areas	B-32	670	S.Y.		1.38	1.38	1.69
010 Large areas	"	1,500			.62	.62	.76
07-001 BASE COURSE Crushed 3/4" stone @ $10.50 per ton, delivered, 3" deep	B-36	4,000		1.65	.31	1.96	2.21
010 6" deep		3,000		3.35	.42	3.77	4.21
020 9" deep		2,200		5	.57	5.57	6.20
030 12" deep		1,800		6.65	.69	7.34	8.20
035 Bank run gravel @ $4.50 per ton, delivered, spread to sub-grade							
037 6" deep	B-10B	3,000	S.Y.	1.37	.29	1.66	1.85
039 9" deep		2,200		2.05	.39	2.44	2.72
040 12" deep		1,800		2.73	.48	3.21	3.57
070 Liquid applications, emulsion	B-45	3,000	Gal.	1.05	.18	1.23	1.39
080 Prime and seal, cut back asphalt		3,000	"	1.20	.18	1.38	1.55
100 Macadam penetration, 2 gal. per S.Y., 4" thick		3,000	S.Y.	2.15	.18	2.33	2.60
110 6" thick, 3 gal. per S.Y.		2,000		3.25	.27	3.52	3.92
120 8" thick, 4 gal. per S.Y.		1,500		4.35	.36	4.71	5.25
600 Stabilization fabric, polypropylene, 6 oz./S.Y.	B-6	10,000		1.35	.06	1.41	1.56
10-001 BITUMINOUS Paving, wearing course, @ $27.30 per ton, 1-1/2" thick	B-25	3,300		2.23	.63	2.86	3.29
010 3" thick		1,650		4.45	1.26	5.71	6.55
030 (26) Binder course, @ $25.50 per ton, 1-1/2" thick		3,300		2.08	.63	2.71	3.13
040 2" thick		2,300		2.77	.91	3.68	4.25
050 3" thick		1,650		4.16	1.26	5.42	6.25
060 4" thick		1,200		5.54	1.74	7.28	8.40

Figure 8.33

MEANS TELEPHONE QUOTATION

DATE **1986**

PROJECT **Office Building**

TIME

FIRM QUOTING **Landscaping, Inc.**

PHONE ( )

ADDRESS

BY

ITEM QUOTED **Landscaping & Sprinklers**

RECEIVED BY **EBW**

WORK INCLUDED	AMOUNT OF QUOTATION
Automatic sprinkler system	8400
Top soil	4246
Sodding	4725
Trees	6182
Shrubs	4730
(Area x 15,700 SF or 1745 SY)	
TOTAL BID	28283

DELIVERY TIME

DOES QUOTATION INCLUDE THE FOLLOWING:

If ☐ NO is checked, determine the following:

STATE & LOCAL SALES TAXES	☒ YES	☐ NO	MATERIAL VALUE
DELIVERY TO THE JOB SITE	☒ YES	☐ NO	WEIGHT
COMPLETE INSTALLATION	☒ YES	☐ NO	QUANTITY
COMPLETE SECTION AS PER PLANS & SPECIFICATIONS	☒ YES	☐ NO	DESCRIBE BELOW

EXCLUSIONS AND QUALIFICATIONS

Maintenance : Routine   60 Days

Guarantee :   Sprinkler   1 Year
              Dead Replacement   90 Days

ADDENDA ACKNOWLEDGEMENT

TOTAL ADJUSTMENTS

ADJUSTED TOTAL BID

ALTERNATES

ALTERNATE NO.

ALTERNATE NO.

ALTERNATE NO.

ALTERNATE NO.

ALTERNATE NO.

ALTERNATE NO.

ALTERNATE NO.

Figure 8.34

Division 3: Concrete

All cast in place concrete work involves the same basic elements: formwork, reinforcing, concrete, placement and finishing. There are two methods that can be used to estimate the concrete portion of a project. All of the above components may be grouped together to form systems or assemblies, such as an 8" foundation wall, 24" x 24" column, and a 1' x 2' strip footing. Prices for such systems are shown in Figure 8.35. A more accurate, but time consuming method is to quantify and price the individual components of the concrete work.

Note that the costs in Figure 8.35 are primarily shown per cubic yard of concrete. Prices may also be separated for minimum, average or maximum reinforcing. Care should be taken when using this pricing method to assure that the proposed system closely matches the priced system. For example, one foundation wall system cost cannot be developed to accurately price different size walls. An 8" inch wall will require 81 square feet of formwork contact area for every cubic yard of concrete. In contrast, a 12" wall will require 54 square feet of forms. The ratio of square feet of form contact area to concrete volume is different for the two wall thicknesses. Reinforcing quantities may also differ per cubic yard. If systems are used for concrete pricing, all variables must be considered.

In the charts below, SFCA is square feet of formwork contact area.

Wall	SFCA/SF Wall	SFCA/CY Concrete
8" wall	2.0	81.0
12" wall	2.0	54.0
16" wall	2.0	40.5

Columns	SFCA/LF Column	SFCA/CY Concrete
12" square	4.0	108.0
16" square	5.3	81.0
24" square	8.0	54.0

Unless the estimator has prices for all possible cast-in-place concrete system variations, the most accurate estimating method is to determine the costs for each component of the concrete work.

Cast in Place Concrete

Before beginning the quantity takeoff, the estimator should carefully review the specifications for requirements that may not be indicated on the plans. Such items may include concrete type (regular or lightweight), concrete strengths, and curing time. Specified additives — such as colors and air entrainment — must also be included in the takeoff, along with protection during curing. In addition to the specifications and plans, details and sections showing concrete work will usually be provided. Reinforcing requirements and accessories will be indicated on these drawings.

When estimating concrete work by individual component, it might be possible to apply the dimensions and quantities calculated for one component to another. It is helpful to take off quantities for all components of one type of concrete work at the same time. For example, the square feet of form contact area may also be the same area that will require finishing.

3.3 Cast in Place Concrete	CREW	DAILY OUTPUT	UNIT	BARE COSTS			TOTAL INCL O&P
				MAT.	INST.	TOTAL	
14-001 CONCRETE IN PLACE Including forms (4 uses), reinforcing							
005 steel, including finishing unless otherwise indicated							
010 Average for concrete framed building,							
011 (35) including finishing	C-17B	15.75	C.Y.	98	120	218	280
013 Average for substructure only, simple design, incl. finishing		29.07		69	65	134	170
015 (47) Average for superstructure only, including finishing	↓	13.42	↓	105	140	245	315
020 Base, granolithic, 1" x 5" high, straight	C-10	175	L.F.	.12	2.81	2.93	4.01
022 (50) Cove	"	140	"	.12	3.51	3.63	4.98
030 Beams, 5 kip per L.F., 10' span	C-17A	6.28	C.Y.	168	285	453	595
035 25' span		7.40		135	240	375	495
050 Chimney foundations, minimum		26.70		89	67	156	195
051 (122) Maximum		19.70		102	91	193	240
070 Columns, square, 12" x 12", minimum reinforcing		4.60		180	390	570	755
072 (49) Average reinforcing	↓	4.10		255	435	690	910
074 Maximum reinforcing	C-17B	3.84		380	495	875	1,125
080 16" x 16", minimum reinforcing	C-17A	6.25		160	285	445	585
082 Average reinforcing	"	4.93		250	360	610	795
084 Maximum reinforcing	C-17B	4.34		420	435	855	1,075
090 24" x 24", minimum reinforcing	C-17A	9.08	↓	140	195	335	435
092 Average reinforcing	"	6.90		210	260	470	605
094 Maximum reinforcing	C-17A	5.65	C.Y.	345	315	660	835
100 36" x 36", minimum reinforcing	C-17B	13.39		130	140	270	345
102 Average reinforcing		9.61		200	195	395	495
104 Maximum reinforcing		7.50		325	250	575	715
120 Columns, round, tied, 16" diameter, minimum reinforcing		13.02		225	145	370	455
122 (49) Average reinforcing		8.30		375	230	605	735
124 Maximum reinforcing		6.05		510	315	825	1,000
130 20" diameter, minimum reinforcing		17.35		210	110	320	385
132 Average reinforcing		10.43		340	180	520	630
134 Maximum reinforcing		7.47		460	255	715	865
140 24" diameter, minimum reinforcing		22.18		200	85	285	340
142 Average reinforcing		11.86		290	160	450	545
144 Maximum reinforcing		8.10		460	235	695	835
150 36" diameter, minimum reinforcing		32.40		180	58	238	280
152 Average reinforcing	↓	16.57	↓	245	115	360	430
154 Maximum reinforcing		11.15	↓	335	170	505	610
170 Curbs, formed in place, 6" x 18", straight,	C-15	400	L.F.	2.90	3.51	6.41	8.25
175 Curb and gutter	"	170	"	4.65	8.25	12.90	17
190 Elevated slabs, flat slab, 125 psf Sup. Load, 20' span	C-17A	13.36	C.Y.	110	135	245	315
195 30' span	C-17B	18.25		105	105	210	260
210 Flat plate, 125 psf Sup. Load, 15' span	C-17A	10.28		115	175	290	375
215 25' span	C-17B	17.01		97	110	207	265
230 Waffle const., 30" domes, 125 psf Sup. Load, 20' span		14.10		120	135	255	320
235 30' span	↓	17.02		113	110	223	280
250 One way joists, 30" pans, 125 psf Sup. Load, 15' span	C-17A	11.07		110	160	270	355
255 25' span		11.04		125	160	285	365
270 One way beam & slab, 125 psf Sup. Load, 15' span		7.49		125	240	365	480
275 25' span		10.15		120	175	295	385
290 Two way beam & slab, 125 psf Sup. Load, 15' span	↓	8.22		120	215	335	445
295 25' span	C-17B	12.23	↓	105	155	260	335
310 Elevated slabs including finish, not							
311 including forms or reinforcing							
315 Regular concrete, 4" slab	C-8	2,685	S.F.	.64	.56	1.20	1.45
320 6" slab		2,585		1.02	.58	1.60	1.89
325 2-1/2" thick floor fill		2,685		.44	.56	1	1.23
330 Lightweight, 110# per C.F., 2-1/2" thick floor fill		2,585		.56	.58	1.14	1.39

Figure 8.35

An example of this quantity takeoff method is shown in Figures 8.36 and 8.37. Footing, Column and Beam Schedules which are normally included on foundation plans, are shown in Figure 8.41. Note on Figure 8.37 that volume (to determine quantity of concrete) is not converted to cubic yards for each system until total cubic feet are determined. This eliminates the effect of rounding errors and helps to assure that such conversions are done consistently and accurately. If concrete is taken off and priced in this way, the quantities and prices of a given project can be used to develop historical costs for future projects.

No matter what format estimators use to compile and list quantities for concrete work, each of these quantities must be computed. Once the format has been established, it should be used throughout the estimate and on all future estimates, establishing consistency and minimizing errors and omissions.

Figure 8.38 graphically illustrates the relationship of the different components of concrete work based on a complete, concrete-framed structure. The way in which the components relate will vary for different and individual types of concrete work, but this pie chart suggests the relative importance of each component.

Formwork: As seen in Figure 8.38, for a complete concrete framed building, formwork can account for more than one third of all concrete costs. For some individual concrete systems using beams, columns and walls, job-built formwork can account for 50% − 60%, or more, of the costs.

Prefabricated, modular forms can help to significantly reduce formwork costs. This is because these forms can be used over and over again, in some cases, hundreds of times. The initial purchase price of prefabricated forms is higher than job-built, but the effective higher cost decreases with each reuse. These prefabricated forms are only useful and cost effective for repetitive, standard, modular concrete work. To illustrate how the cost of formwork (whether prefabricated or job-built) decreases with each use, please refer to Figure 8.39. This table shows the costs per 100 SFCA (square feet of contact area) for job-built foundation wall forms, 8' high. Costs for the first use of the forms include construction, erection, stripping and cleaning. Costs for reuse include the same erection, stripping and cleaning costs plus an allowance for 10% material replacement. The difference in cost between the first use and the reuse is the bulk of initial materials and construction labor. The effective costs of the formwork based on the number of uses are calculated below. Costs are from Figure 8.39.

$$\frac{\text{Cost of First Use } + \text{ (Cost per Reuse x No. of Reuses)}}{\text{No. of Uses}} = \frac{\text{Cost per Use}}{\text{(for No. of Uses)}}$$

Using the costs in Figure 8.39:

Two Uses:

$$\frac{\$264.80 + (\$183.30 \times 1)}{2} = \$224.05 \text{ per use for two uses}$$

Three Uses:

$$\frac{\$264.80 + (\$183.30 \times 2)}{3} = \$210.47 \text{ per use for three uses}$$

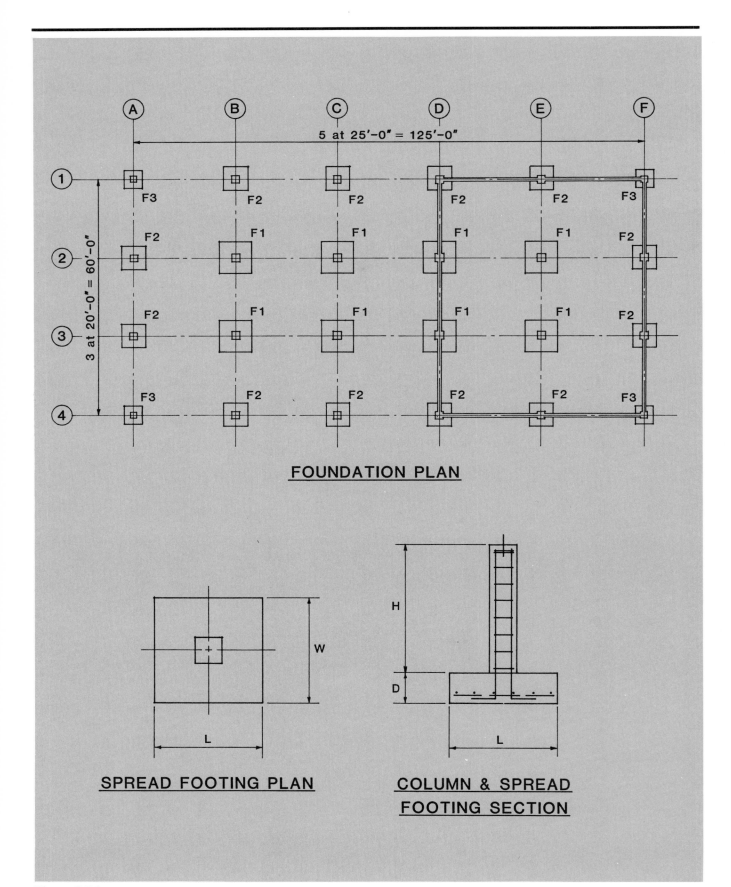

FOUNDATION PLAN

SPREAD FOOTING PLAN

COLUMN & SPREAD FOOTING SECTION

Figure 8.36

PROJECT **Sample Project**

ESTIMATE NO.

LOCATION ARCHITECT DATE

TAKE OFF BY EXTENSIONS BY: CHECKED BY:

DESCRIPTION	NO.	DIMENSIONS			Concrete Volume	UNIT	Form Area	UNIT	Finished Area	UNIT	MISC.	UNIT
Spread Footings						CF		SF		SF		
F-1	8	8	8	1.83	937		469		512			
F-2	12	6	6	1.33	575		383		432			
F-3	4	4.5	4.5	1	81		72		81			
Totals					1593	CF	924	SF	1025	SF		
					59	CY						
Wall Footings												
Column Line 1,4	2	38.75	2	1	155		155		155			
Column Line D,F	2	43.5	2	1	174		174		174			
Totals					329	CF	329	SF	329	SF		
					13	CY						
Walls												
Column Line 1,4	2	51.5	1	11	1133		2266		1133			
Column Line D,F	2	61.5	1	11	1353		2706		1353			
Pilasters	10	1.5	1.5	11	83		440		55			
Corners	10 x 8										80	Ea.
Brick Shelf												
Column Line 1		51.5	.33	1	(17)		52		—			
Column Line F		61.5	.33	1	(21)		62		—			
Totals					2531	CF	5526	SF	2541	SF		
					94	CY						
Set Anchor Bolts											48	Ea.
Keyway	2	39									78	
	2	44									88	
											166	LF
Columns C-1	8	2	2	12	384		768					
C-2	12	1.67	1.67	12	400		960		ALL			
C-3	4	1.33	1.33	12	85		256		↓			
Totals					869	CF	1984	SF	1984	SF		
					32	CY						

Figure 8.37

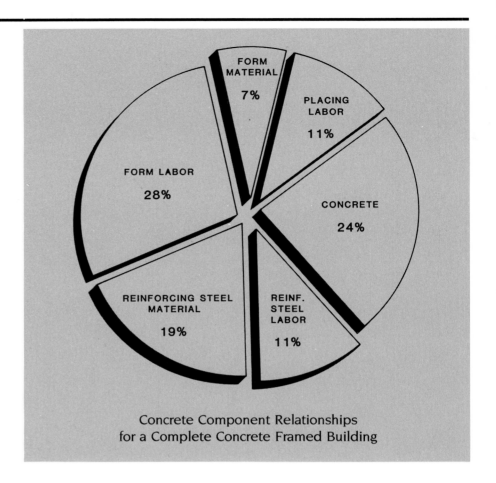

Concrete Component Relationships
for a Complete Concrete Framed Building

Figure 8.38

Foundation Wall, 8' High	First Use			Reuse		
	Quantities	Material	Installation	Quantities	Material	Installation
5/8" exterior plyform @ $615/M.S.F.	110 S.F.	$ 67.65		11.0 S.F.	$ 6.75	
Lumber @ $315 per M.B.F.	140 B.F.	44.10		14.0 B.F.	4.40	
Accessories	Allow	15.25		Allow	13.85	
Make up, crew C-2 at $20.37 per						
man-hour	5.0 M.H.		$101.85	1.0 M.H.		$ 20.35
Erect and strip	6.5 M.H.		132.40	6.5 M.H.		132.40
Clean and move	1.5 M.H.		30.55	1.5 M.H.		30.55
Total per 100 S.F.C.A.	13.0 M.H.	$127.00	$264.80	9.0 M.H.	$25.00	$183.30

Figure 8.39

Four Uses:

$$\frac{\$264.80 + (\$183.30 \times 3)}{4} = \$203.68 \text{ per use for four uses}$$

The estimator should figure on reuse of forms within a project as well as from one project to the next. To determine the optimum number of forms required, a preliminary schedule (as described in Chapter 5) can be extremely useful. For a building with hundreds of similar columns, only a certain percentage of that number of forms need be built. The appropriate number of forms is determined by the sequence of construction and by the curing time before the forms can be stripped and reused. (See Chapter 5 and Figures 5.4 and 5.5.) Curing time is often the limiting factor when determining the required number and reuse of forms.

Reinforcing: The size and quantities of reinforcing steel can vary greatly with the type of structure, design load, concrete strength and type of steel. Steel material prices should always be verified by local suppliers. Labor costs will also vary depending upon the size of reinforcing. Reinforcing is priced and purchased by weight. While a smaller and lighter bar may be installed faster than a larger, heavier bar, more tonnage is installed faster with the heavier reinforcing. For example, in slabs and footings, a rodman can install a ton of heavy bars in about nine hours, while a ton of light bars requires about fifteen hours.

Specified sizes for reinforcing are shown in sections and details. Quantities are measured from the plans as linear feet for each size; this figure must then be converted to weight. Conversion factors are given in Figure 8.40. Accessories, dowels and splicing should be priced separately. If post-tensioning is specified, the estimator must be sure to include all requirements, coatings, wrapping, etc. Grouting after tensioning may also be required.

When the plans show the complete concrete design but are not sufficient to serve as placing drawings, suppliers will often provide the detailing service by preparing reinforcing steel placing drawings. This service should not be substituted for and does not take the place of structural engineering services. In conjunction with the drawings, the suppliers may produce material lists to aid the estimator. For large projects, the Concrete Reinforcing Steel Institute (CRSI) may provide these services to all prospective bidders.

Welded wire fabric for slabs should be measured allowing a 10% overlap. (Material costs for welded wire fabric, as presented in *Building Construction Cost Data* include a 10% overlap.) Weights, sizes and new designations of welded wire fabric are shown in Figure 8.40.

Because of the quantity and weight involved, handling costs for reinforcing must also be added. Unloading, sorting and crane placement costs can add 5% to 7% percent to the cost of reinforcing.

Placing Concrete: There are many ways to transport concrete from the truck to the installation locations. The most economical method is by direct chute because little labor or equipment is required from truck to forms; gravity does the work. The construction of an elaborate chute system, while an expensive initial cost, may be less costly overall than alternative methods.

Reinforcing Bars

Bar Size Designation	Weight Pounds Per Foot	Nominal Dimensions - Round Sections		
		Diameter Inches	Cross-Sectional Area-Sq. Inches	Perimeter Inches
#3	.376	.375	.11	1.178
#4	.668	.500	.20	1.571
#5	1.043	.625	.31	1.963
#6	1.502	.750	.44	2.356
#7	2.044	.875	.60	2.749
#8	2.670	1.000	.79	3.142
#9	3.400	1.128	1.00	3.544
#10	4.303	1.270	1.27	3.990
#11	5.313	1.410	1.56	4.430
#14	7.650	1.693	2.25	5.320
#18	13.600	2.257	4.00	7.090

Common Stock Styles of Welded Wire Fabric

	New Designation	Old Designation	Steel Area Per Foot				Approximate Weight Per 100 Sq. Ft.	
			Longitudinal		Transverse			
	Spacing - Cross Sectional Area (IN.)-(Sq. IN. 100)	Spacing Wire Gauge (IN.)-(AS & W)	IN.	CM	IN.	CM	LB	KG
Rolls	6 x 6-W1.4 x W1.4	6 x 6-10 x 10	0.028	0.071	0.028	0.071	21	9.53
	6 x 6-W2.0 x W2.0	6 x 6-8 x 8 (1)	0.040	0.102	0.040	0.102	29	13.15
	6 x 6-W2.9 x W2.9	6 x 6-6 x 6	0.058	0.147	0.053	0.147	42	19.05
	6 x 6-W4.0 x W4.0	6 x 6-4 x 4	0.080	0.203	0.080	0.203	58	26.31
	4 x 4-W1.4 x W1.4	4 x 4-10 x 10	0.042	0.107	0.042	0.107	31	14.06
	4 x 4-W2.0 x W2.0	4 x 4-8 x 8 (1)	0.060	0.152	0.060	0.152	43	19.50
	4 x 4-W2.9 x W2.9	4 x 4-6 x 6	0.087	0.221	0.087	0.221	62	28.12
	4 x 4-W4.0 x W4.0	4 x 4-4 x 4	0.120	0.305	0.120	0.305	85	38.56
Sheets	6 x 6-W2.9 x W2.9	6 x 6-6 x 6	0.058	0.147	0.058	0.147	42	19.05
	6 x 6-W4.0 x W4.0	6 x 6-4 x 4	0.080	0.203	0.080	0.203	58	26.31
	6 x 6-W5.5 x W5.5	6 x 6-2 x 2 (2)	0.110	0.279	0.110	0.279	80	36.29
	6 x 6-W4.0 x W4.0	4 x 4-4 x 4	0.120	0.305	0.120	0.305	85	38.56

NOTES
1. Exact W-number size for 8 gauge is W2.1
2. Exact W-number size for 2 gauge is W5.4

Figure 8.40

The estimator should visualize the process and use experience to determine the most economical approach. The number of forms, size of the pours and size of the finishing crews will all have a direct bearing on the choice of proper placement method. If the size of the pour is large and adequate finishing workers and laborers are available, pumping concrete is the fastest, but most expensive method. If a crane is available on-site, placement with the crane and a bucket may be the most feasible. Conveyors, wheelbarrows and even hand carried buckets may be used depending upon the type of work involved. Motorized carts may also be used in conjunction with each of the above mentioned methods. Temporary ramps and runways will be required for these carts. Costs are presented in *Building Construction Cost Data* for each method of placing concrete for different types of structures. Only an analysis of each individual project will determine the most feasible and economical method of concrete placement.

Finishing Concrete: Requirements for concrete finishes are usually found in the specifications portion of the construction documents. For floors, walks, and other horizontal surfaces, not only must the type of finish be included (broom, trowel, etc.), but also any required surface treatments and additives. Such treatments may include hardeners, colors, and abrasives. Costs for floor finishing will also depend upon the allowable tolerances for floor leveling. Typical tolerances may allow a 1/8" inch variation in 10'. Closer required tolerances will require more labor and finishing costs.

Wall finishing may vary from patching voids and tie holes to creating hammered or sandblasted finishes. Architectural finishes may also be achieved using special form surface materials, such as boards or strips.

Spread Footings: Plans for a building with spread footings (as in Figure 8.36) generally include a footing schedule that lists, counts and defines each type and size of spread footing. Reinforcing data is usually included. An example footing schedule is shown in Figure 8.41; it includes information on reinforcing requirements. When the schedule is provided, it eliminates the repetition of detailing on the plans and simplifies the estimator's task. Dimensions can be transferred directly onto the Quantity Sheet (see Figure 8.37). Using this form and the footing schedule, the procedure is as follows:

- Write down the number of each size and the dimensions of each of the spread footings shown on the plans.
- Extend each of these lines to obtain the Volume, Form Area, and Finish Area.
- Total the extensions.
- Count the total number of footings on the plan to make sure none has been left out.

When working with these plans for spread footings, take off related items such as anchor bolts, templates, base plates and reinforcing steel. Reinforcing steel may be transferred to a separate sheet. These other items should be computed and totaled on the same Quantity Sheet from which they were derived in order to avoid errors and omissions.

Continuous Wall Footings and Grade Beams: Wall footings transmit loads directly to the soil. Grade Beams are self-supporting structural members that carry wall loads across unacceptable soil to spread footings, caissons or support piles. The sequence for quantity takeoff is the same as discussed above. Again, dimensions should be recorded and extended on a Quantity Sheet.

Wall footings are stepped when grade changes necessitate changes in footing elevation. Figure 8.42 illustrates a stepped footing. Notice that in plan view, the footing may easily be mistaken as continuous. Where stepped footings occur, extra formwork (2 x Area A plus Area B) and extra concrete (W x Area A) are required in addition to the quantities for the continuous footing. Accessories should also be taken off at the same time using the pertinent dimensions and derived quantities.

Footing Schedule			
Ident.	No.	Size	Reinforcing
F-1	8	8'0" x 8'0" x 1'10"	9-#6 e.w.
F-2	12	6'0" x 6'0" x 1'4"	8-#5 e.w.
F-3	4	4'6" x 4'6" x 1'0"	5-#5 e.w.

Column Schedule			
Ident.	No.	Size	Reinforcing
C-1	8	24" x 24" x 12'	8-#11 ties #4 @ 22"
C-2	12	20" x 20" x 12'	8- #9 ties #3 @ 18"
C-3	4	16" x 16" x 12'	8- #9 ties #3 @ 16"

Beam Schedule			
Ident.	No.	Size	Reinforcing
B-1 Ext.	1	1' x 2'6" x 60'	See Re-Bar Schedule
B-2 Ext.	2	1' x 2'4" x 75'	
B-3 Int.	2	8" x 1'6" x 60'	
B-4 Int.	2	6" x 1'6" x 125'	

Figure 8.41

Pile Caps: Pile Caps are basically spread footings on piles. The shape is not always rectangular, so that the form area is determined by the perimeter x depth. Concrete volume should be not deducted for the protrusion of the piles into the cap.

Piers: Piers are used to extend the bearing of the superstructure down to the footing. They vary in length to accommodate sub-surface conditions, original site grades and frost penetration. Piers are often included on the Footing Schedule.

Walls: Walls are separated by height during takeoff. Generally this is done in 4' increments such as under 4', 4' to 8', and 8' to 12'. Different forming and placing costs may be used for each of these heights.

- Using a quantity sheet, define each wall. If all walls have footings, the wall footing schedule can be used as a basis.
- Write in the dimensions for each of these walls.
- From these dimensions, compute the Volume and Form Area for each wall, dividing them into convenient modular categories. Brick shelves and slab seats should be listed and deducted from concrete volume.
- Total the extensions.

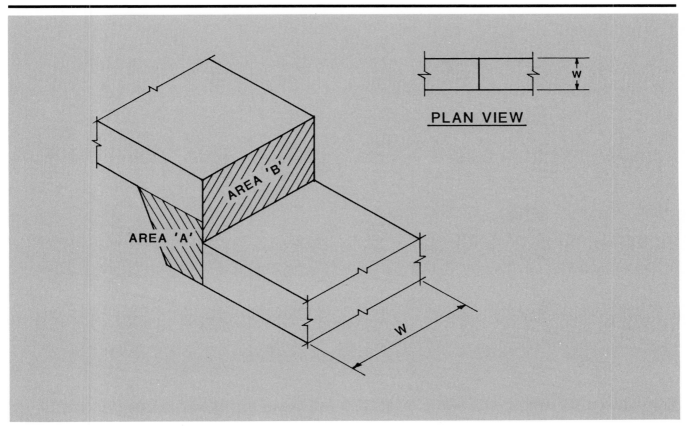

Figure 8.42

- Upon examination of the wall sections and details, list all associated items: beams seats, anchor bolts, base plates, chamfers, pilasters, rustications, architectural finishes, openings and reinforcing steel. Where pilasters occur, figure the wall forming straight through and then add the area of the pilasters as a separate item. Costs are different for walls and pilasters. The additional materials will be used in waste, bracing and framing.
- Building a perimeter wall with many angles and corners will take more time and more material to form than a wall with four square corners. Note the number of corners on the Quantity Sheet so that an allowance for material and labor can be made when pricing the wall forming.

The above procedure will be identical for foundation walls and retaining walls. If retaining walls are battered, be sure to note this. Formwork erection time may be up to 20% slower as a result. For special architectural effects, the use of form liners, rustication strips, retarders, and sandblasting must be considered.

Columns: Columns are commonly listed in a schedule similar to that used for spread footings. An example is shown in Figure 8.41. Quantities are derived using the same procedure discussed above. When estimating columns, the following associated items must be considered:

- Height Measurement from floor slab below to underside of beam or slab.
- Multiple use of forms.
- Chamfer strips.
- Finishing requirements.
- Capitals.
- Reinforcing steel.
- Clamps, inserts, and placing pockets.

Beams: As with footings and columns, cast-in-place beams are also often listed on a schedule. If not otherwise designated, interior and exterior beams should be listed separately. The following principles should be used when estimating beams:

- The depths given in schedules represent design depths. Slab thickness must be deducted when calculating volume and contact area.
- Exterior and interior beams should be listed separately. An exterior beam requires forming for the full design depth on one side. The access and bracing of this exterior form make it more costly to erect and strip.
- Formwork or volume should not be deducted for columns.
- Beams and slabs are usually placed simultaneously. Beam quantities should be separated by floor to be included with slab placement.
- The support method should be determined — whether the formwork is hung from beams, supported with adjustable horizontal shores, or shored from the structure below. Reshoring costs must be included if required.
- Finishing requirements and design will affect the multiple use of forms.

Calculations for Formed, Cast-in-Place Concrete:

Spread Footings and Pile Caps:

Volume	— Length (L) x Width (W) x Depth (D)
Form Area	— (2L + 2W) x D
Finish Area	— L x W

Continuous Footings:

Volume	— Length (L) x Width (W) x Depth (D)
Form Area	— 2L x D
Finish Area	— L x W

Rectangular Columns:

Volume	— Length (L) x Width (W) x Height (H)
Form Area	— (2L + 2W) x H
Finish Area	— (2L + 2W) x H

Round Columns:

Volume	— 3.146 x Radius (R) x R x Height (H)
Form Area	— 3.146 x Diameter (D) x H
Finish Area	— 3.146 x D x H

Walls:

Volume	— Length (L) x Height (H) x Thickness (T)
Form Area	— L x H x 2
Finish Area	— L x H (for each side)

Beams:

Exterior:

Volume	— L x W x (Design depth (d) — Slab thickness (t))
Form Area	— (L x W) + (L x d) + (L x (d — t))
Finish Area	— Same as form area

Interior:

Volume	— Length x Width x (d — t)
Form Area	— (L x W) + 2 (L x (d — t))
Finish Area	— Same as form area

Slabs: Concrete slabs can be divided into two categories: slabs on grade including sidewalks and concrete paving, and elevated slabs. Several items must be considered when estimating slabs on grade.

- Granular Base
- Fine Grading
- Vapor Barrier
- Edge Forms and Bulkheads
- Expansion Joints
- Contraction Joints
- Screeds
- Welded Wire Fabric and Reinforcing
- Concrete Material
- Finish and Topping
- Curing and Hardeners
- Control Joints
- Concrete "Outs"
- Haunches
- Drops

Quantities for most of the items above can be derived from basic dimensions: length, width, and slab thickness. When these quantities are calculated, some basic rules can be used:

- Allow about 25% compaction for granular base.
- Allow 10% overlap for vapor barrier and welded wire fabric.
- Allow 5% extra concrete for waste.
- No deductions should be made for columns or "outs" under 10 S.F.
- If screeds are separated from forming and placing costs, figure 1 L.F. of screed per 10 S.F. of finish area.

Elevated slabs, while similar to slabs on grade, require special consideration. For all types of elevated slabs, edge forms should be estimated carefully. Stair towers, elevator shafts and utility chases all require edge forms. The appropriate quantities for each of these "outs" should be deducted from the concrete volume and finish area. Edge form materials and installation will vary depending upon the slab type and thickness. Special consideration should be given to pipe chases that require concrete placement after the pipes are in position. This is done in order to maintain the fireproofing integrity. Hand mixing and placing may be necessary.

When estimating beam supported slabs, beams should not normally be deducted from the floor form area. The extra costs for bracing and framing at the beams will account for the difference. When concrete for the beams and slab is placed at the same time, the placement costs will be the same for both.

Slab placement costs should be increased based on the beam volume. Separate costs for beam concrete placement should not be included. For hung slabs, separation of costs for beams and slab is even more difficult. These costs may be treated as one item.

Metal decking for elevated slabs is usually installed by the steel erector. When determining concrete quantities, measure the slab thickness to the middle of the corrugation.

Cast-in-place concrete joist and dome (or waffle) slabs are more difficult to estimate. Pans and domes are shored with either open or closed deck forming. For concrete joist systems, quantities for concrete can be calculated from Figure 8.43. Volume of beams must be added separately. Volume of waffle slabs, because of the varying sizes of solid column heads, should be estimated differently. Total volume from top of slab to bottom of pan should be calculated. The volume of the actual number of domes (voids) is then deducted. Volumes for standard domes are listed in Figure 8.44.

Stairs: When taking off cast-in-place stairs, a careful investigation should be made to ensure that all inserts, such as railing pockets, anchors, nosings, and reinforcing steel have been included. Also indicate on your quantity sheet any special tread finishes; these can sometimes represent a considerable cost.

Stairs cast on fill are most easily estimated and recorded by the square foot. The calculation is — slant length times width. Because of the commonly used ratios adopted by designers, this method works for high or low risers with wide or narrow treads. Shored cast in place stairs can be estimated in the same way — slant length times width.

Concrete Quantities (CF concrete/SF floor) for Single & Multiple Span Concrete Joist Construction						
	Width					
	20″ Forms			30″ Forms		
Depth (Rib/Slab)	5″ Rib 25″ O.C.	6″ Rib 26″ O.C.	7″ Rib 27″ O.C.	5″ Rib 35″ O.C.	6″ Rib 36″ O.C.	7″ Rib 37″ O.C.
8″/3″	0.40	0.42	—	0.36	0.37	—
8″/4½″	0.53	0.55	—	0.48	0.50	—
10″/3″	0.45	0.47	—	0.39	0.41	—
10″/4½″	0.57	0.61	—	0.51	0.53	—
12″/3″	0.49	0.52	—	0.42	0.45	—
12″/4½″	0.62	0.65	—	0.55	0.57	—
14″/3″	0.54	0.57	—	0.45	0.48	—
14″/4½″	0.66	0.69	—	0.58	0.61	—
16″/3″	—	0.63	0.66	—	0.52	0.55
16″/4½″	—	0.75	0.79	—	0.65	0.68
20″/3″	—	0.75	0.79	—	0.61	0.64
20″/4½″	—	0.87	0.91	—	0.74	0.77

Figure 8.43

	Standard Dome Sizes and Volumes									
	19″ Domes				30″ Domes					
Depth	6″	8″	10″	12″	8″	10″	12″	14″	16″	20″
Volume (CF per dome)	1.09	1.41	1.90	2.14	3.85	4.78	5.53	6.54	7.44	9.16

Figure 8.44

Treads and landings of prefabricated metal pan stairs should be identified on the takeoff sheet. The cost of hand placing the fill concrete should be included in Division 3.

For all cast-in-place, formed concrete work, the following factors can affect the number of pans to rent, the S.F. of forms to build, the number of shores to provide, etc.:

- Placement rate of concrete for crew.
- Concrete pump or crane and bucket rental cost per pour.
- Finishing rate for concrete finishers.
- Curing time before stripping and reshoring.
- Forming and stripping time.
- Number of reuses of forms.

Experience (or consultation with an experienced superintendent) will tell the estimator which combination of these six items will limit the quantity of forms to be built, or the number of pans to be rented.

Precast Concrete

Typical precast units are estimated and purchased by the square foot or linear foot. The manufacturer will most often deliver precast units. Costs for delivery are sometimes separate from the purchase price and must be included in the estimate. Most manufacturers also have the capability to erect these units, and, because of experience, are best suited to the task.

Each type and size of precast unit should be separated on the quantity or estimate sheet. Typical units are shown in Figure 8.45. The estimator should verify the availability of specified units with local suppliers. For types that are seldom used, casting beds may have to be custom built, thus increasing cost.

Connections and joint requirements will vary with the type of unit, from welding or bolting embedded steel to simple grouting. Toppings must also be included, whether lightweight or regular concrete on floors, insulating concrete for roofs. The specifications and construction details must be examined carefully.

Sample Estimate: Division 3

When performing the estimate for the sample division building project, a number of principles mentioned above, are applied. The most important is common sense, together with the ability to visualize the construction process. Most information for the quantity takeoff would normally be supplied on drawings, details and in the specifications. Even when all data is provided, however, the estimator must be familiar with standard materials and practices.

Concrete work is composed of many components, most of which are based on similar dimensions. It makes sense to organize all takeoff data on a Quantity Sheet as shown in Figure 8.37. A partial takeoff for Division 3 of the sample project is shown in Figure 8.46. Note that every quantity that is to be priced has been converted to the appropriate units and delineated on the sheet. As the quantities are transferred to the pricing sheets, colored pencil checkmarks will ensure inclusion of all items. The estimate sheets for Division 3 are shown in Figures 8.47 to 8.52.

Most quantities are derived from the plan in Figure 8.5. Heights are determined from the building section in Figure 8.10. Dimensioned details are provided in complete plans and specifications. The spread footing quantities are easily obtained from the drawings. Care must be exercised when estimating the continuous footings. Note on Figure 8.46 that the complete perimeter is used for a gross quantity and that a deduction is included where the spread footings interrupt the continuous footing. The keyway and dowel supports, as shown in Section A-A in Figure 8.5, continue across the spread footings. Thus, the linear dimension of the keyway and dowel supports will be greater than that of the continuous footing. (Note that the keyway and dowel supports are included in more than the perimeter footings.) The steps in the perimeter footing between column lines 4 and 5 (Figure 8.5) are not listed separately due to their insignificant effect on the total cost. This is a judgement call of the type that should only be made based on experience.

Quantities for the perimeter wall are calculated with no deduction for the pilasters. Such a deduction should be more than compensated by extra costs for framing and bracing at the connections. Pilaster formwork should be recorded separately. Costs used for placing the pilaster concrete are the same as for the perimeter wall because placement for both will occur simultaneously.

Reinforcing quantities are taken from Circle Reference Number 47 in *Building Construction Cost Data*. These figures are based on pounds per cubic yard of concrete. When detailed information is available, actual linear quantities and counts of splices and accessories of each size and type should be taken off and priced for greater accuracy. Note that the costs used for welded wire fabric as presented in *Building Construction Cost Data* (Figure 8.53) include a 10% overlap so that quantities in this case are derived from actual dimensions.

(55) Prestressed Precast Concrete Structural Units

Type	Location	Depth	Span in Ft.		Live Load Lb. per S.F.
Double Tee	Floor	28" to 34"	60 to 80		50 to 80
	Roof	12" to 24"	30 to 50		40
	Wall	Width 8'	Up to 55' high		Wind
Multiple Tee	Roof	8" to 12"	15 to 40		40
	Floor	8" to 12"	15 to 30		100
Plank	Roof		Roof	Floor	
		4"	13	12	40 for Roof
	or	6"	22	18	
		8"	26	25	
		10"	33	29	100 for Floor
	Floor	12"	42	32	
Single Tee	Roof	28" 32" 36" 48"	40 80 100 120		40
AASHO Girder	Bridges	Type 4 5 6	100 110 125		Highway
Box Beam	Bridges	15" 27" 33"	40 to 100		Highway

Figure 8.45

170

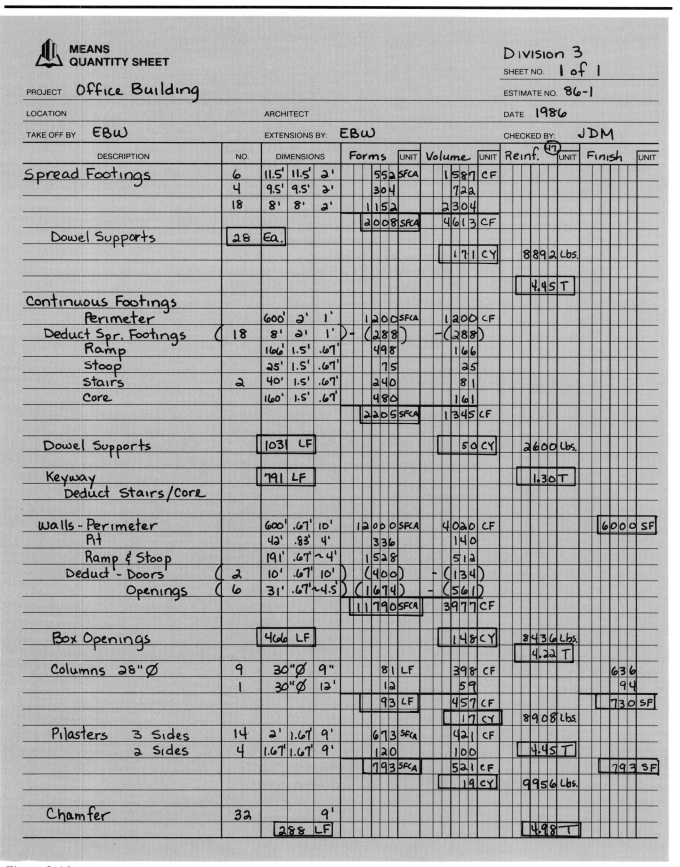

Figure 8.46

MEANS CONSOLIDATED ESTIMATE

PROJECT: Office Building
LOCATION
TAKE OFF BY: EBW   QUANTITIES BY: EBW   PRICES BY: RSM   EXTENSIONS BY: SLM   CHECKED: JDM

CLASSIFICATION
ARCHITECT

Division 3
SHEET NO. 1 of 6
ESTIMATE NO. 86-1
DATE 1986

DESCRIPTION	SOURCE/DIMENSIONS			QUANTITY	UNIT	MATERIAL UNIT COST	MATERIAL TOTAL	LABOR UNIT COST	LABOR TOTAL	EQUIPMENT UNIT COST	EQUIPMENT TOTAL	SUBCONTRACT UNIT COST	SUBCONTRACT TOTAL
Division 3: Concrete													
Formwork													
Spread Footings	3.1	45	515	2008	SFCA	.32	643	1.53	3072				
Dowel Supports	3.1	45	610 615	28	Eq.	14.95	419	34.50	966				
Continuous Footings	3.1	45	015	2205	SFCA	.27	595	1.31	2889				
Dowel Supports	3.1	45	050	1031	LF	.50	515	1.27	1309				
Keyway (excl. stairs & core)	3.1	45	150	791	LF	.07	55	.30	237				
Walls:													
Pit (10")	3.1	65	200	336	SFCA	1.27	427	2.64	887				
Ramp & Stoops (8")	3.1	65	200	1528	SFCA	1.27	1941	2.64	4034				
Perimeter (8"x10')	3.1	65	215	9936	SFCA	.50	4963	1.94	19256				
	12,000	SFCA											
Deduct Openings													
Garage	(400)												
Above Grade	(1674)												
Box Openings	3.1	65	015	464	LF	1.15	5363.49	3.49	1626				
Sub Totals							(10094)		(34276)				

Figure 8.47

172

MEANS CONSOLIDATED ESTIMATE

Division 3
SHEET NO. 2 of 6

PROJECT Office Building CLASSIFICATION ESTIMATE NO. 86-1

LOCATION ARCHITECT DATE 1986

TAKE OFF BY EBW QUANTITIES BY EBW PRICES BY RSM EXTENSIONS BY SLM CHECKED JDM

DESCRIPTION	SOURCE/DIMENSIONS			QUANTITY	UNIT	MATERIAL UNIT COST	MATERIAL TOTAL	LABOR UNIT COST	LABOR TOTAL	EQUIPMENT UNIT COST	EQUIPMENT TOTAL	SUBCONTRACT UNIT COST	SUBCONTRACT TOTAL	
Division 3: (Cont'd) Formwork (Cont'd)														
Columns - 28" Ø 9@9', 1@12'	3.1	25	185	93	LF	14.75	1372	5.05	470					
Pilasters	3.1	65	860	793	SFCA	1.44	1142	3.62	2871					
Chamfer 3/4"	3.1	05	245	288	LF	.40	115	.30	86					
4" Slab Edge Form @ Pit & Openings	3.1	55	300	65	LF	.16	10	1.06	69					
Waffle Slab (1st Floor)	3.1	35	450	18,220	SF	2.23	40631	2.41	43910					
		18,900 SF												
Deduct - Stairs		(600 SF)												
Shaft		(80 SF)												
Opening Edge Forms	3.1	35	500	273	SFCA	1.82	497	5.15	1406					
Perimeter Edge Forms	3.1	35	710	600	SFCA	.40	240	1.81	1086					
Perimeter Work Deck	3.1	35	800	200	LF	5	1000	7.05	1410					
Bulkhead Forms	3.1	35	600	500	LF	.96	480	1.96	980					
Sub Totals							45487		52288					

Figure 8.48

MEANS CONSOLIDATED ESTIMATE

PROJECT: Office Building
LOCATION
TAKE OFF BY: EBW QUANTITIES BY: EBW PRICES BY: RSM EXTENSIONS BY: SLM
CLASSIFICATION
ARCHITECT
CHECKED: JDM

DESCRIPTION	SOURCE/DIMENSIONS			QUANTITY	UNIT	MATERIAL UNIT COST	MATERIAL TOTAL	LABOR UNIT COST	LABOR TOTAL	EQUIPMENT UNIT COST	EQUIPMENT TOTAL	SUBCONTRACT UNIT COST	SUBCONTRACT TOTAL
Division 3: (Cont'd)													
Reinforcing Steel													
Footings	3.2	04	050	5.75	T	500	2875	330	1897				
Walls	3.2	04	070	4.22	T	505	2131	230	971				
Columns	3.2	04	025	9.43	T	500	4715	305	2876				
Waffle Slab	3.2	04	040	23.59	T	510	12031	240	5662				
WWF: 6 x 6 10/10													
Elevated Slabs				37,800	SF								
Garage Slab				18,900									
Penthouse Floor				2,100									
Deduct - Stair				(1,120)									
Elevator				(360)									
				57,320	SF								
Total WWF	3.2	06	001	573.2	CSF	7.65	4385	9.95	5703				
Sub Totals							26137		17109				

MEANS CONSOLIDATED ESTIMATE

Division 3

SHEET NO. 4 of 6

PROJECT Office Building | CLASSIFICATION | ESTIMATE NO. 86-1

LOCATION | ARCHITECT | DATE 1986

TAKE OFF BY EBW | QUANTITIES BY EBW | PRICES BY RSM | EXTENSIONS BY SLM | CHECKED JDM

DESCRIPTION	SOURCE/DIMENSIONS			QUANTITY	UNIT	MATERIAL UNIT COST	MATERIAL TOTAL	LABOR UNIT COST	LABOR TOTAL	EQUIPMENT UNIT COST	EQUIPMENT TOTAL	SUBCONTRACT UNIT COST	SUBCONTRACT TOTAL
Division 3: (cont'd)													
Cast In Place Concrete													
Spread Footings													
Concrete-Incl. 5% Waste	3.3	12	015	180	CY	48.90	8802						
Placing	3.3	38	260	180	CY			7.30	1314	.49	88		
Continuous Footings													
Concrete-Incl. 5% Waste	3.3	12	015	52	CY	48.90	2543						
Placing	3.3	38	190	52	CY			6.70	348	.45	23		
Walls													
Concrete-Incl. 5%	3.3	12	030	155	CY	52.20	8091						
Placing	3.3	38	495	155	CY			12.90	1999	6.65	1031		
Finishing	3.3	28	001	6000	SF	.01	60	.28	1680				
Columns													
Concrete-Incl. 5%	3.3	12	030	18	CY	52.20	940						
Placing	3.3	38	100	18	CY			7.85	141	4.04	73		
Finishing	3.3	28	001	730	SF	.01	7	.28	204				
Pilasters													
Concrete-Incl. 5%	3.3	12	030	20	CY	52.20	1044						
Placing-(Use wall costs above)				20	CY			12.90	258	6.65	133		
Finishing	3.3	28	001	793	SF	.01	8	.28	222				
SubTotals							21495		6166		1348		

Figure 8.50

MEANS CONSOLIDATED ESTIMATE

PROJECT Office Building

LOCATION

TAKE OFF BY EBW QUANTITIES BY EBW PRICES BY RSM EXTENSIONS BY SLM

CLASSIFICATION

ARCHITECT

DESCRIPTION	SOURCE/DIMENSIONS			QUANTITY	UNIT	MATERIAL		LABOR		EQUIPMENT		SUBCONTRACT	
						UNIT COST	TOTAL	UNIT COST	TOTAL	UNIT COST	TOTAL	UNIT COST	TOTAL
Division 3: (Cont'd)													
Cast In Place Concrete (Cont'd)													
Slab on Grade													
Concrete - Incl. 5%	3.3	12	015	348	CY	48.90	17017						
Placing	3.3	38	460	348	CY			4.88	1698	.33	115		
Finishing	3.3	26	015	18,210	SF			.27	4917				
Pt Slab													
Concrete - Incl. 5%	3.3	12	015	3	SY	48.90	147						
Placing	3.3	38	460	3	SY			4.88	15	.33	1		
Finishing	3.3	26	015	80	SF			.27	22				
Waffle Slab													
Concrete - Incl. 5%	3.3	12	030 100	555	CY	57.42	31868						
Placing	3.3	38	160	555	CY			7.30	4051	3.77	2092		
Finishing	3.3	26	020	18,900	SF			.29	5481				
5'la" Elevated Slabs													
4" Lt. Wt. Concrete - Incl. 5%	3.3	12	030 101	462	CY	66.29	30626						
Placing	3.3	38	140	462	CY			10	4620	5.15	2379		
Finishing	3.3	26	020	37,800	SF			.29	10962				
Curing - 3 Floors	3.3	16	030	567	CSF	1.70	964	2.68	1520				
Stair Treads & Landings	3.3	48	175	1436	SF	2.30	3303	1.54	2211				
Sub Total							83925		35497		4587		

Figure 8.51

MEANS CONSOLIDATED ESTIMATE

Division 3
SHEET NO. 6 of 6
ESTIMATE NO. 86-1
DATE 1986
CHECKED JDM

PROJECT Office Building
LOCATION
CLASSIFICATION
ARCHITECT

TAKE OFF BY EBW | QUANTITIES BY EBW | PRICES BY RSM | EXTENSIONS BY SLM

DESCRIPTION	SOURCE/DIMENSIONS	QUANTITY	UNIT	MATERIAL UNIT COST	MATERIAL TOTAL	LABOR UNIT COST	LABOR TOTAL	EQUIPMENT UNIT COST	EQUIPMENT TOTAL	SUBCONTRACT UNIT COST	SUBCONTRACT TOTAL
Division 3: (Cont'd)											
Sheet 1					10094		34276				
Sheet 2					454871		522488				
Formwork SubTotals					555581		865644				
Sheet 3					26137		17109				
Reinforcing SubTotals					26137		17109				
Sheet 4					21495		6166		1348		
Sheet 5					83925		35497		4587		
Concrete In Place SubTotals					105420		41663		5935		
Division 3 Totals					187138		145336		5935		

Figure 8.52

3.2 Reinforcing Steel		CREW	DAILY OUTPUT	UNIT	BARE COSTS			TOTAL INCL O&P
					MAT.	INST.	TOTAL	
103	#9 bars	C-5	68	Ea.	11.60	23	34.60	46
104	#10 bars		68		12.60	23	35.60	47
105	#11 bars		68		15.70	23	38.70	50
106	#14 bars		62		19.85	25	44.85	58
107	#18 bars	↓	62	↓	29	25	54	68
108								
120	Full tension, grade 60 steel, columns,							
122	slabs or beams, #6, 7, 8 bars	C-5	68	Ea.	11.50	23	34.50	46
123	#9 bars		68		13.10	23	36.10	47
124	#10 bars		68		14.35	23	37.35	49
125	#11 bars		68		17.05	23	40.05	52L
126	#14 bars		62		23	25	48	61
127	#18 bars	↓	62		37	25	62	77
140	If equipment handling not required, deduct			↓		50%		
160	Mechanical threaded type, bar threading not included,							
170	straight bars, #10 & #11	C-5	190	Ea.	10.10	8.30	18.40	23
175	#14 bars		170		13.60	9.30	22.90	28
180	#18 bars		100		21.80	15.80	37.60	46
200	#11 to #14 transition		190		13.05	8.30	21.35	26
210	#11 to #18 & #14 to #18 transition		100		23	15.80	38.80	48
240	Bent bars, #10 & #11		140		19.80	11.30	31.10	38
250	#14		120		26	13.15	39.15	47
260	#18		90		39	17.55	56.55	68
280	#11 to #14 transition		100		26	15.80	41.80	51
290	#11 to #18 & #14 to #18 transition	↓	90	↓	39	17.55	56.55	68
06-001	WELDED WIRE FABRIC Rolls, 6 x 6 = #10/10 (W1.4/W1.4) 21 lb.	2 Rodm	35	C.S.F.	7.65	9.95	17.60	24
020	6 x 6 = #8/8 (W2.1/W2.1) 30 lb. per C.S.F.		31		10.50	11.25	21.75	29
030	6 x 6 = #6/6 (W2.9/W2.9) 42 lb. per C.S.F.		29		14.80	12	26.80	35
040	6 x 6 = #4/4 (W4/W4) 58 lb. per C.S.F.		27		19.80	12.90	32.70	42
050	4 x 4 = #10/10 (W1.4/W1.4) 31 lb. per C.S.F.		31		11.75	11.25	23	30
060	4 x 4 = #8/8 (W2.1/W2.1) 44 lb. per C.S.F.		29		14.05	12	26.05	34
065	4 x 4 = #6/6 (W2.9/W2.9) 61 lb. per C.S.F.		27		20	12.90	32.90	42
070	4 x 4 = #4/4 (W4/W4) 85 lb. per C.S.F.		25		30	13.90	43.90	55
080	2 x 2 = #14 galv. @ 21 lb., beam & column wrap		6.50		13.40	54	67.40	98
090	2 x 2 = #12 galv. for gunite reinforcing	↓	6.50	↓	18.50	54	72.50	105
095	Material prices for above include 10% lap							
098								
100	Specially fabricated heavier gauges, in sheets	4 Rodm	50	C.S.F.		13.90	13.90	22L
101	Material only, minimum			Ton	580		580	640M
102	Average				675		675	745M
103	Maximum			↓	835		835	920M

3.3 Cast in Place Concrete		CREW	DAILY OUTPUT	UNIT	BARE COSTS			TOTAL INCL O&P
					MAT.	INST.	TOTAL	
01-001	AGGREGATE Expanded shale, C.L. lots, 43.5 to 52 lb. per C.F., minimum			Ton	32		32	35M
005	Maximum			"	37		37	41M
010	Lightweight vermiculite or perlite, 4 C.F. bag, C.L. lots			Bag	5		5	5.50M
015	L.C.L. lots			"	5.65		5.65	6.20M
025	Sand & stone, loaded at pit, crushed bank gravel			Ton	4.45		4.45	4.89M
030	Fill, bank run				2.25		2.25	2.47M
035	Sand, washed, for concrete				6.55		6.55	7.20M
040	For plaster or brick				7		7	7.70M
045	Stone, 3/4" to 1-1/2"				7.75		7.75	8.50M
050	3/8" roofing stone & 1/2" pea stone			↓	8.75		8.75	9.60M

(42)

Figure 8.53

178

Concrete material costs for the waffle slab include a cost for high early strength. The 2nd and 3rd floor elevated slabs include percentages for high early strength and for lightweight aggregate. The appropriate percentages are obtained from Figure 8.54 and added to the unit costs before entry on the estimate sheet. Costs for concrete are readily available from local suppliers and should always be verified.

Figures 8.54 (bottom) and 8.55 show costs for complete concrete systems in place. These systems are most often priced per cubic yard of concrete. The costs are based on averages for each type and size of system as listed. These figures provide an excellent checklist to quickly compare costs of similar systems estimated by individual components for possible omissions or duplications. For the sample estimate such a comparison can be made. The component costs for spread footings from the estimate sheets of Division 3 are added:

Spread Footings:

Bare Costs

	Material	Labor	Total
Formwork	$ 643	$3,072	$ 3,715
Reinf.	2,225	1,468	3,693
Concrete	8,802		8,802
Placing (incl. equip.)		$1,402	$ 1,402
Total	$11,670	$5,942	$17,612
$/CY (171 CY)	64.83	33.01	97.84

Reinforcing costs, separated for the spread footings only, are obtained from the appropriate quantities, from Figure 8.46, and the unit costs from Figure 8.49. Comparison to line 385 in Figure 8.55, verifies that costs for the building's spread footings are good. Similar crosschecks can be made throughout the estimate to help prevent gross errors.

Quantities and prices for all components of each of the concrete systems have been separately itemized. By organizing the estimate in this way, costs and quantities can be compared to historical figures and used as a comparison for future projects.

Division 4: Masonry

Masonry is generally estimated by the piece (brick, block, etc.) or by wall area (per square foot). Quantities based on square feet of surface area are a function of:

- Size of the masonry unit.
- Bond (pattern or coursing).
- Thickness of mortar joints.
- Thickness of wall.

Similar to other divisions, masonry estimates should be performed in as detailed a manner as is practical. The masonry specifications will contain pertinent information which should be noted before proceeding with the quantity takeoff. Such items as mortar types, joint reinforcing, and cleaning requirements should all be described and defined. Typical mortar types (mixtures) most commonly specified are shown in Figure 8.56. Required mortar additives (coloring, anti-hydro, bonding agents, etc.) will be specified and should be noted.

3.3 Cast in Place Concrete	CREW	DAILY OUTPUT	UNIT	BARE COSTS			TOTAL INCL O&P
				MAT.	INST.	TOTAL	
130	Non-metallic, 55 lb. bags, natural (grey), minimum			Lb.	.30		.30	.33M
131	Maximum				.40		.40	.44M
132	Non-metallic, colors, mininum				.35		.35	.38M
134	Maximum				.45		.45	.49M
140	Non-metallic, non-slip, 100 lb. bags, minimum				.35		.35	.38M
142	Maximum				.45		.45	.49M
150	Solution type, 300 to 400 S.F. per gallon			Gal.	4.80		4.80	5.30M
151								
155	Release agent, for tilt slabs			Gal.	7.50		7.50	8.25M
157	For forms, average				5		5	5.50M
160	Sealer, hardener and dustproofer, clear, 450 S.F., minimum				7		7	7.70M
162	Maximum				16.50		16.50	18.15M
170	Colors (300-400 S.F. per gallon)				15		15	16.50M
171								
180	Set accelerator for below freezing, 1 to 1-1/2 gal. per C.Y.			Gal.	4.20		4.20	4.62M
190	Set retarder, 2 to 4 fl. oz. per bag of cement			"	12.80		12.80	14.10M
200	Waterproofing, integral 1 lb. per bag of cement			Lb.	.72		.72	.79M
210	Powdered metallic, 40 lbs. per 100 S.F., minimum				.77		.77	.84M
212	Maximum				1		1	1.10M
220	Water reducing admixture, average			Gal.	7.75		7.75	8.50M
10-001 (45)	CONCRETE, FIELD MIX FOB forms 2250 psi			C.Y.	44.60		44.60	49M
002	3000 psi				47.45		47.45	52M
12-001 (43)	CONCRETE, READY MIX Regular weight, 2000 psi				45.55		45.55	50M
010	2500 psi				47.25		47.25	52M
015 (42)	3000 psi				48.90		48.90	54M
020	3500 psi				50.55		50.55	56M
025	3750 psi				51.50		51.50	57M
030	4000 psi				52.20		52.20	57M
035	4500 psi				54.15		54.15	60M
040	5000 psi				55.15		55.15	61M
100	For high early strength cement, add				10%			
101	For structural lightweight with regular sand, add				27%			
200	For all lightweight aggregate, add				50%			
300	For integral colors, 2500 psi, 5 bag mix							
310	Red, yellow or brown, 1.8 lb. per bag, add			C.Y.	12.60		12.60	13.85M
320	9.4 lb. per bag, add				66		66	73M
340	Black, 1.8 lb. per bag, add				13.10		13.10	14.40M
350	7.5 lb. per bag, add				55		55	61M
370	Green, 1.8 lb. per bag, add				27		27	30M
380	7.5 lb. per bag, add				115		115	125M
14-001	CONCRETE IN PLACE Including forms (4 uses), reinforcing							
005	steel, including finishing unless otherwise indicated							
010 (35)	Average for concrete framed building,							
011	including finishing	C-17B	15.75	C.Y.	98	120	218	280
013 (47)	Average for substructure only, simple design, incl. finishing		29.07		69	65	134	170
015	Average for superstructure only, including finishing		13.42		105	140	245	315
020 (50)	Base, granolithic, 1" x 5" high, straight	C-10	175	L.F.	.12	2.81	2.93	4.01
022	Cove	"	140	"	.12	3.51	3.63	4.98
030	Beams, 5 kip per L.F., 10' span	C-17A	6.28	C.Y.	168	285	453	595
035	25' span		7.40		135	240	375	495
050 (122)	Chimney foundations, minimum		26.70		89	67	156	195
051	Maximum		19.70		102	91	193	240
070 (49)	Columns, square, 12" x 12", minimum reinforcing		4.60		180	390	570	755
072	Average reinforcing		4.10		255	435	690	910
074	Maximum reinforcing	C-17B	3.84		380	495	875	1,125
080	16" x 16", minimum reinforcing	C-17A	6.25		160	285	445	585
082	Average reinforcing	"	4.93		250	360	610	795
084	Maximum reinforcing	C-17B	4.34		420	435	855	1,075
090	24" x 24", minimum reinforcing	C-17A	9.08		140	195	335	435
092	Average reinforcing	"	6.90		210	260	470	605

Figure 8.54

3.3	Cast in Place Concrete	CREW	DAILY OUTPUT	UNIT	BARE COSTS			TOTAL INCL O&P
					MAT.	INST.	TOTAL	
094	Maximum reinforcing	C-17A	5.65	C.Y.	345	315	660	835
100	36" x 36", minimum reinforcing	C-17B	13.39		130	140	270	345
102	Average reinforcing		9.61		200	195	395	495
104	Maximum reinforcing		7.50		325	250	575	715
120	Columns, round, tied, 16" diameter, minimum reinforcing		13.02		225	145	370	455
122	Average reinforcing		8.30		375	230	605	735
124	Maximum reinforcing		6.05		510	315	825	1,000
130	20" diameter, minimum reinforcing		17.35		210	110	320	385
132	Average reinforcing		10.43		340	180	520	630
134	Maximum reinforcing		7.47		460	255	715	865
140	24" diameter, minimum reinforcing		22.18		200	85	285	340
142	Average reinforcing		11.86		290	160	450	545
144	Maximum reinforcing		8.10		460	235	695	835
150	36" diameter, minimum reinforcing		32.40		180	58	238	280
152	Average reinforcing		16.57		245	115	360	430
154	Maximum reinforcing	▼	11.15	▼	335	170	505	610
170	Curbs, formed in place, 6" x 18", straight,	C-15	400	L.F.	2.90	3.51	6.41	8.25
175	Curb and gutter	"	170	"	4.65	8.25	12.90	17
190	Elevated slabs, flat slab, 125 psf Sup. Load, 20' span	C-17A	13.36	C.Y.	110	135	245	315
195	30' span	C-17B	18.25		105	105	210	260
210	Flat plate, 125 psf Sup. Load, 15' span	C-17A	10.28		115	175	290	375
215	25' span	C-17B	17.01		97	110	207	265
230	Waffle const., 30" domes, 125 psf Sup. Load, 20' span	▼	14.10		120	135	255	320
235	30' span	▼	17.02		113	110	223	280
250	One way joists, 30" pans, 125 psf Sup. Load, 15' span	C-17A	11.07		110	160	270	355
255	25' span		11.04		125	160	285	365
270	One way beam & slab, 125 psf Sup. Load, 15' span		7.49		125	240	365	480
275	25' span		10.15		120	175	295	385
290	Two way beam & slab, 125 psf Sup. Load, 15' span	▼	8.22		120	215	335	445
295	25' span	C-17B	12.23	▼	105	155	260	335
310	Elevated slabs including finish, not							
311	including forms or reinforcing							
315	Regular concrete, 4" slab	C-8	2,685	S.F.	.64	.56	1.20	1.45
320	6" slab		2,585		1.02	.58	1.60	1.89
325	2-1/2" thick floor fill		2,685		.44	.56	1	1.23
330	Lightweight, 110# per C.F., 2-1/2" thick floor fill		2,585		.56	.58	1.14	1.39
340	Cellular concrete, 1-5/8" fill, under 5000 S.F.		2,000		.25	.75	1	1.27
345	Over 10,000 S.F.		2,200		.21	.69	.90	1.14
350	Add per floor for 3 to 6 stories high	▼	31,800	▼		.05	.05	.06
352	For 7 to 20 stories high	▼	21,200	▼		.07	.07	.09
380	Footings, spread under 1 C.Y.	C-17B	31.82	C.Y.	71	59	130	160
385	Over 5 C.Y.	C-17C	70.45		68	28	96	115
390	Footings, strip, 18" x 9", plain	C-17B	34.22		61	55	116	145
395	36" x 12", reinforced		49.07		67	39	106	130
400	Foundation mat, under 10 C.Y.		32.32		113	59	172	205
405	Over 20 C.Y.	▼	47.37		100	40	140	165
420	Grade walls, 8" thick, 8' high	C-17A	10.16		100	175	275	365
425	14' high	C-20	7.30		150	230	380	465
426	12" thick, 8' high	C-17A	13.50		120	130	250	320
427	14' high	C-20	11.60		113	145	258	315
430	15" thick, 8' high	C-17B	20.01		85	95	180	225
435	12' high	C-20	14.80		95	110	205	255
450	18' high	"	12	▼	109	140	249	305
451								
465	Ground slab, not including finish, 4" thick	C-17C	75.28	C.Y.	61	27	88	105
470	6" thick	"	113.47	"	58	17.70	75.70	89
475	Ground slab, incl. troweled finish, not incl. forms							
476	or reinforcing, over 10,000 S.F., 4" thick slab	C-8	3,520	S.F.	.71	.43	1.14	1.35
482	6" thick slab		3,610		1.05	.42	1.47	1.71
484	8" thick slab	▼	3,275	▼	1.44	.46	1.90	2.19

Figure 8.55

It is important that mortar specifications be followed carefully. What little money may be saved by "skimping" on the mortar is not really worth the risks involved.

When all requirements in the specifications have been noted, the plans must be carefully reviewed. Drawings and details of masonry work are usually interspersed throughout the plans. All sheets should be checked. Walls and partitions of different masonry types and sizes are estimated separately. Requirements which must be listed and estimated individually include:

- Number and type of masonry units
- Bonding patterns
- Special coursing
- Openings
- Lintels and accessories

Brick Mortar Mixes*					
Type	Portland Cement	Hydrated Lime	Sand** (Maximum)	Strength	Use
M	1	1/4	3-3/4	High	General use where high strength is required, especially good compressive strength; work that is below grade and in contact with earth.
S	1	1/2	4-1/2	High	Okay general for use, especially good where high lateral strength is desired.
N	1	1	6	Medium	General use when masonry is exposed above grade; best to use when high compressive and lateral strengths are not required.
O	1	2	9	Low	Do not use when masonry is exposed to severe weathering; acceptable for non-loadbearing walls of solid units and interior non-loadbearing partitions of hollow units.

*The water used should be of the quality of drinking water. Use as much water as is needed to bring the mix to a suitably plastic and workable state.

**The sand should be damp and loose. A general rule for sand content is that it should not be less than 2-1/4 or more than 3 times the sum of the cement and lime volumes.

Figure 8.56

- Joint size (mortar quantities) and finish
- Grouting (cores, pilasters, door jambs, and bond beams, incl. reinforcing)
- Joint reinforcing
- Wall ties
- Flashing, reglets, weepholes
- Control joints
- Cleaning (water or chemical)
- Scaffolding and equipment

Each type of specified masonry unit should be identified on a takeoff sheet, not only by the kind of unit (brick, block, etc.) but also by type of construction (wall, arch, foundation, etc.). The square feet and/or linear feet of each listing should be measured from the plans and elevations. It should be remembered that exterior measurements of a building's perimeter include an overlap of the thickness of the walls for every outside corner. This is accepted accuracy and should be included, since corners tend to require more cutting and waste.

When measuring exterior dimensions at inside corners, however, the estimator must add to the actual dimensions to account for the extra material and labor involved to construct the inside corners.

Openings or "outs" should be deleted from overall quantity only if greater than 2 square feet. Lintels should be listed separately at this time by type and size (steel angle, precast, etc.). Responsibility for purchase of steel lintels should be established. Often, loose lintels are supplied by the steel fabricator and only installed by the masonry contractor.

When the overall square foot quantities of masonry work have been determined, the number of units may be calculated. Figure 8.57 lists different types of masonry units and corresponding quantities. Note that quantities per square foot as shown are based on certain joint sizes. If different joint sizes are specified, quantities should be adjusted. In Figure 8.57, quantities are listed not only by the type of unit but also by bond and coursing. Typical brick and block types and joints, bonds and coursing are shown in Figures 8.58 to 8.60. The descriptions of different bonds in Figure 8.59 include suggested waste allowance percentages which should be added to the quantities before pricing.

It is difficult to develop accurate unit price data for masonry due to fluctuation of both material prices and labor productivity. The estimator should always call suppliers to verify material costs and availability. All unit prices for brick masonry in *Building Construction Cost Data* (Figure 8.61) include the material cost per thousand pieces in the Line Description. If local costs are different, the material unit costs should be adjusted.

Productivity is affected by the type and complexity of work and can be severely affected by weather. Assume that a crew (including masons, helpers and appropriate equipment) can install approximately 600 standard bricks per man per day. This productivity rate assumes fairly straight runs (few openings) and good weather. For complicated work (many openings and corners), assume the same crew can install 400 bricks per man per day. Even for a simple building elevation as shown in Figure 8.62, both rates would apply. The high productivity portions (HP) are those areas, between rows of windows, with no openings. Low productivity portions (LP) are those areas which include the window jambs, headers and sills.

Brick Quantities

Type Brick	Nom. Sz. (incl. mortar) L H W	Modular Coursing	Number of Brick per S.F.	C.F. of Mortar per M Bricks, Waste Included 1 Wythe	2 Wythe	Bond Type	Description	Factor
Standard	8 x 2-2/3 x 4	3C=8"	6.75	13.0	16.5	Common	full header every fifth course	+20%
Economy	8 x 4 x 4	1C=4"	4.50	14.6	19.6		full header every sixth course	+16.7%
Engineer	8 x 3-1/5 x 4	5C=16"	5.63	13.6	17.6	English	full header every second course	+50%
Fire	9 x 2-1/2 x 4-1/2	2C=5"	6.40	550# fireclay	—	Flemish	alternate headers every course	+33.3%
Jumbo	12 x 4 x 6 or 8	1C=4"	3.00	34.0	41.4		every sixth course	+5.6%
Norman	12 x 2-2/3 x 4	3C=8"	4.50	17.8	22.8	Header = W x H exposed		+100%
Norwegian	12 x 3-1/5 x 4	5C=16"	3.75	18.5	24.4	Rowlock = H x W exposed		+100%
Roman	12 x 2 x 4	2C=4"	6.00	17.0	20.7	Rowlock stretcher = L x W exposed		+33.3%
SCR	12 x 2-2/3 x 6	3C=8"	4.50	26.7	31.7	Soldier = H x L exposed		—
Utility	12 x 4 x 4	1C=4"	3.00	19.4	26.8	Sailor = W x L exposed		−33.3%

Top spanning headers: Running Bond — No. of Brick per S.F. of Wall - Single Wythe 1/2" Jts.; For Other Bonds Standard Size Add to S.F. Quantities in Table to Left.

Concrete Block Quantities

Concrete Blocks Nominal Size (incl. 3/8" joint)	Approximate weight per S.F. Standard	Lightweight	Blocks per 100 S.F.	Mortar per M block Partitions	Back up
2" x 8" x 16"	20 PSF	15 PSF	113	16 C.F.	36 C.F.
4"	30	20		31	51
6"	42	30		46	66
8"	55	38		62	82
10"	70	47		77	97
12"	85	55		92	112

Glass Block Quantities

Size	Per 100 S.F. No. of Block	Mortar 1/4" Joint	Per 1000 Block Asphalt Emulsion	Caulk	Expansion Joint	Panel Anchors	Wall Mesh
6" x 6"	410 ea.	5.0 C.F.	.17 gal.	1.5 gal.	80 L.F.	20 ea.	500 L.F.
8" x 8"	230	3.6	.33	2.8	140	36	670
12" x 12"	102	2.3	.67	6.0	312	80	1000
Approximate quantity per 100 S.F.			.07 gal.	.6 gal	32 L.F.	9 ea.	51, 68, 102 L.F.

Figure 8.57

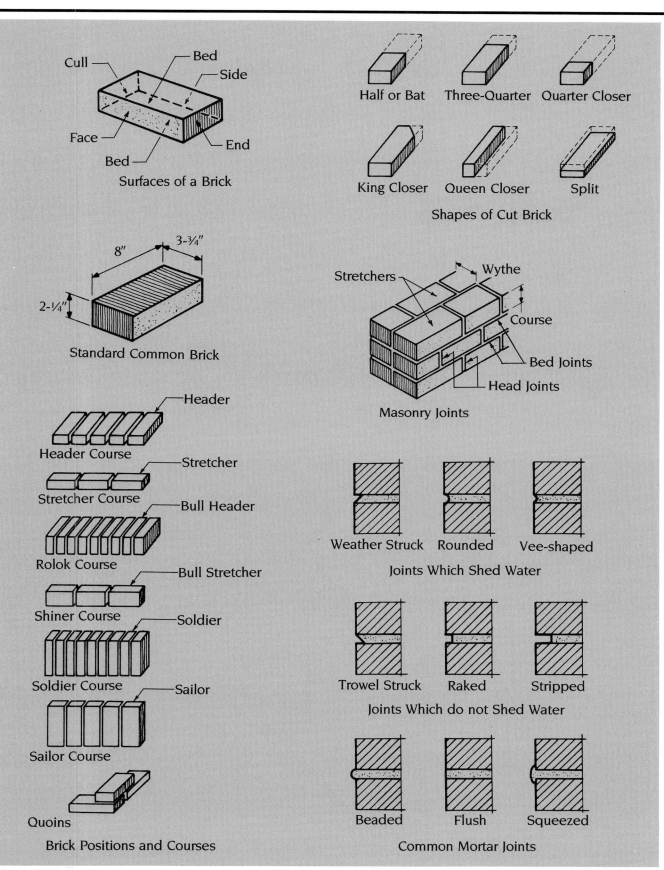

Cull
Bed
Side
Face
End
Bed

Surfaces of a Brick

Half or Bat   Three-Quarter   Quarter Closer

King Closer   Queen Closer   Split

Shapes of Cut Brick

8"   3-¾"   2-¼"

Standard Common Brick

Header
Header Course

Stretcher
Stretcher Course

Bull Header
Rolok Course

Bull Stretcher
Shiner Course

Soldier
Soldier Course

Sailor
Sailor Course

Quoins

Brick Positions and Courses

Stretchers   Wythe
Course
Bed Joints
Head Joints

Masonry Joints

Weather Struck   Rounded   Vee-shaped

Joints Which Shed Water

Trowel Struck   Raked   Stripped

Joints Which do not Shed Water

Beaded   Flush   Squeezed

Common Mortar Joints

Figure 8.58

185

Running or Stretcher Bond	The face brick are all stretchers and are tied to the backing by metal or reinforcing. Waste – 5%.
Common or American Bond	Every sixth course of stretcher bond is usually a header course. Waste – 4%.
Flemish Bond	Each course has alternate headers and stretchers with the alternate headers centered over the stretcher. Waste – 3 to 5%.
English Bond	Consists of alternate headers and stretchers with the vertical joints in the header and stretcher aligning or breaking over each other. Waste – 8 to 15%.
Stack Bond	Has no overlapping of units since all vertical joints are aligned. Usually this pattern is bonded to the backing with rigid steel ties. Waste – 3%.
English Cross or Dutch Bond	Built up of interlocking crosses. This wall consists of two headers and a stretcher forming a cross. Waste – 8%.

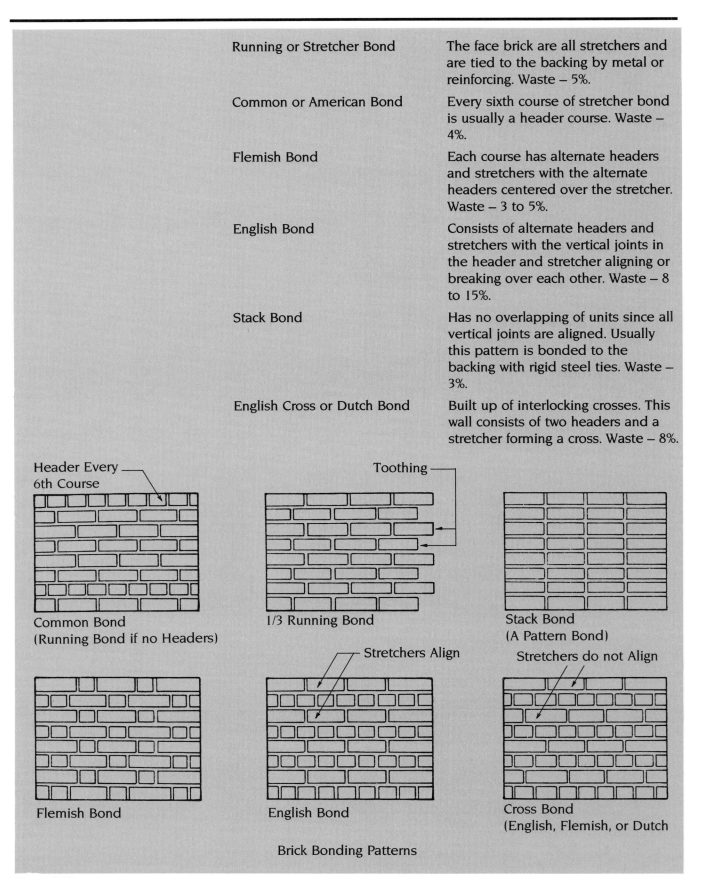

Header Every 6th Course

Common Bond
(Running Bond if no Headers)

Toothing

1/3 Running Bond

Stack Bond
(A Pattern Bond)

Flemish Bond

Stretchers Align

English Bond

Stretchers do not Align

Cross Bond
(English, Flemish, or Dutch

Brick Bonding Patterns

Figure 8.59

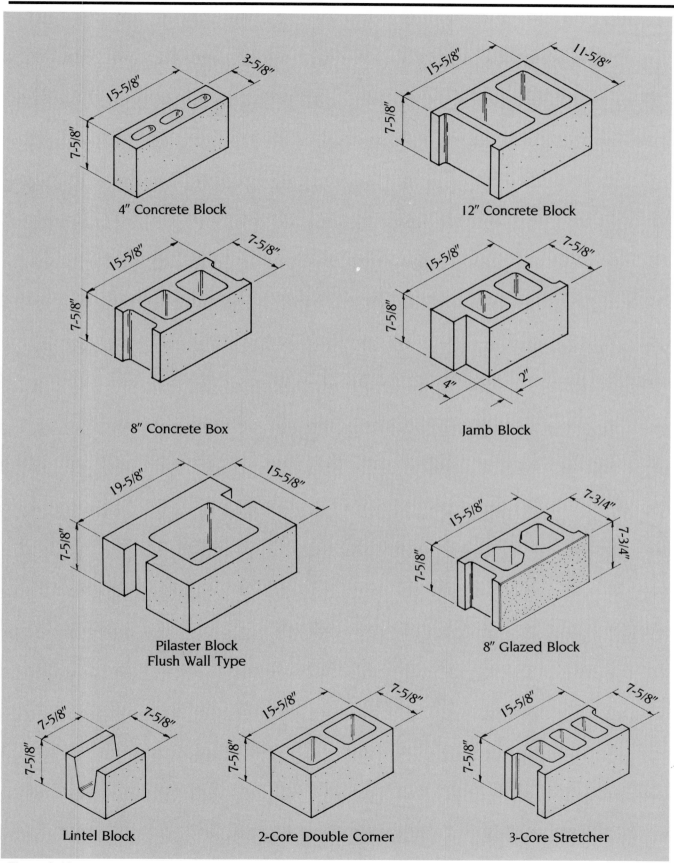

4" Concrete Block

12" Concrete Block

8" Concrete Box

Jamb Block

Pilaster Block
Flush Wall Type

8" Glazed Block

Lintel Block

2-Core Double Corner

3-Core Stretcher

Figure 8.60

4.2 Brick Masonry		CREW	DAILY OUTPUT	UNIT	BARE COSTS			TOTAL INCL O&P
					MAT.	INST.	TOTAL	
030	Common face brick	B-9	1,200	S.F.	.15	.67	.82	1.09
040	Wire cut face brick	"	900	"	.15	.89	1.04	1.40
54-001	STEPS With select common at $205 per M	D-1	.30	M	243	975	1,218	1,650
56-001	VENEER 4" thick, sel. common, 8" x 2-2/3" x 4" @ $205/M (6.75/S.F.)	D-2	1.55	M	263	535	798	1,050
005	Standard 8" x 2-2/3" x 4", running bond, red face, $225 per M		1.50		285	550	835	1,100
010	Buff or gray face, brick at $260 per M (6.75/S.F.)		1.50		320	550	870	1,150
015	(61) Full header every 6th course (7.88/S.F.)		1.45		320	570	890	1,175
020	English, full header every 2nd course (10.13/S.F.)		1.40		320	590	910	1,200
025	(62) Flemish, alternate header every course (9.00/S.F.)		1.35		320	615	935	1,225
030	Flemish, alt. header every 6th course (7.13/S.F.)		1.45		320	570	890	1,175
032	(59) Full headers throughout (13.50/S.F.)		1.40		320	590	910	1,200
034	Rowlock course (13.50 per S.F.)		1.35		320	615	935	1,225
036	Rowlock stretcher (4.50 per S.F.)		1.40		320	590	910	1,200
038	Soldier course (6.75 per S.F.)		1.35		320	615	935	1,225
040	Sailor course (4.50 per S.F.)		1.30		320	635	955	1,250
045	Glazed face, 8" x 2-2/3" x 4" $750 per M, running bond		1.40		825	590	1,415	1,750
047	Full header every 6th course (7.88 per S.F.)		1.35		825	615	1,440	1,775
050	Jumbo 12" x 4" x 6" running bond, $900 per M (3.00 per S.F.)		1.30		1,056	635	1,691	2,075
060	Norman 12" x 2-2/3" x 4" run. bond, $395 per M (4.50 per S.F.)		1.45		482	570	1,052	1,350
065	Norwegian 12" x 3-1/5" x 4" at $455 per M (3.75 per S.F.)		1.40		553	590	1,143	1,450
070	Economy 8" x 4" x 4" at $380 per M (4.50 per S.F.)		1.40		464	590	1,054	1,350
075	Engineer 8" x 3-1/5" x 4" at $265 per M (5.63 per S.F.)		1.45		332	570	902	1,175
080	Roman 12" x 2" x 4" at $470 per M (6.00 per S.F.)		1.50		549	550	1,099	1,400
085	SCR 12" x 2-2/3" x 6" at $555 per M (4.50 per S.F.)		1.40		668	590	1,258	1,575
090	Utility 12" x 4" x 4" at $650 per M (3.00 per S.F.)		1.35		766	615	1,381	1,725
092	8" x 8" x 4" at $930 per M (2.25 per S.F.)		.99		1,069	835	1,904	2,375
094	8" x 16" x 4" at $1820 per M (1.13 per S.F.)	▼	.51		2,057	1,625	3,682	4,575
101	For battered walls, add					30%		
102	For corbels, add					60%		
103	For curved walls, add					30%		
104	For pits and trenches, deduct		▼			20%		
105	Std., sel. common, 8" x 2-2/3" x 4" $205 per M (6.75 per S.F.)	D-2	230	S.F.	1.80	3.60	5.40	7.10
150	Standard 8" x 2-2/3" x 4", running bond, red face, @ $225 per M		220		1.95	3.76	5.71	7.50
155	Buff or gray face, brick at $260 per M (6.75 per S.F.)		220		2.15	3.76	5.91	7.75
160	Full header every 6th course (7.88 per S.F.)		185		2.50	4.48	6.98	9.15
165	English, full header every 2nd course (10.13 per S.F.)		140		3.25	5.90	9.15	12
170	Flemish, alter. header every course (9.00 per S.F.)		150		2.90	5.50	8.40	11.05
180	Flemish, alt. header every 6th course (7.13/S.F.)		205		2.30	4.04	6.34	8.30
182	Full headers throughout (13.50 per S.F.)		105		4.30	7.90	12.20	16
184	Rowlock course (13.50 per S.F.)		100		4.30	8.30	12.60	16.55
186	Rowlock stretcher (4.50 per S.F.)		310		1.45	2.67	4.12	5.40
188	Soldier course (6.75 per S.F.)		200		2.15	4.14	6.29	8.25
190	Sailor course (4.50 per S.F.)		290		1.45	2.86	4.31	5.65
195	Glazed face, brick at $750 per M, running bond		210		5.60	3.94	9.54	11.80
197	Full header every 6th course (7.88 per S.F.)		170		6.50	4.87	11.37	14.10
200	Jumbo 12" x 4" x 6" running bond, @ $900 per M (3.00 per S.F.)		435		3.15	1.90	5.05	6.20
205	Norman, 12" x 2-2/3" x 4" running bond, @ $395/M (4.50/S.F.)		320		2.15	2.59	4.74	6.05
210	Norwegian 12" x 3-1/5" x 4" at $455/M (3.75 per S.F.)		375		2.05	2.21	4.26	5.40
220	Economy 8" x 4" x 4" $380 per M (4.50 per S.F.)		310		2.10	2.67	4.77	6.10
230	Engineer 8" x 3-1/5" x 4" at $265 per M (5.63 per S.F.)		260		1.85	3.18	5.03	6.60
240	Roman 12" x 2" x 4" at $470 per M (6.00 per S.F.)		250		3.30	3.31	6.61	8.35
250	SCR 12" x 2-2/3" x 6" at $555 per M (4.50 per S.F.)		310		3	2.67	5.67	7.10
260	Utility 12" x 4" x 4" at $650 per M (3.00 per S.F.)		450		2.30	1.84	4.14	5.15
262	8" x 8" x 4" at $930 per M (2.25 per S.F.)		440		2.40	1.88	4.28	5.35
264	8" x 16" x 4" at $1820 per M (1.13 per S.F.)	▼	455		2.35	1.82	4.17	5.20
270	For cavity wall construction, add					15%		
280	For stacked bond, add					10%		
290	For interior veneer construction, add			▼		15%		

Figure 8.61

188

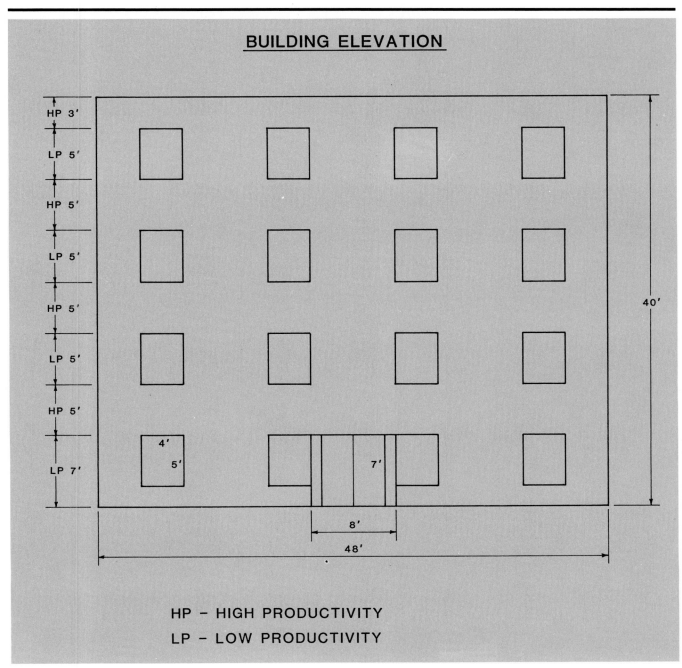

Figure 8.62

Total wall area	1920 SF
Deduct openings	−376 SF
Total masonry area	1544 SF
Standard brick (Fig. 8.57)	x 6.75 brick/SF
Total bricks	10,422 bricks
5% waste (Running bond, Fig. 8.59)	521
	10,943 bricks

56% of the wall area is high productivity and 44% is low productivity.

56%	of	10,943	=	6,128 bricks (HP)
44%	of	10,943	=	4,815 bricks (LP)

HP area: $\dfrac{6,128 \text{ bricks}}{600 \text{ bricks/days}} = 10$ days

LP area: $\dfrac{4,815 \text{ bricks}}{400 \text{ bricks/day}} = 12$ days

From quick, simple calculations, the estimator has the material quantity and the time required. A material cost is obtained from a supplier and the cost per day for the crew is multiplied by the time durations. Total costs for the work are obtained. Unit costs are determined by dividing the total costs — material *or* labor *or* both — by the appropriate units — square feet *or* per thousand brick.

Temperature and humidity variations can have a significant impact on masonry work. Not only are the general working conditions affected, but the drying time and workability of mortar have an effect on productivity. Figure 8.63 is a graphic representation of the relative effects of temperature and humidity. The numbers in the grid are factors to be multiplied by a maximum productivity. The following procedure can be used to derive this theoretical maximum (based on ideal weather conditions, 75 degrees F., 60% humidity — see Figure 8.63). For a given month, assume the productivity of a crew to be 500 units per day per mason. A record of the local, average temperature and humidity for that month is obtained from the National Weather Service, for example, 60 degrees F., 75% relative humidity. The factor for those conditions is 0.765, from Figure 8.63.

$$\frac{500 \text{ units/day}}{0.765} = 654 \text{ units/day (theoretical maximum)}$$

This theoretical maximum serves as a practical example for using the chart to predict productivity based on anticipated weather conditions.

BRICK PRODUCTIVITY TABLE

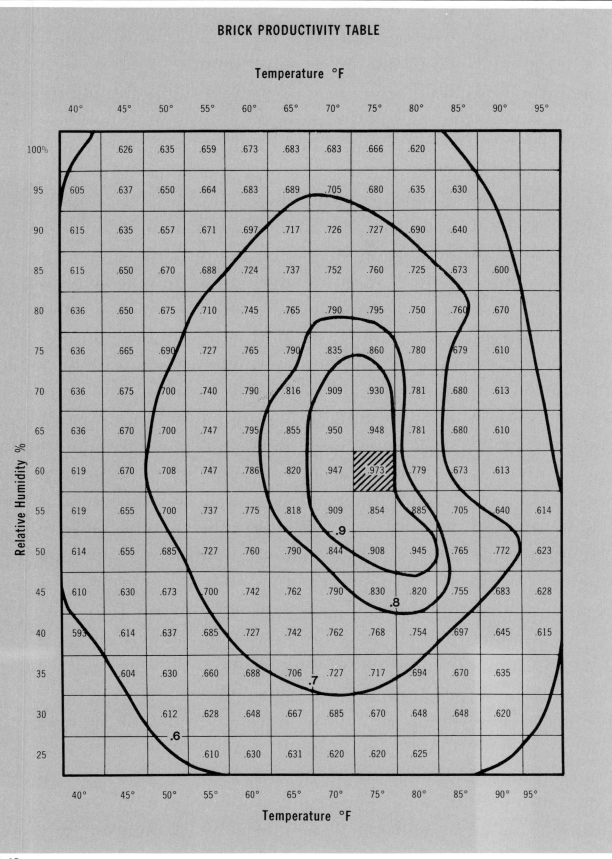

Figure 8.63

Sample Estimate: Division 4

For the masonry portion sample building project, assume that good historical records are available. The following data have been developed from past jobs:

Productivity:

Regular block	– 150 SF block/mason/day
8″ x 16″ x 8″	– 170 block/mason/day
Split face block	– 125 SF block/mason/day
8″ x 16″ x 6″	– 142 block/mason/day
Mortar	– 62 CF/M block
(Figure 8.57)	10 CF/mason/day

Bare Costs:

Mason	$20.00/hr., $160.00/day
Mason's helper	$15.00/hr., $120.00/day
Mortar	$2.25/CF
Mixer	$40.00/day
Scaffolding	$10.00/section/month
Forklift	$170.00/day
Masonry saw	$30.00/day

Even though the mixer and scaffolding are owned, costs are charged to each job. A crew of four masons and two helpers will be available and used for this job. Costs are developed as follows:

Material:

Regular block:

> 9,430 SF x 113 block/100 SF = 10,656 block
> (10,656 + 5% waste) x $0.78 Ea.
> 11,189 block x $0.78 = $8,727

Split face:

> 2,040 SF x 113 block/100 SF = 2,305 block
> (2,305 + 5% waste) x $1.15 Ea.
> 2,420 block x $1.15 = $2,783

Mortar:

> 62 CF/M block x 12,961 block = 804 CF
> 804 CF x $2.25 CF = $1,809

Reinforcing:

> 6,000 LF x $175/MLF = $1,050

Lintels:

> Labor costs included below.
> Material costs included in Division 5.

Total Material Costs:

Regular Block	$ 8,727
Split Face Block	2,783
Mortar	1,899
Reinforcing	1,050
	$14,459

Labor:

Regular block:

$$\frac{9{,}430 \text{ SF}}{150 \text{ SF/mason/day x 4 masons}} = 16 \text{ days}$$

Split block:

$$\frac{2{,}040 \text{ SF}}{125 \text{ SF/mason/day x 4 masons}} = 4 \text{ days}$$

4 masons x $160/day x 20 days = $12,800

2 helpers x $120/day x 20 days = $ 4,800

1 helper x $30/hour x 20 hours = $ 600 (overtime)

Total Labors Costs:

Masons	$12,800
Helpers	5,400
	$18,200

Equipment:

Mixer:
$40/day x 20 days = $800

Scaffolding:
24 sections x $10/section/month x 1 month = $240

Crane:
4 hours x $100/hour = $400

Forklift:
10 days x $170/day = $1,700

Masonry saw:
10 days x $30/day = $300

Total Equipment Costs:

Mixer	$ 800
Scaffolding	240
Crane	400
Forklift	1,700
Masonry saw	300
	$3,440

The costs are entered as shown in Figure 8.64. Unit costs for materials should be obtained from or verified by local suppliers. The most accurate prices are those developed from recent data. A thorough and detailed cost control and accounting system is important for the development of such costs. Overtime costs for one helper are for mixing mortar before the start of the workday.

MEANS CONSOLIDATED ESTIMATE

Division 4

SHEET NO. 1 of 1

PROJECT Office Building | CLASSIFICATION | ESTIMATE NO. 86-1

LOCATION | ARCHITECT | DATE 1986

TAKE OFF BY EBW | QUANTITIES BY EBW | PRICES BY RSM | EXTENSIONS BY SLM | CHECKED JDM

DESCRIPTION	SOURCE/DIMENSIONS	QUANTITY	UNIT	MATERIAL UNIT COST	MATERIAL TOTAL	LABOR UNIT COST	LABOR TOTAL	EQUIPMENT UNIT COST	EQUIPMENT TOTAL	SUBCONTRACT UNIT COST	SUBCONTRACT TOTAL
Division 4: Masonry											
Regular Block 8"x16"x 8"		11,189	Ea.	.78	8727						
Split Face Block 8"x 16"x 6"		2,420	Ea.	1.15	2783						
Mortar		804	CF	2.25	1809						
Reinforcing		6	MLF	175	1050						
Labor: Masons		80	MD			160	12800				
Helpers - Reg.		40	MD			120	4800				
OT		20	Hr.			30	600				
Equip: Mixer		20	Day					40	800		
Scaffolding (24 Sections)		1	Mo					240	240		
Crane		4	Hr.					100	400		
Forklift		10	Day					170	1700		
Masonry Saw		10	Day					30	300		
Division 4 Totals					14369		18200		3440		

Figure 8.64

Division 5: Metals

The metals portion of a building project, and the corresponding estimate should be broken down into basic components: structural metals, metal joists, metal decks, miscellaneous metals, ornamental metals, expansion control and fasteners. The items in a building project are shown on many different sheets of the drawings and may or may not be thoroughly listed in the specifications. This is especially true of the miscellaneous metals that are listed under Division 5. A complete and detailed review of the construction documents is therefore necessary, noting all items and requirements. Most structural steel work is subcontracted to specialty fabricators and erectors. However, the estimator for the general contractor may perform a takeoff to assure that all specific work is included. Pricing based on total weight (tonnage) can be used to verify subcontractor prices.

Structural Metals

The various structural members should be identified and separately listed by type and size. For example:

	Size	Length	Quantity
Columns:	W8 x 67	12'–6"	16
	W12 x 58	12'–6"	8
Beams:	W14 x 30	30'–0"	10
	W14 x 30	28'–0"	6
	W14 x 26	30'–0"	16
	W24 x 55	30'–0"	12

The quantities may be converted to weight (tonnage) for pricing. This figure is based on weight per linear foot. Base plates, leveling plates, anchor bolts and other accessories should be taken off and listed at this time. Connections should also be noted. Costs for structural steel in *Building Construction Cost Data* (Figures 8.65 and 8.66) are given for both individual members and for complete projects including bolted connections. If specified, costs for high strength steel and/or high strength bolts must be added separately (Figure 8.66). Welded connections should be listed by fillet size and length and priced separately. Light gauge and special framing for items such as hanging lintels, fascias, and parapets, should be taken off and priced separately. The amount of this type of metal work will vary depending upon design and project requirements.

For development of a budget cost or verification of a subcontractor bid, the estimator can apply average allowance percentages to gross tonnage for:

Base plates	–	2 to 3%
Column splices &		
Beam connections	–	8 to 10%
Total allowance	–	10 to 13% of main members

Erection costs can be determined in two ways. The first method is to base labor and equipment costs on gross tonnage, as shown in Figure 8.66. The second method is to base costs on the number of pieces. A typical crew and crane can set 35 to 60 pieces per day on the average. Based on normal sizes of beams, girders and columns, this is equivalent

5.1 Structural Metals	CREW	DAILY OUTPUT	UNIT	BARE COSTS			TOTAL INCL O&P
				MAT.	INST.	TOTAL	
710 Fixed glass, no screens, 3030 (3' x 3')	E-1	14	Opng.	80	41	121	150
720 6040 (6' x 4')		12		140	48	188	225
740 Prefinished storm sash, 3030 (3' x 3')		70		28	8.20	36.20	43
760 6040 (6' x 4')	↓	60	↓	40	9.60	49.60	58
780 Siding and roofing, see division 7.4							
780							
781 Skylight, fiberglass panels, to 30 S.F.	E-1	10	Ea.	150	58	208	250
782 Larger sizes, add for excess over 30 S.F.	"	300	S.F.	1.25	1.92	3.17	4.24
800 Roof vents, circular with damper, birdscreen							
801 and operator hardware, painted							
810 26 ga., 12" diameter	1 Sswk	4	Ea.	100	43	143	180
815 20" diameter		3		140	58	198	245
820 24 ga., 24" diameter		2		160	87	247	310
825 Galvanized	↓	2		145	87	232	295
830 Continuous, 26 ga., 10' long, 9" wide	2 Sswk	4		200	87	287	355
840 12" wide	"	4	↓	235	87	322	395
40-001 SPACE FRAME Steel 4' modular, 40' to 70' spans, 5.5 psf, minimum	E-2	556	S.F.	7.85	3.57	11.42	13.50
020 Maximum		365		11.25	5.45	16.70	19.80
040 5' modular, 4.5 psf minimum		585		6.75	3.39	10.14	12.05
050 Maximum	↓	405		9.65	4.89	14.54	17.30
070 Add to above for galvanizing, 4' modular				1		1	1.10M
080 5' modular				.90		.90	.99M
45-001 STRESSED SKIN Roof and ceiling system, spans to 100', minimum	E-2	1,150	↓	2.80	1.72	4.52	5.45
020 Maximum	"	760	↓	5.60	2.61	8.21	9.70
47-001 STRUCTURAL STEEL MEMBERS Common WF sizes, spans 10' to 45'							
002 including bolted connections and erection							
010 W 6 x 9	E-2	600	L.F.	5.45	3.30	8.75	10.50
030 W 8 x 10		600		5.65	3.30	8.95	10.70
050 X 31		500		12.90	3.96	16.86	19.60
070 W 10 x 22		660		12.65	3	15.65	18
090 X 49		540		18.95	3.67	22.62	26
110 W 12 x 14		880		7.05	2.25	9.30	10.85
130 X 22		880		9.90	2.25	12.15	13.95
150 X 26		880		11.40	2.25	13.65	15.60
170 X 72		640		26	3.10	29.10	33
190 W 14 x 26		990		10.60	2	12.60	14.40
210 X 30		900		11.85	2.20	14.05	16.05
230 X 34		810		13.10	2.45	15.55	17.75
250 X 120		720		43	2.75	45.75	51
270 W 16 x 26		1,000		10	1.98	11.98	
290 X 31		900		11.95	2.20	14.15	16.15
310 X 40	↓	800		14.60	2.48	17.08	19.45
330 W 18 x 35	E-5	960		12.75	2.74	15.49	17.85
350 x 40		960		14.20	2.74	16.94	19.45
370 X 50		912		18.20	2.88	21.08	24
390 X 55		912		20	2.88	22.88	26
410 W 21 x 44		1,064		15.60	2.47	18.07	21
430 x 50		1,064		17.70	2.47	20.17	23
450 X 62		1,036		21	2.53	23.53	27
470 X 68		1,036		24	2.53	26.53	30
490 W 24 x 55		1,110		20	2.37	22.37	
510 X 62		1,110		22	2.37	24.37	28
530 X 68		1,110		23	2.37	25.37	29
550 X 76		1,110		26	2.37	28.37	32
570 X 84		1,080		28	2.43	30.43	34
590 W 27 x 94		1,190		32	2.21	34.21	38
610 W 30 x 99		1,200		34	2.19	36.19	40
630 X 108		1,200		37	2.19	39.19	44
650 X 116		1,160		40	2.26	42.26	47
670 W 33 x 118	↓	1,176	↓	40	2.23	42.23	47

Figure 8.65

5.1	**Structural Metals**	CREW	DAILY OUTPUT	UNIT	BARE COSTS MAT.	INST.	TOTAL	TOTAL INCL O&P
690	W33 x 130	E-5	1,134	L.F.	44	2.32	46.32	52
710	X 141		1,134		48	2.32	50.32	56
730	W 36 x 135		1,170		46	2.24	48.24	54
750	X 150		1,170		51	2.24	53.24	59
770	X 194		1,125		67	2.33	69.33	77
790	X 230		1,125		80	2.33	82.33	91
810	X 300	↓	1,035	↓	105	2.54	107.54	120
50-001	**STRUCTURAL STEEL PROJECTS** Bolted, unless mentioned otherwise							
020	Apts., nursing homes, etc., steel bearing, 1 to 2 stories	E-5	10.30	Ton	825	255	1,080	1,275
030	⑦¹ 3 to 6 stories	"	10.10		840	260	1,100	1,275
040	7 to 15 stories	E-6	14.20		865	265	1,130	1,325
050	⑦² Over 15 stories	"	13.90		895	270	1,165	1,375
070	Offices, hospitals, etc., steel bearing, 1 to 2 stories	E-5	10.30		800	255	1,055	1,225
080	3 to 6 stories	E-6	14.40		830	260	1,090	1,300
090	7 to 15 stories		14.20		865	265	1,130	1,325
100	Over 15 stories	↓	13.90		890	270	1,160	1,375
110	For multi-story masonry wall bearing construction, add					30%		
130	Industrial bldgs., 1 story, beams & girders, steel bearing	E-5	12.90		815	205	1,020	1,175
140	Masonry bearing	"	10	↓	815	265	1,080	1,275
150	Industrial bldgs., 1 story, under 10 tons,							
151	steel from warehouse, trucked	E-2	7.50	Ton	960	265	1,225	1,425
160	1 story with roof trusses, steel bearing	E-5	10.60		955	250	1,205	1,400
170	Masonry bearing	"	8.30		955	315	1,270	1,500
190	Monumental structures, banks, stores, etc., minimum	E-6	13		835	290	1,125	1,325
200	Maximum	"	9		1,450	420	1,870	2,200
220	Churches, minimum	E-5	11.60		750	225	975	1,150
230	Maximum	"	5.20		1,075	505	1,580	1,900
280	Power stations, fossil fuels, minimum	E-6	11		750	345	1,095	1,325
290	Maximum		5.70		1,275	660	1,935	2,350
295	Nuclear fuels, non-safety steel, minimum		7		855	540	1,395	1,700
300	Maximum		5.50		1,175	685	1,860	2,275
304	Safety steel, minimum		2.50		1,275	1,500	2,775	3,550
307	Maximum	↓	1.50		1,600	2,500	4,100	5,350
310	Roof trusses, minimum	E-5	13		855	200	1,055	1,225
320	Maximum		8.30		1,400	315	1,715	1,975
321	Schools, minimum		14.50		825	180	1,005	1,150
322	Maximum	↓	8.30		1,275	315	1,590	1,850
340	Welded construction, simple commercial bldgs., 1 to 2 stories	E-7	7.60		855	345	1,200	1,425
350	7 to 15 stories	E-9	8.30		965	470	1,435	1,725
370	Welded rigid frame, 1 story, minimum	E-7	15.80		855	165	1,020	1,175
380	Maximum	"	5.50		1,125	480	1,605	1,900
400	⑦³ High strength steels, add to A36 price, minimum				75		75	83M
410	Maximum			↓	150		150	165M
430	Column base plates, light	2 Sswk	2,000	Lb.	.40	.17	.57	.71
440	Heavy plates	E-2	15,000	"	.35	.13	.48	.57
460	Castellated beams, light sections, to 50#/L.F., minimum		10.70	Ton	1,050	185	1,235	1,400
470	Maximum		7		1,300	285	1,585	1,825
490	Heavy sections, over 50# per L.F., minimum		11.70		915	170	1,085	1,250
500	Maximum	↓	7.80	↓	1,200	255	1,455	1,675
520	⑦⁴ High strength bolts in place, light reaming, 3/4" bolts, average	2 Sswk	165	Ea.	.85	2.10	2.95	4.24
530	7/8" bolts, average	"	160	"	1.25	2.17	3.42	4.78
550	⑫¹ Steel domes							
551								
570	⑦² Steel estimating weights per S.F.							
571								
590	⑦⁹ Galvanizing structural steel, under 1 ton, add to above			Ton	350		350	385M
600	Over 20 ton, add to above			"	250		250	275M
610	Cold galvanizing, brush	1 Psst	1,600	S.F.	.15	.10	.25	.33
611								

Figure 8.66

to approximately 25 tons per day. The installation rate (number of pieces per day) will not only vary due to crew size, speed and efficiency, but will also be affected by job conditions (relative access or mobility) and the weight of the pieces. A crew may set more smaller, lighter pieces (but less total tonnage) per day than larger or heavier pieces.

Metal Joists and Decks

The estimator will frequently find H-Series Open Web Joists used for the direct support of floor and roof decks in buildings. When long clear spans are desired, the designer will specify often the Longspan Steel Joist LH-Series; these are suitable for the direct support of floors and roof decks. Deep Longspan Steel Joists DLH-Series may be specified for the direct support of roof decks. Some plans will not indicate each joist in place, but rather the designation and spacing. The overall length of each span will be dimensioned. Required bridging may or may not be shown, as this may be defined in the specifications. The quantity takeoff sheet should indicate the joist designation, quantity, length and weight per lineal foot for total tonnage. Extensions of bottom chords, bridging (whether diagonal or horizontal) and any other related items must also be tabulated. The weight of joists per linear foot is usually not specified on the drawings, but is shown in manufacturers' catalogues.

Metal roof deck or form deck (sometimes termed centering) is often used on open web joist construction. Metal deck used on structural steel framing are manufactured in open type, cellular or composite configuration. The finish may be either galvanized painted, or black.

Metal joists are most often priced by the ton. Installation costs may be determined in the same way as for structural steel. Metal deck is taken off and priced by the square foot based on type (open, cellular, composite) gauge and finish.

Miscellaneous and Ornamental Metals

A thorough review of all drawings and specifications is necessary to ensure that all miscellaneous metal requirements are included. Listed below are typical miscellaneous and ornamental metals and the appropriate takeoff units. All items should be listed and priced separately.

Item	Unit	Item	Unit
Aluminum	Lb.	Frames	S.F.
Area Walls	Ea.	Ladders	V.L.F.
Bumper Rails	L.F.	Lampposts	Ea.
Checkered Plate	Lb.	Lintels	Lb.
Castings Misc.	Lb.	Pipe Support Framing	Lb.
Chain Link Fabric	C.S.F.	Railing	L.F.
Corner Guards	L.F.	Solar Screens	S.F.
Crane Rail	Lb.	Stairs	Riser
Curb Edging	L.F.	Toilet Part. Supports	Stall
Decorative Covering	S.F.	Window Guards	S.F.
Door Frames	Ea.	Wire	L.F.
Fire Escapes	Lb.	Wire Rope	L.F.
Floor Grating	S.F.		

Expansion Control and Fasteners

This portion of Division 5 includes fasteners for wood construction (nails, timber connectors, lag screws) as well as those for metal. Expansion anchors, shear studs and expansion joint assemblies are also included. It is up to the estimator to determine how costs for these items are to be listed in the estimate. Wood fasteners may be included in Division 6; shear studs may be considered part of the structural steel or metal deck installation. As previously emphasized, it is not as important *where* items are included as long as all required items *are* included.

Sample Estimate: Division 5

The increased use of computers and the development of estimating software in the construction industry provides the estimator with tools to increase speed, improve documentation and to lessen the chance of mathematical error. In essence, estimates can be produced better and faster with the use of these tools. R.S. Means has developed a series of estimating software packages. One such program is called CAD/COST. In addition to its thorough estimating functions and Means' cost data base, the CAD/COST software has a unique feature that allows the estimator to produce computer generated drawings. The components of these drawings are automatically quantified and priced. Thus, an estimate is produced directly from the drawing. Unit prices used may be from the Means data base or may be developed by the user.

Figure 8.67 is an example of a computer generated drawing that the estimator (contractor or engineer) might produce to aid in estimating the structural steel portion of the sample building project. Such a drawing would compile data from the specifications and from different plans, sections and details of the construction documents. The drawing in Figure 8.67 is of the framing for the second and third floors. Similar drawings might show column heights, base plates, and roof and penthouse framing, including metal joists and bridging. These are not construction or shop drawings and are used only for takeoff. Figure 8.68 is a typical estimate sheet generated by the Means' CAD/COST program from the drawing in Figure 8.67. Note that all information, as provided in *Building Construction Cost Data*, is displayed for each item on the estimate sheet (in this case, burdened, or including overhead and profit).

For the sample project, the estimator is developing costs for comparison to and verification of subcontract bids. Depending on the estimating accuracy, an estimate developed as a crosscheck may be included in the project bid if no reasonable subcontract bids are submitted. This practice involves risk; but often, no other option is available. A computer generated estimate as described above would be ideal for such a purpose.

Returning to pencil and paper, the quantity sheets for the structural steel, metal joists and deck are shown in Figures 8.69 and 8.70.

Quantities are calculated and subtotalled by the pound. The total weight is not converted to tons until it is entered on the estimate sheet. In this way, errors due to rounding can be avoided. Quantities are entered and priced on the estimate sheets in Figures 8.71 to 8.73.

In Figure 8.71, the 10% addition for connections is included; it is based on the above discussion of allowances for structural steel. Base plate weights are added after the connections. Because this portion of the estimate is to be used for verification, a single price per ton for all structural steel is used (from Figure 8.66, line 5.1-50-080). Note that the price per ton includes bolting. High strength bolts are specified for the project and require more labor than standard bolts. Standard bolts, are usually used for connecting and are replaced with high strength bolts during the bolting up procedure. No deduction (from the $1300 per ton) is used for deleting the standard bolting. The approximate quantity of high strength bolts may be determined from Figure 8.74, Circle Reference Number 77.

Material costs only are included for the anchor bolts and lintels. These items will be installed by different trades.

On Sheet 3 of the estimate (Figure 8.73) the subtotals for Division 5 are separated and listed according to the major subdivisions of metals work. These costs may be used as part of the historical cost development for estimating and comparison to future projects.

Division 6: Wood and Plastics

Wood frame construction is still dominant in the residential construction industry in the United States. However, its use for large scale commercial buildings has declined. There are many reasons for this trend; among them are: design criteria, cost and, in some localities, building and fire code restrictions. Nevertheless, the use of wood framing for smaller suburban office buildings is still common.

Material prices for lumber fluctuate more and with greater frequency than any other building material. For this reason, when the material list is complete it is important to obtain current, local prices for the lumber. Installation costs depend on productivity. For Division 6, accurate cost records from past jobs can be most helpful. The estimate can be tailored to the productivity of specific crews as shown in Division 4 of the Sample Estimate.

Carpentry work can be broken down into the following categories: rough carpentry, finish carpentry and millwork, and laminated framing and decking. The rough carpentry materials can be sticks of lumber or sheets of plywood — job site fabricated and installed, or may consist of trusses, and truss joists, and panelized roof systems — prefabricated, delivered and erected by a specialty subcontractor.

Rough carpentry

Lumber is usually estimated in board feet and purchased in 1000 board foot quantities. A board foot is 1" x 12" x 12" (nominal) or 3/4" x 11-1/2" x 12" milled (actual). To determine board feet of a piece of framing, the nominal dimensions can be multiplied, and the result divided by 12. The final result represents the number of board feet per linear foot of that framing size.

Example: 2 x 10 joists

$$2 \times 10 = 20$$

$$\frac{20}{12} = 1.67 \ \frac{\text{Board feet}}{\text{Linear foot}}$$

The Quantity Sheet should indicate species, grade, and any type of wood preservative or fire retardant treatment specified or required by code.

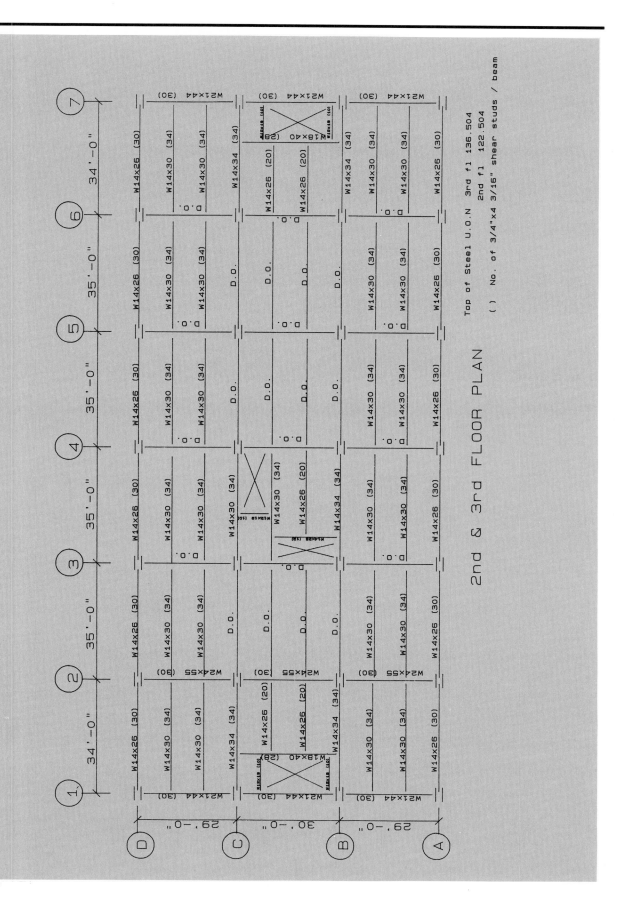

2nd & 3rd FLOOR PLAN

Top of Steel U.O.N 3rd fl 136.504
2nd fl 122.504

( ) No. of 3/4"x4 3/16" shear studs / beam

Figure 8.67

201

```
=================================================================================================

NO. 1                        BURDENED ITEMIZED JOB REPORT                 02-05-1986  15:14:20  PAGE  1
-------------------------------------------------------------------------------------------------

PROJECT   : Office Building                    LOCATION  : Kingston, Massachusetts
ARCHITECT : ANNON                              OWNER     : RSM, Inc.
QUANTITIES: rjg                                ENTERED BY: rjg


=================================================================================================


                                    5 METALS


-------------------------------------------------------------------------------------------------
  5.1 STRUCTURAL METALS
-------------------------------------------------------------------------------------------------
DESCRIPTION                            CREW  QUANTITY  UNIT    D/O   MATERIAL   LABOR   EQUIP   TOTAL    SUB
LINE NO.            TAG
ASMBLY# RENUMBER1    RENUMBER2  PER1 PER2
-------------------------------------------------------------------------------------------------
STRUCT STL, WF, 10' - 45' SPAN, W 12 X 22
  051 470 1300 00  M                    E2    49.80   L.F.   880.00   10.89    1.71    0.99    13.59
  -                          100% 100%                               542.32   85.39   49.18   676.89

STRUCT STL, WF, 10' - 45' SPAN, W 14 X 26
  051 470 1900 00  M                    E2   539.10   L.F.   990.00   11.66    1.52    0.88    14.06
  -                          100% 100%                              6285.91  821.70  473.21  7580.81

STRUCT STL, WF, 10' - 45' SPAN, W 14 X 30
  051 470 2100 00  M                    E2  1410.40   L.F.   900.00   13.04    1.68    0.97    15.68
  -                          100% 100%                             18384.57 2364.71 1361.82 22111.09

STRUCT STL, WF, 10' - 45' SPAN, W 14 X 34
  051 470 2300 00  M                    E2   166.00   L.F.   810.00   14.41    1.86    1.07    17.35
  -                          100% 100%                              2392.06  309.24  178.09  2879.40

STRUCT STL, WF, 10' - 45' SPAN, W 18 X 40
  051 470 3500 00  M                    E5    58.10   L.F.   960.00   15.62    2.13    1.02    18.77
  -                          100% 100%                               907.52  123.76   59.41  1090.69

STRUCT STL, WF, 10' - 45' SPAN, W 21 X 44
  051 470 4100 00  M                    E5   155.80   L.F.  1064.00   17.16    1.92    0.92    20.00
  -                          100% 100%                              2673.53  299.44  143.74  3116.71

STRUCT STL, WF, 10' - 45' SPAN, W 24 X 55
  051 470 4900 00  M                    E5   394.25   L.F.  1110.00   22.00    1.84    0.88    24.73
  -                          100% 100%                              8673.50  726.33  348.66  9748.49

=================================================================================================
                                         SUB TOTAL :        39859    4731    2614   47204       0
-------------------------------------------------------------------------------------------------
  5.8 EXPANSION CONTROL & FASTENERS
-------------------------------------------------------------------------------------------------
DESCRIPTION                            CREW  QUANTITY  UNIT    D/O   MATERIAL   LABOR   EQUIP   TOTAL    SUB
LINE NO.            TAG
ASMBLY# RENUMBER1    RENUMBER2  PER1 PER2
-------------------------------------------------------------------------------------------------
WELDED SHEAR CONN 3/4" X 4-3/16"
  058 450 0300 00  M                    E10 1450.00    EA.   1030.00    0.48    0.26    0.31    1.06
  -                          100% 100%                               701.80  377.28  452.17  1531.26
=================================================================================================
                                         SUB TOTAL :          702     377     452    1531       0
=================================================================================================
                                    DIVISION TOTAL :        40561    5108    3066   48735       0
=================================================================================================
```

Figure 8.68

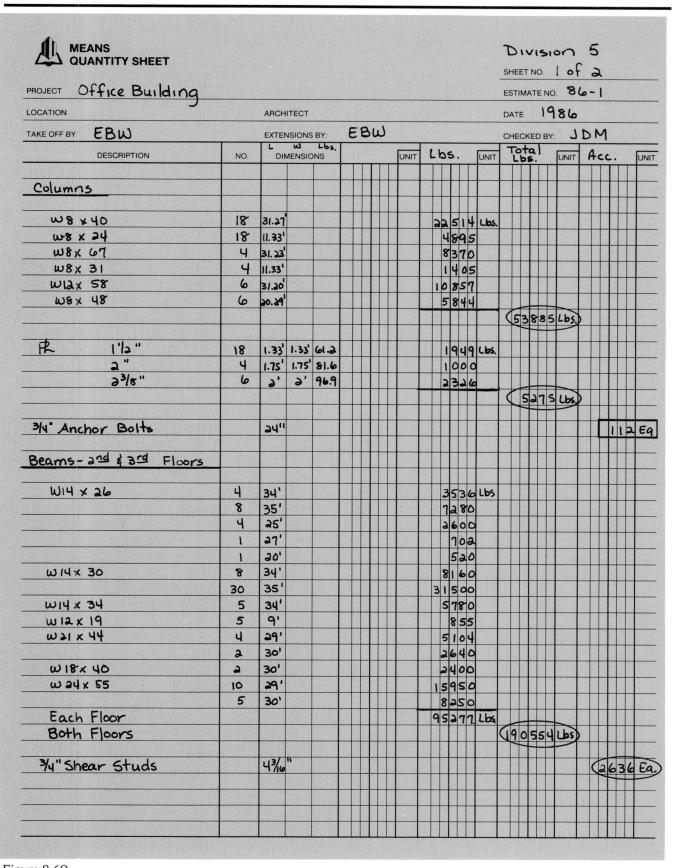

Figure 8.69

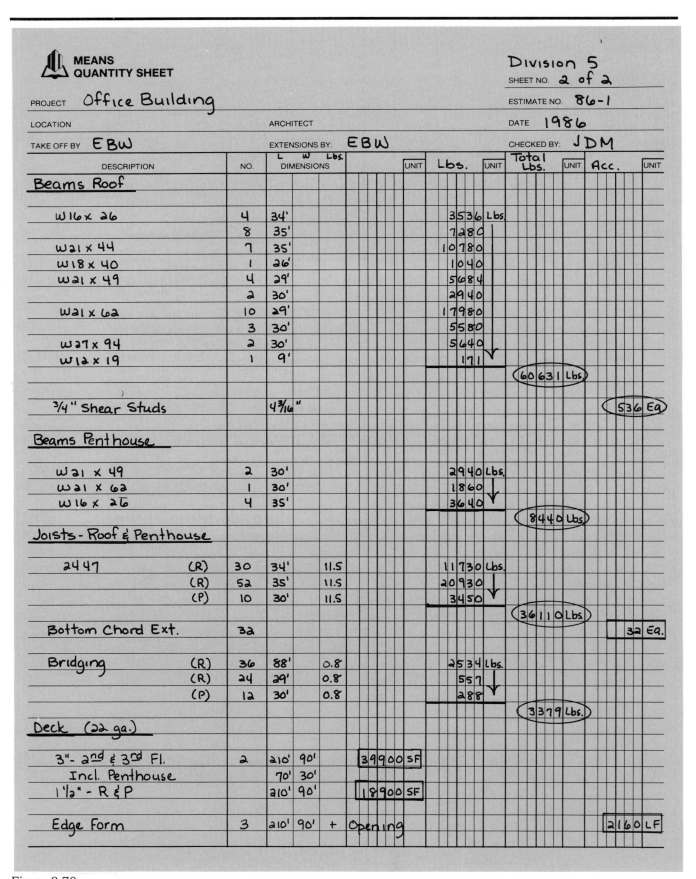

MEANS
QUANTITY SHEET

PROJECT Office Building

Division 5
SHEET NO. 2 of 2

ESTIMATE NO. 86-1

LOCATION   ARCHITECT   DATE 1986

TAKE OFF BY EBW   EXTENSIONS BY: EBW   CHECKED BY: JDM

DESCRIPTION	NO.	L / DIMENSIONS	W	Lbs.	UNIT	Lbs.	UNIT	Total Lbs.	UNIT	Acc.	UNIT
Beams Roof											
W16 x 26	4	34'				3536	Lbs.				
	8	35'				7280					
W21 x 44	7	35'				10780					
W18 x 40	1	26'				1040					
W21 x 49	4	29'				5684					
	2	30'				2940					
W21 x 62	10	29'				17980					
	3	30'				5580					
W27 x 94	2	30'				5640					
W12 x 19	1	9'				171					
								60631 Lbs.			
3/4" Shear Studs		4 3/16"								536	Ea.
Beams Penthouse											
W21 x 49	2	30'				2940	Lbs.				
W21 x 62	1	30'				1860					
W16 x 26	4	35'				3640					
								8440 Lbs.			
Joists - Roof & Penthouse											
2447 (R)	30	34'	11.5			11730	Lbs.				
(R)	52	35'	11.5			20930					
(P)	10	30'	11.5			3450					
								36110 Lbs.			
Bottom Chord Ext.	32									32	Ea.
Bridging (R)	36	88'	0.8			2534	Lbs.				
(R)	24	29'	0.8			557					
(P)	12	30'	0.8			288					
								3379 Lbs.			
Deck (22 ga.)											
3" - 2nd & 3rd Fl.	2	210'	90'		39900	SF					
Incl. Penthouse		70'	30'								
1 1/2" - R & P		210'	90'		18900	SF					
Edge Form	3	210'	90'	+	Opening					2160	LF

Figure 8.70

MEANS CONSOLIDATED ESTIMATE

Division 5

SHEET NO. 1 of 3

PROJECT Office Building | CLASSIFICATION | ESTIMATE NO. 86-1

LOCATION | ARCHITECT | DATE 1986

TAKE OFF BY EBW | QUANTITIES BY EBW | PRICES BY RSM | EXTENSIONS BY SLM | CHECKED JDM

DESCRIPTION	SOURCE/DIMENSIONS			QUANTITY	UNIT	MATERIAL UNIT COST	MATERIAL TOTAL	LABOR UNIT COST	LABOR TOTAL	EQUIPMENT UNIT COST	EQUIPMENT TOTAL	SUBCONTRACT UNIT COST	SUBCONTRACT TOTAL		
Division 5: Metals															
Structural Steel															
Columns				53,885	Lbs.										
2nd & 3rd Fl. Beams				190,554											
Roof				60,631											
Penthouse				8,440											
				313,510	Lbs.										
10% Connections				31,351											
				344,861	Lbs.										
Base PL				5,275											
				350,136	Lbs.										
Total	5.1	50	080	175	T							1300	227500		
High Strength Bolts 20/Ton (77)	5.1	50	520	3,500	Ea.							4.24	14840		
Anchor Bolts (Mat. Only)	3.1	05	050	112	Ea.							2.20	246		
Sub Total													242586		

Figure 8.71

MEANS CONSOLIDATED ESTIMATE

PROJECT Office Building

LOCATION

TAKE OFF BY EBW   QUANTITIES BY EBW   PRICES BY RSM   EXTENSIONS BY SLM

CLASSIFICATION

ARCHITECT

DESCRIPTION	SOURCE/DIMENSIONS			QUANTITY	UNIT	MATERIAL		LABOR		EQUIPMENT		SUBCONTRACT	
						UNIT COST	TOTAL	UNIT COST	TOTAL	UNIT COST	TOTAL	UNIT COST	TOTAL
Division 5: (Cont'd)													
Metal Joists & Decks													
Joists				36,110	Lbs.								
Bridging				3,379									
				39,489	Lbs.								
Total	5.1	50	080	19.75	T							1300	25675
Bottom Chord Extensions	5.2	40	165	32	Ea.							5.20	166
Composite													
Deck - 3" 22 ga.	5.2	30	570	40,570	SF							1.19	48279
Roof - 1½" 22 ga.	5.2	30	240	18,900	SF							.88	16632
Edge Form	5.2	30	710	2,160	LF							3	6480
Shear Studs 3/4" x 4 3/16"	5.8	45	030	3,172	Ea.							1.35	4282
SubTotal													101514

Figure 8.72

MEANS CONSOLIDATED ESTIMATE

Division 5

SHEET NO. 3 of 3

PROJECT Office Building — CLASSIFICATION — ESTIMATE NO. 86-1

LOCATION — ARCHITECT — DATE 1986

TAKE OFF BY EBW — QUANTITIES BY EBW — PRICES BY RSM — EXTENSIONS BY SLM — CHECKED JDM

DESCRIPTION	SOURCE/DIMENSIONS			QUANTITY	UNIT	MATERIAL UNIT COST	MATERIAL TOTAL	LABOR UNIT COST	LABOR TOTAL	EQUIPMENT UNIT COST	EQUIPMENT TOTAL	SUBCONTRACT UNIT COST	SUBCONTRACT TOTAL
Division 5: (Cont'd)													
Miscellaneous Metals													
Stairs 3'-6" w/Rails	5.4	64	020	188	R							175	32900
Landings 10'-8' x 4'	5.4	64	150	320	SF							32	10240
Exterior Alum. Rails	5.4	64	001	150	LF							66	9900
Lintels (Mat. Only)	4.1	45	025	34	Ea.							10.23	348
Sub Total													53388
Sheet 1: Structural Steel													242586
Sheet 2: Metal Joists & Deck													101514
Sheet 3: Miscellaneous													53388
Division 5 Total													397488

Figure 8.73

CIRCLE REFERENCE NUMBERS

⑦⑥ Structural Steel Extras (Div. 5.1)

Principal Extras in Dollars Per Ton

Item quantity — using 5 tons per size as base price. Under 5 tons to 3 tons inclusive add $5 per ton. Under 3 tons to 2 tons inclusive add $10 per ton. Under 2 tons to 1 ton inclusive add $15 per ton. Under 1 ton to 1/2 ton add $50 per ton. Under 1/2 ton add $100 per ton.

Lightest beams in each size add $45 for 24"; $45 for 14"; $70 for 8"; and $80 for 6" depth.

Equal leg angles add $55 for 8" x 8"; $50 for 6" x 6"; $54 for 5" x 5" x 5/16"; $50 for other gauges of 5" x 5"; $31 for 4" x 4" x 1/4"; $28 for 4" x 4" x 3/4"; $46 for 3" x 3" x 3/16"; $42 for 3" x 3" x 1/2".

Special 14" column sections add $75 for 455 lb. to $85 for 730 lb. in A36 steel.

Standard beams add $45 for 24" to 10"; $47 for 8"; $55 for 6"; and $125 for 3" depth.

Standard channels $40 for 15"; $40 for 12"; $60 for 8"; $60 for 6"; $80 for 4"; and $100 for 3" depth.

Unequal leg angles add $60 for 8" x 6"; $60 for 8" x 4"; $50 for 6" x 4"; $38 for 5" x 3" x 1/4" to $35 for 5" x 3" x 1/2"; $41 for 4" x 3" x 1/4" to $37 for 4" x 3" x 1/2".

Most common WF sections add $25 to a maximum of $80 per ton.

*Cambering $20 to $40 per ton, varies with wt./ft. and length.

Galvanizing under 1 ton $350; over 20 tons $250 per ton. For color coating of galvanizing add 40% to prices.

Government Specifications, medium grade $24, high tensile $77 per ton.

High strength steels see ⑦③

*Length 10' to 20', $25; 20' to 30', $10; 30' to 40', $5; 60' to 65', $4; 40' to 50', $3; 65' to 80', $21; 80' to 90', $24; 90' to 100', $26.

Milling, one or two ends, 10' to 25' inclusive, members weighing 10 thru 50 lbs., $80; 51 lbs. thru 200 lbs., $48; 201 lbs. thru 426 lbs., $36; over 426 lbs., $24. Members over 25' weighing 10 thru 50 lbs., $70; 51 lbs. thru 200 lbs., $43; 201 lbs. thru 426 lbs., $31; over 426 lbs., $24.

Special testing runs $5 to $7 per ton. Handling and loading runs from $2 under 10,000 lbs.; $3 under 6000 lbs.; $4 under 4000 lbs.

*Splitting beams to produce T's $35 for heavy beams to $60 for light members.

Note: * Subject to mill tolerance.

⑦⑦ High Strength Bolts (Div. 5.1-50-520)

In factory buildings, common bolts are used in secondary connections.

Allow 20 field bolts per ton of steel for a 6 story office building, apartment house or light industrial building. For 6 to 12 stories allow 18 bolts and above 12 stories, 25 bolts. On power stations 20 to 25 bolts per ton are needed.

Cost per bolt, nut and washer combination, material only. Under 5000 lbs. A325 and A490.

Length	1½"		2"		2½"		3"		3½"		4"		5"		6"		7"		8"	
ASTM Designation	A325	A490	A325	A490	A325	A490	A325	A490	A325	A490	A325	A490	A325	A490	A325	A490	A325	A490	A325	A490
5/8" diameter	$.49	$.64	$.51	$.67	$.55	$.73	$.60	$.79	$.67	$.84	$.72	$.90	$.81	$1.02	—	—	—	—	—	—
3/4"	.66	.86	.70	.91	.75	.99	.81	1.07	.86	1.14	.96	1.22	1.08	1.37	1.20	1.51	1.48	1.88	1.64	—
7/8"	—	—	1.12	1.48	1.16	1.53	1.24	1.64	1.32	1.75	1.40	1.86	1.56	2.07	1.72	2.29	2.00	2.58	2.21	$2.81
1"	—	—	—	—	1.70	2.25	1.81	2.40	1.91	2.54	2.02	2.69	2.23	2.98	2.45	3.26	2.66	3.55	3.06	3.96
1-1/8"	—	—	—	—	3.17	—	3.20	4.33	3.33	4.51	3.47	4.70	3.73	5.07	4.00	5.44	4.27	5.81	4.77	6.18
1-1/4" ▼	—	—	—	—	—	—	3.80	5.30	3.91	5.30	4.08	5.53	4.41	6.00	4.74	6.45	5.07	6.91	5.41	7.37

⑦⑧ Subpurlins (Div. 5.2-10)

Table is based on subpurlins 32-3/4" O.C. with simple spans, 40 psf, L.L., material only, 10,000 lb. to 30,000 lb. lots.

Type	Bulb Tees, Painted			Truss Tees, Painted							
	Wt. per L.F.	Cost per L.F.	Max. Span	Size	Wt. per L.F.	Cost per L.F.	Max. Span	Size	Wt. per L.F.	Cost per L.F.	Max. Span
112	1.44#	$ .42	5'-6"	2"	1.1 #	$.53	5'-9"	2-1/2"	1.39#	$ .69	8'-7"
158	1.63	.47	6'-5"		1.27	.62	7'-3"		1.85	.96	10'-0"
168	1.85	.52	7'-8"		1.33	.65	7'-7"	3"	1.14	.58	7'-3"
178	2.13	.60	8'-9"		1.78	.91	8'-9"		1.88	1.01	9'-2"
218	3.06	.89	10'-2"	2-1/2"	1.12	.56	6'-7"	3-1/2"	1.17	.61	9'-7"
228	3.69	1.16	12'-1"		1.34	.67	8'-3"		1.9	1.04	11'-2"

Figure 8.74

Sills, Posts, and Girders used in subfloor framing should be taken off by length and quantity. The standard lengths available vary by species and dimensions. Cut-offs are often used for blocking. Careful selection of lengths will decrease the waste factor required.

Floor Joists, shown or specified by size and spacing, should be taken off by nominal length and the quantity required. Add for double joists under partitions, headers and cripple joists at openings, overhangs, laps at bearings, and blocking or bridging.

Ceiling Joists, similar to floor joists, carry roof loads and or/ceiling finishes. Soffits and suspended ceilings should be noted and taken off separately. Ledgers may be a part of the ceiling joist system. In a flat roof system, the rafters are called joists and are usually shown as a ceiling system.

Studs required are noted on the drawings by spacing, usually 16″ O.C. or 24″ O.C., with the stud size given. The linear feet of partitions with the same stud size, height and spacing, and divided by the spacing will give the estimator the approximate number of studs required. Additional studs for openings, corners, double top plates, sole plates, and intersecting partitions must be taken off separately. An allowance for waste should be included (or heights should be recorded as a standard length). A rule of thumb is to allow one stud for every linear foot of wall, for 16″ O.C.

Number and Size of Openings are important. Even though there are no studs in these areas, the estimator must take off headers, subsills, king studs, trimmers, cripples, and knee studs. Where bracing and fire blocking are noted, indicate the type and quantity.

Roof Rafters vary with different types of roofs. A hip and valley, because of its complexity, has a greater material waste factor than most other roof types. Although straight gable, gambrel, and mansard roofs are not as complicated, care should be taken to ensure a good material takeoff. Roof pitches, overhangs, and soffit framing all affect the quantity of material and therefore, the costs. Rafters must be measured along the slope, not the horizontal. (See Figure 8.80.)

Roof Trusses are usually furnished and delivered to the job site by the truss fabricator. The high cost of job site labor and new gang nailing technology have created a small boom in truss manufacturing. Many architects' designs of wood frame and masonry bearing wall structures now include wood trusses of both the trussed rafter type and the flat chord type (also used for floors). Depending upon the size of truss, hoisting equipment may be needed for erection. The estimator should obtain prices and weights from the fabricator and should determine whether or not erection is included in the fabricator's cost. Architecturally exposed trusses are typically more expensive to fabricate and erect.

Tongue and Groove Roof Decks of various woods, solid planks, or laminated construction are nominally 2″ to 4″ thick and are often used with glued laminated beams or heavy timber framing. The square foot method is used to determine quantities and consideration is given to roof pitches and non-modular areas for the amount of waste involved. The materials are purchased by board foot measurement. The conversion from square foot to board foot must allow for net sizes as opposed to board measure. In this way, loss of coverage due to the available tongue and mill lengths can be taken into account.

Sheathing on walls can be plywood of different grades and thicknesses, wallboard, or solid boards nailed directly to the studs. Insulating sheets with air infiltration barriers are often used as sheathing in colder climates. Plywood can be applied with the grain vertical, horizontal, or rarely, diagonal to the studding. Solid boards are usually nailed diagonally, but can be applied horizontally when lateral forces are not present. For solid board sheathing, add 15% to 20% more material to the takeoff when using tongue and groove, as opposed to square edge sheathing. Wallboard can be installed either horizontally or vertically, depending upon wall height and fire code restrictions. When estimating quantities of plywood or wall board sheathing, the estimator calculates the number of sheets required by measuring the square feet of area to be covered and then dividing by sheet size. Applying these materials diagonally or on non-modular areas will create waste. This waste factor must be included in the estimate. For diagonal application of boards, plywood, or wallboard, include an additional 10% to 15% material waste factor.

Subfloors can be CDX type plywood (with the thickness dependent on the load and span), solid boards laid diagonally or perpendicular to the joists, or tongue and groove planks. The quantity takeoff for subfloors is similar to sheathing (noted above).

Stressed Skin Plywood includes prefabricated roof panels, with or without bottom skin or tie rods, and folded plate roof panels with intermediate rafters. Stressed skin panels are typically custom prefabricated. Takeoff is by the square foot or panel.

Structural Joists are prefabricated "beams" with wood flanges and plywood or tubular steel webs. This type of joist is spaced in accordance with the load and requires bridging and blocking supplied by the fabricator. Quantity takeoff should include the following: type, number required, length, spacing, end-bearing conditions, number of rows, length of bridging, and blocking.

Grounds are normally 1" x 2" wood strips used for case work or plaster; the quantities are estimated in L.F.

Furring (1" x 2" or 3") wood strips are fastened to wood masonry or concrete walls so that wall coverings may be attached thereto. Furring may also be used on the underside of ceiling joists to fasten ceiling finishes. Quantities are estimated by L.F.

Lumber and Plywood Treatments can sometimes double the costs for material. The plans and specifications should be carefully checked for required treatments — against insects, fire or decay — as well as grade, species and drying specifications.

An alternative method to pricing rough carpentry by the piece or linear foot is to determine quantities (in board feet) based on square feet of surface area. Appendix B of this book contains charts and tables that may be used for this second method. Also included are quantities of nails required for each type and spacing of rough framing. A rule of thumb for this method can be used to determine linear feet of framing members (such as studs, joists) based on square feet of surface area (wall, floor, ceiling):

Spacing of Framing Members	Board Feet per Square Foot Surface
12″ O.C.	1.2 BF/SF
16″ O.C.	1.0 BF/SF
24″ O.C.	0.8 BF/SF

The requirements for rough carpentry, especially those for temporary construction, may not all be directly stated in the plans and specifications. These additional items may include blocking, temporary stairs, wood inserts for metal pan stairs, and railings, along with various other requirements for different trades. Temporary construction may also be included in Division 1 of the General Requirements.

Finish Carpentry and Millwork

Finish carpentry and millwork — wood rails, paneling, shelves, casements and cabinetry — are common in buildings that have no other wood.

Upon examination of the plans and specifications, the estimator must determine which items will be built on-site, and which will be fabricated off-site by a millwork subcontractor. Shop drawings are often required for architectural woodwork and are usually included in the subcontract price.

Window and Door Trim may be taken off and priced by the "set" or by the linear foot. Check for jamb extensions at exterior walls. The common use of pre-hung doors and windows makes it convenient to take off this trim with the doors and windows. Exterior trim, other than door and window trim, should be taken off with the siding, since the details and dimensions are interrelated.

Paneling is taken off by the type, finish, and square foot (converted to full sheets). Be sure to list any millwork that would show up on the details. Panel siding and associated trim are taken off by the square foot and linear foot, respectively. Be sure to provide an allowance for waste.

Decorative Beams and Columns that are non-structural should be estimated separately. Decorative trim may be used to wrap exposed structural elements. Particular attention should be paid to the joinery. Long, precise joints are difficult to construct in the field.

Cabinets, Counters and Shelves are most often priced by the linear foot or by the unit. Job-fabricated, prefabricated, and subcontracted work should be estimated separately.

Stairs should be estimated by individual component unless accurate, complete system costs have been developed from previous projects. Typical components and units for estimating are shown in Figure 8.75. The cost development of a residential wood stair system is shown in Figure 8.76.

A general rule for budgeting millwork is that total costs will be two to three times the cost of the materials. Millwork is often ordered and purchased directly by the owner; when installation is the responsibility of the contractor, costs for handling, storage and protection should be included.

6.2 Finish Carpentry	CREW	DAILY OUTPUT	UNIT	BARE COSTS			TOTAL INCL O&P
				MAT.	INST.	TOTAL	
73-001 SOFFITS Wood fiber, no vapor barrier, 15/32" thick	F-2	525	S.F.	.40	.64	1.04	1.36
010 5/8" thick		525		.50	.64	1.14	1.47
030 As above, 5/8" thick, with factory finish		525		.58	.64	1.22	1.56
050 Hardboard, 3/8" thick, slotted		525		.62	.64	1.26	1.60
100 Exterior AC plywood, 1/4" thick		420		.38	.80	1.18	1.57
110 1/2" thick	↓	420	↓	.54	.80	1.34	1.74
115 For aluminum soffit, see division 7.6-54							
76-001 STAIR PARTS Balusters, turned, 30" high, pine, minimum	1 Carp	28	Ea.	3.73	5.70	9.43	12.40
010 Maximum		26		5	6.15	11.15	14.40
030 30" high birch balusters, minimum		28		4.75	5.70	10.45	13.50
040 Maximum		26		6	6.15	12.15	15.50
060 42" high, pine balusters, minimum		27		4.40	5.95	10.35	13.45
070 Maximum		25		5.20	6.40	11.60	15
090 42" high birch balusters, minimum		27		6.25	5.95	12.20	15.45
100 Maximum		25	↓	6.60	6.40	13	16.55
105 Baluster, stock pine, 1-1/16" x 1-1/16"		240	L.F.	.46	.67	1.13	1.47
110 1-5/8" x 1-5/8"		220	"	.93	.73	1.66	2.08
120 Newels, 3-1/4" wide, starting, minimum		7	Ea.	31	23	54	67
130 Maximum		6		150	27	177	205
150 Landing, minimum		5		45	32	77	96
160 Maximum		4	↓	145	40	185	215
180 Railings, oak, built-up, minimum		60	L.F.	3.75	2.67	6.42	8
190 Maximum		55		8	2.91	10.91	13
210 Add for sub rail	↓	110	↓	1.60	1.45	3.05	3.87
211							
230 Risers, Beech, 3/4" x 7-1/2" high	1 Carp	64	L.F.	3.75	2.50	6.25	7.75
240 Fir, 3/4" x 7-1/2" high		64		.97	2.50	3.47	4.69
260 Oak, 3/4" x 7-1/2" high		64		3	2.50	5.50	6.90
280 Pine, 3/4" x 7-1/2" high		66		.97	2.42	3.39	4.58
285 Skirt board, pine, 1" x 10"		55		1.26	2.91	4.17	5.60
290 1" x 12"		52	↓	1.54	3.08	4.62	6.15
300 Treads, oak, 1-1/16" x 9-1/2" wide, 3' long		18	Ea.	14.15	8.90	23.05	28
310 4' long		17		19.80	9.40	29.20	35
330 1-1/16" x 11-1/2" wide, 3' long		18		17	8.90	25.90	32
340 6' long	↓	14	↓	36	11.45	47.45	56
360 Beech treads, add			↓	40%			
380 For mitered return nosings, add			L.F.	1.83		1.83	2.01M
79-001 STAIRS, PREFABRICATED							
011 Box stairs, 3' wide, oaktards, no handrails, 2' high	2 Carp	5	Flight	110	64	174	215
020 4 ft. high		4		185	80	265	320
030 6 ft. high		3.50		290	91	381	450
040 8 ft. high		3		360	105	465	550
060 With pine treads for carpet, 2 ft. high		5		67	64	131	165
070 4 ft. high		4		115	80	195	240
080 6 ft. high		3.50		180	91	271	330
090 8 ft. high	↓	3	↓	210	105	315	385
110 For 4' wide stairs, add			↓	10%			
150 Prefabricated stair rail with balusters, 5 risers	2 Carp	15	Ea.	105	21	126	145
160							
170 Basement stairs, prefabricated, soft wood,							
171 open risers, 3' wide, 8' high	2 Carp	4	Flight	120	80	200	250
190 Open stairs, prefabricated prefinished poplar, metal stringers,							
191 treads 3'-6" wide, no railings							
200 3 ft. high	2 Carp	5	Flight	295	64	359	415
210 4 ft. high		4		370	80	450	525
220 6 ft. high		3.50		640	91	731	835
230 8 ft. high	↓	3	↓	940	105	1,045	1,200
250 For prefab. 3 piece wood railings & balusters, add for							
260 3 ft. high stairs	2 Carp	15	Ea.	100	21	121	140

Figure 8.75

Laminated Construction

Laminated construction should be listed separately, as it is frequently supplied by a specialty subcontractor. Sometimes the beams are supplied and erected by one subcontractor, and the decking installed by the general contractor or another subcontractor. The takeoff units must be adapted to the system: square foot — floor, linear foot — members, or board foot — lumber. Since the members are factory fabricated, the plans and specifications must be submitted to a fabricator for takeoff and pricing.

Sample Estimate:
Division 6

The estimate for Division 6 — Wood and Plastics — of the sample project is minimal and straightforward. The estimate sheet is shown in Figure 8.77. The only item included for rough carpentry is fire retardant treated blocking. Blocking requirements may or may not be shown on the drawings or stated in the specifications, but in this case, previous experience dictates that an allowance be included. The only other carpentry for the project involves wall paneling at the elevator lobby of each floor, and vanities in the women's rest rooms. For custom quality finish work, it is recommended that the craftsman to perform the work be consulted. This person is able to call upon experience to best estimate the required time.

(84) Wood Stair, Residential (Div. 6.2-76)

One Flight with 8'-6" Story Height, 3'-6" Wide Oak Treads Open One Side, Built in Place				
Item	Quantity	Unit Cost	Bare Costs	Costs Incl. Subs O & P
Treads 10-1/2" x 1-1/16" thick	11 Ea.	$ 16.25	$ 178.75	$ 196.35
Landing tread nosing	1 Ea.	3.00	3.00	3.30
Risers 3/4" thick	12 Ea.	10.50	126.00	138.60
Single end starting step (range $100 to $155)	1 Ea.	00.00	100.00	110.00
Balusters (range $3.70 to $9.60)	22 Ea.	4.75	104.50	114.95
Newels, starting & landing (range $32 to $155)	2 Ea.	32.00	64.00	70.40
Rail starter (range $34 to $85)	1 Ea.	45.00	45.00	49.50
Handrail (range $3.90 to $7.90)	26 L.F.	4.25	110.50	121.55
Cove trim	50 L.F.	.43	21.50	23.65
Rough stringers three - 2 x 12's, 14' long	84 B.F.	.40	33.60	36.95
Carpenters installation: Bare Cost	36 Hrs.	$ 20.00	$ 720.00	
Cost incl. Subs O & P		29.00		$1,044.00
	Total per Flight		$1,506.85	$1,909.25

Figure 8.76

MEANS CONSOLIDATED ESTIMATE

Division 6

SHEET NO. 1 of 1

PROJECT Office Building | CLASSIFICATION | ESTIMATE NO. 86-1

LOCATION | ARCHITECT | DATE 1986

TAKE OFF BY EBW | QUANTITIES BY EBW | PRICES BY RSM | EXTENSIONS BY SLM | CHECKED JDM

DESCRIPTION	SOURCE/DIMENSIONS			QUANTITY	UNIT	MATERIAL UNIT COST	MATERIAL TOTAL	LABOR UNIT COST	LABOR TOTAL	EQUIPMENT UNIT COST	EQUIPMENT TOTAL	SUBCONTRACT UNIT COST	SUBCONTRACT TOTAL
Division 6: Wood & Plastics													
Rough Carpentry													
Blocking	6.1	02	274	0.1	MBF	315	31	1200	120				
Fire Treatment	6.1	57	040	0.1	MBF	200	20						
Finish Carpentry													
Paneling@Elevator Lobby	6.2	58	260	1800	SF	1.30	2340	.84	1512				
Vanities	6.2	88	815	6	Ea.	190	1140	48	288				
Arch: Woodwork													
Vanity Top	6.4	80	150	24	LF	2.50	60	6.40	154				
Backsplash	6.4	80	260	24	LF	.75	18	4.44	107				
Cutouts	6.4	80	390	9	Ea.			13.35	120				
Division 6 Totals							3609		2301				

Figure 8.77

Division 7: Moisture & Thermal Control

This division includes materials for sealing the outside of a building — for protection against moisture and air infiltration, as well as insulation and associated accessories. When reviewing the plans and specifications, the estimator should visualize the construction process, and thus determine all probable areas where these materials will be found in or on a building. The technique used for quantity takeoff depends on the specific materials and installation methods.

Waterproofing

- Dampproofing
- Vapor Barriers
- Caulking and Sealants
- Sheet and Membrane
- Integral Cement Coatings

A distinction should be made between dampproofing and waterproofing. Dampproofing is used to inhibit the migration of moisture or water vapor. In most cases, dampproofing will not stop the flow of water (even at minimal pressures). Waterproofing, on the other hand, consists of a continuous, impermeable membrane and is used to prevent or stop the flow of water.

Dampproofing usually consists of one or two bituminous coatings applied to foundation walls from about the finished grade line to the bottom of the footings. The areas involved are calculated from the total height of the dampproofing and the length of the wall. After separate areas are figured and added together to provide a total square foot area, a unit cost per square foot can be selected for the type of material, the number of coats, and the method of application specified for the building.

Waterproofing at or below grade with elastomeric sheets or membranes is estimated on the same basis as dampproofing, with two basic exceptions. First, the installed unit costs for the elastomeric sheets do not include bonding adhesive or splicing tape, which must be figured as an additional cost. Second, the membrane waterproofing under slabs must be estimated separately from the higher cost installation on walls. In all cases, unit costs are per square foot of covered surface.

For walls below grade, protection board is often specified to prevent damage to the barrier when the excavation is backfilled. Rigid foam insulation installed outside of the barrier may also serve a protective function. Metallic coating material may be applied to floors or walls, usually on the interior or dry side, after the masonry surface has been prepared (usually by chipping) for bonding to the new material. The unit cost per square foot for these materials depends on the thickness of the material, the position of the area to be covered and the preparation required. In many cases, these materials must be applied in locations where access is difficult and under the control of others. The estimator should make an allowance for delays caused by this problem.

Caulking and sealants are usually applied on the exterior of the building except for certain special conditions on the interior. In most cases, caulking and sealing is done to prevent water and/or air from entering a building. Caulking and sealing are usually specified at joints, expansion joints, control joints, door and window frames and in places where dissimilar materials meet over the surface of the building exterior. To estimate the installed cost of this type of material, two things must be determined. First, the estimator must note (from the specifications) the kind of material to be used for each caulking or sealing job. Second, the dimensions of the joints to be caulked or sealed must be measured on the plans, with attention given to any requirements for backer rods. With this information, the estimator can select the applicable cost per linear foot and multiply it by the total length in feet. The result is an estimated cost for each kind of caulking or sealing on the job. Caulking and sealing may often be overlooked as incidental items. They may, in fact, represent a significant cost, depending upon the type of construction.

The specifications may require testing of the integrity of installed waterproofing in certain cases. If required, adequate time must be allowed and costs included in the estimate.

Insulation

- Batt or Roll
- Blown-in
- Board (Rigid and Semi-rigid)
- Cavity Masonry
- Perimeter Foundation
- Poured in Place
- Reflective
- Roof
- Sprayed

Insulation is primarily used to reduce heat transfer through the exterior enclosure of the building. The type and form of this insulation will vary according to its location in the structure and the size of the space it occupies. Major insulation types include mineral granules, fibers and foams, vegetable fibers and solids, and plastic foams. These materials may be required around foundations, on or inside walls, and under roofing. Many different details of the drawings must be examined in order to determine types, methods and quantities of insulation. The cost of insulation depends on the type of material, its form (loose, granular, batt or boards), its thickness in inches, the method of installation, and the total area in square feet.

It is becoming popular to specify insulation by "R" value only. The estimator may have the choice of materials, given a required "R" value and a certain cavity space (which may dictate insulation thickness). For example, the specifications may require an "R" value of 11, and only 2" of wall cavity is available for the thickness of the insulation. From Figures 8.78 and 8.79, it is seen that only rigid urethane (line 7.2-80-256) meets the design criteria. Note that if more cavity space were available, 3-1/2" non-rigid fiberglass (line 7.2-85-042) would be a much less expensive alternative. The estimator may have to do some shopping to find the least expensive material for the specified "R" value and thickness. Installation costs may vary from one material to another. Also, wood blocking and/or nailers are often required to match the insulation thickness in some instances.

Working with the above data, the estimator can accurately select the installed cost per square foot and estimate the total cost. The estimate for insulation should also include associated costs, such as cutting and patching for difficult installation, or requirements for air vents and other accessories.

Insulation is not only used for controlling heat transfer. It is also specified for use in internal walls and ceilings for controlling *sound* transfer. Although the noise reduction coefficient of batt insulation is not as great as specialized sound attenuation blankets, the costs are considerably less.

Shingles

Most residences and many smaller types of commercial buildings have sloping roofs covered with some form of shingle or watershed material. The materials used in shingles vary from the more common granular-covered asphalt and fiberglass units to wood, metal, clay, concrete, or slate.

The first step in estimating the cost of a shingle roof is to determine the material specified, shingle size and weight, and installation method. With this information, the estimator can select the accurate installed cost of the roofing material.

In a sloping roof deck, the ridge and eave lengths, as well as the ridge to eaves dimension, must be known or measured before the actual roof area can be calculated. When the plan dimensions of the roof are known and the sloping dimensions are not known, the actual roof area can still be estimated, providing the slope of the roof is known. Figure 8.80 is a table of multipliers that can be used for this purpose. The roof slope is given in both the inches of rise per foot of horizontal run, and in the degree of slope, which allows direct conversion of the horizontal plan dimension into the dimension on the slope.

After the roof area has been estimated in square feet, it must be divided by 100 to convert it into roofing squares (the conventional "unit" for roofing — one square equals 100 square feet). To determine the quantity of shingles required for hips or ridges, add one square for each 100 linear feet of hips and/or ridges.

When the total squares of roofing have been calculated, the estimator should make an allowance for waste based on the design of the roof. A minimum allowance of 3% to 5% is needed if the roof has two straight sides with two gable ends and no breaks. At the other extreme, any roof with several valleys, hips, and ridges may need a waste allowance of 15% or more to cover the excess cutting required.

Accessories that are part of a shingle roof include drip edges, flashings at chimneys, dormers, skylights, vents, valleys, and walls. These are necessary to complete the roof and should be included in the estimate for the shingles.

Roofing and Siding

In addition to shingles, many types of roofing and siding are used on commercial and industrial buildings. These are made of several kinds of material and come in many forms for both roofing and siding — panels, sheets, membranes, and boards.

The materials used in roofing and siding panels include: aluminum, mineral fiber-cement, epoxy, fibrous glass, steel, vinyl, many types of synthetic sheets and membranes, coal tar, asphalt felt, tar felt and asphalt asbestos felt. Most of the latter materials are used in job-fabricated, built-up roofs and as backing for other materials, such as shingles.

7.2 Insulation	CREW	DAILY OUTPUT	UNIT	BARE COSTS			TOTAL INCL O&P
				MAT.	INST.	TOTAL	
030 Foam type on roofs, incl. preparation							
060 Urethane, 3 lb./C.F., 1" thick, R7.7	G-2	770	S.F.	.05	.68	.73	.99
070 2" thick, R15.4	"	475	"	.15	1.11	1.26	1.67
75-001 VAPOR BARRIER See division 7.1-15							
77-001 VENTS, ONE-WAY For insulated decks, 1 per M.S.F., plastic, minimum	1 Rofc	40	Ea.	4.75	3.76	8.51	11
010 Maximum		20		52	7.50	59.50	69
030 Aluminum		30		12.50	5	17.50	21
050 Copper	↓	28		14.70	5.35	20.05	24
080 Fiber board baffles, 12" wide for 16" O.C. rafter spacing	1 Carp	90		.43	1.78	2.21	3.05
090 For 24" O.C. rafter spacing	"	110	↓	.64	1.45	2.09	2.81
80-001 WALL INSULATION, RIGID							
004 Fiberglass, 1.5#/C.F., unfaced, 1" thick, R4.1	1 Carp	1,000	S.F.	.18	.16	.34	.43
006 1-1/2" thick, R6.2		1,000		.35	.16	.51	.62
008 2" thick, R8.3		1,000		.46	.16	.62	.74
012 3" thick, R12.4		800		.70	.20	.90	1.06
037 3#/C.F., unfaced, 1" thick, R4.3		1,000		.50	.16	.66	.78
039 1-1/2" thick, R6.5		1,000		.75	.16	.91	1.06
040 2" thick, R8.7		890		1.01	.18	1.19	1.37
042 2-1/2" thick, R10.9		800		1.26	.20	1.46	1.68
044 3" thick, R13		800		1.50	.20	1.70	1.94
052 Foil faced, 1" thick, R4.3		1,000		.94	.16	1.10	1.27
054 1-1/2" thick, R6.5		1,000		1.18	.16	1.34	1.53
056 2" thick, R8.7		890		1.43	.18	1.61	1.83
058 2-1/2" thick, R10.9		800		1.68	.20	1.88	2.14
060 3" thick, R13		800		2.73	.20	2.93	3.29
067 6#/C.F., unfaced, 1" thick, R4.3		1,000		.91	.16	1.07	1.23
069 1-1/2" thick, R6.5		890		1.37	.18	1.55	1.77
070 2" thick, R8.7		800		1.82	.20	2.02	2.29
072 2-1/2" thick, R10.9		800		2.28	.20	2.48	2.80
074 3" thick, R13		730		2.75	.22	2.97	3.34
082 Foil faced, 1" thick, R4.3		1,000		1.32	.16	1.48	1.68
084 1-1/2" thick, R6.5		890		1.76	.18	1.94	2.20
085 2" thick, R8.7		800		2.21	.20	2.41	2.72
088 2-1/2" thick, R10.9		800		2.63	.20	2.83	3.18
090 3" thick, R13	↓	730	↓	3.10	.22	3.32	3.73
100							
150 Foamglass, 1-1/2" thick, R2.64	1 Carp	800	S.F.	1.42	.20	1.62	1.85
155 2" thick, R5.26		730		1.98	.22	2.20	2.50
170 Perlite, 1" thick, R2.77		800		.28	.20	.48	.60
175 2" thick, R5.55		730		.56	.22	.78	.93
190 Polystyrene, extruded blue, 2.2#/C.F., 3/4" thick, R4		800		.36	.20	.56	.69
194 1-1/2" thick, R8.1		730		.59	.22	.81	.97
196 2" thick, R10.8		730		.78	.22	1	1.18
210 Molded bead board, white, 1" thick, R3.85		800		.15	.20	.35	.45
212 1-1/2" thick, R5.6		730		.23	.22	.45	.57
214 2" thick, R7.7		730		.31	.22	.53	.66
235 Sheathing, insulating foil faced fiberboard, 3/8" thick	↓	670	↓	.20	.24	.44	.57
245							
251 Urethane, no paper backing, 1/2" thick, R2.9	1 Carp	800	S.F.	.22	.20	.42	.53
252 1" thick, R5.8		800		.42	.20	.62	.75
254 1-1/2" thick, R8.7		730		.63	.22	.85	1.01
256 2" thick, R11.7		730		.84	.22	1.06	1.24
271 Fire resistant, 1/2" thick, R2.9		800		.27	.20	.47	.59
272 1" thick, R5.8		800		.57	.20	.77	.92
274 1-1/2" thick, R8.7		730		.78	.22	1	1.18
276 2" thick, R11.7	↓	730	↓	1.04	.22	1.26	1.46
85-001 WALL OR CEILING INSULATION, NON-RIGID							
004 Fiberglass, kraft faced, batts or blankets							

Figure 8.78

7.2	Insulation	CREW	DAILY OUTPUT	UNIT	BARE COSTS			TOTAL INCL O&P
					MAT.	INST.	TOTAL	
006	3-1/2" thick, R11, 11" wide	1 Carp	1,150	S.F.	.20	.14	.34	.42
008	15" wide		1,600		.20	.10	.30	.36
010	23" wide		1,600		.22	.10	.32	.39
014	6" thick, R19, 11" wide		1,000		.32	.16	.48	.58
016	15" wide		1,350		.32	.12	.44	.52
018	23" wide		1,600		.32	.10	.42	.50
020	9" thick, R30, 15" wide		1,150		.50	.14	.64	.75
022	23" wide		1,350		.50	.12	.62	.72
024	12" thick, R38, 15" wide		1,000		.67	.16	.83	.97
026	23" wide	↓	1,350	↓	.67	.12	.79	.91
035								
040	Fiberglass, foil faced, batts or blankets							
042	3-1/2" thick, R11, 15" wide	1 Carp	1,600	S.F.	.22	.10	.32	.39
044	23" wide		1,600		.22	.10	.32	.39
046	6" thick, R19, 15" wide		1,350		.34	.12	.46	.55
048	23" wide		1,600		.34	.10	.44	.52
050	9" thick, R30, 15" wide		1,150		.53	.14	.67	.78
055	23" wide	↓	1,350	↓	.53	.12	.65	.75
070								
080	Fiberglass, unfaced, batts or blankets							
082	3-1/2" thick, R11, 15" wide	1 Carp	1,350	S.F.	.18	.12	.30	.37
083	23" wide		1,600		.18	.10	.28	.34
086	6" thick, R19, 15" wide		1,150		.30	.14	.44	.53
088	23" wide		1,350		.30	.12	.42	.50
090	9" thick, R30, 15" wide		1,000		.48	.16	.64	.76
092	23" wide		1,150		.48	.14	.62	.73
094	12" thick, R38, 15" wide		1,000		.63	.16	.79	.92
096	23" wide	↓	1,150	↓	.63	.14	.77	.89
130	Mineral fiber batts, kraft faced							
132	3-1/2" thick, R13	1 Carp	1,600	S.F.	.50	.10	.60	.69
134	6" thick, R19	↓	1,600		.60	.10	.70	.80
138	10" thick, R30	↓	1,350		.95	.12	1.07	1.22
190	For foil backing 2 sides, add			↓	.06		.06	.06M

7.3	Shingles	CREW	DAILY OUTPUT	UNIT	BARE COSTS			TOTAL INCL O&P
					MAT.	INST.	TOTAL	
05-001	ALUMINUM Shingles, mill finish, .020" thick	1 Carp	2.50	Sq.	115	64	179	220
010	.030" thick	"	2.50		146	64	210	255
030	For colors, anodized finish, add				32		32	35M
040	For bonderized finish, add			↓	64		64	70M
060	Ridge cap, .020" thick	1 Carp	170	L.F.	3.98	.94	4.92	5.75
070	.030" thick		170		5.70	.94	6.64	7.65
090	Valley section for above, .020" thick		170		1.46	.94	2.40	2.97
100	.030" thick	↓	170	↓	1.57	.94	2.51	3.09
120	For 1" factory applied polystyrene insulation, add			Sq.	22.50		22.50	25M
150	Shakes, corrugated, .019" thick, fluropon coated, 46 lb. per sq.	1 Carp	2.30		183	70	253	300
07-001	ALUMINUM Tiles, .019" thick, mission tile		2.50		226	64	290	340
020	Spanish tiles		3		180	53	233	275
10-001	ASBESTOS Mineral fiber strip shingles, 14" x 30", 325 lb. per square		4		105	40	145	175
010	12" x 24", 167 lb. per square		3.50		85	46	131	160
011	Starters, 8" x 30", 255 lb. per 100 L.F.		3	↓	62	53	115	145
012	Hip & ridge shingles, 4-3/4" x 14", 380 lbs. per 100 L.F.		1	C.L.F.	300	160	460	560
020	(91) Shakes, 9.35" x 16", 500 lb. per square (siding)		2.20	Sq.	155	73	228	275
030	Hip & ridge shingles, 5-3/8" x 14"	↓	1	C.L.F.	300	160	460	560

Figure 8.79

The basic data required for estimating either roofing or siding includes the specification of the material, the supporting structure, the method of installation, and the area to be covered. When selecting the current unit price for these materials, the estimator must remember that basic installed unit costs are per square foot for siding and per square for roofing. The major exceptions to this general rule are prefabricated roofing panels and single-ply roofing, which are priced per square foot.

Single-ply roofs

- Chlorinated Polyethylene (CPE)
- Chlorosulfonated Polyethylene
- Ethylene Propylene Diene Monomer (EPDM)
- Polychloroprene (Neoprene)
- Polyisobutylene (PIB)
- Polyvinyl Chloride (PVC)
- Modified Bitumen

Since the early 1970s the use of single-ply roofing membranes in the construction industry has been on the rise. Market surveys have recently shown that of all the single-ply systems being installed, about one in three is on new construction. Materially, these roofs are more expensive

Factors for Converting Inclined to Horizontal					
Roof Slope	Approx. Angle	Factor	Roof Slope	Approx. Angle	Factor
Flat	0	1.000	12 in 12	45.0	1.414
1 in 12	4.8	1.003	13 in 12	47.3	1.474
2 in 12	9.5	1.014	14 in 12	49.4	1.537
3 in 12	14.0	1.031	15 in 12	51.3	1.601
4 in 12	18.4	1.054	16 in 12	53.1	1.667
5 in 12	22.6	1.083	17 in 12	54.8	1.734
6 in 12	26.6	1.118	18 in 12	56.3	1.803
7 in 12	30.3	1.158	19 in 12	57.7	1.873
8 in 12	33.7	1.202	20 in 12	59.0	1.943
9 in 12	36.9	1.250	21 in 12	60.3	2.015
10 in 12	39.8	1.302	22 in 12	61.4	2.088
11 in 12	42.5	1.357	23 in 12	62.4	2.162

Example:

[20' (1.302) 90'] 2 = 4,687.2 S.F. = 46.9 Sq.

OR

[40' (1.302) 90'] = 4,687.2 S.F. = 46.9 Sq.

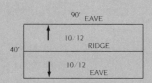

Figure 8.80

than other, more conventional roofs; however, labor costs are much lower because of a faster installation. Re-roofing represents the largest market for single-ply roof today. Single-ply roof systems are normally installed in one of the following ways:

Loose-laid and ballasted: Generally this is the easiest type of single-ply roof to install. Some special consideration must be given, however, when flashing is attached to the roof. The membrane is typically fused together at the seams, stretched out flat and ballasted with stone (1-1/2″ @10-12 PSF) to prevent wind blow-off. This extra load must be considered during design stages. It is particularly important if re-roofing over an existing built-up roof that already weighs 10-15 PSF. A slip-sheet or vapor barrier is sometimes required to separate the new roof from the old.

Partially-adhered: This method of installation uses a series of bar or point attachments which adhere the membrane to a substrate. The membrane manufacturer typically specifies the method to be used based on the material and substrate. Partially-adhered systems do not use ballast material. A slip-sheet may be required.

Fully-adhered: This is generally the most time-consuming of the single-plies to install, because these roofs employ a contact cement, cold adhesive, or hot bitumen to adhere the membrane uniformly to the substrate. Only manufacturer-approved insulation board or substrate should be used to receive the membrane. No ballast is required.

The materials available can be broken down into three categories:

- Thermo-Setting: EDPM, Neoprene, and PIB
- Thermo-Plastic: Hypalon, PVC, and CPE
- Composites: Modified Bitumen

Each has its own requirements and performance characteristics. Most are available in all three installation methods. See Figure 8.81.

Single-ply roof systems are available from many sources. Most if not all manufacturers, however, sell their materials only to franchised installers. As a result, there may be only one source for a price in any given area. Read the specifications carefully. Estimate the system required, exactly as specified; substitutes are usually not allowed.

Sheet Metal

- Copper and Stainless Steel
- Gutters and Downspouts
- Edge Cleats and Gravel Stops
- Flashings
- Trim
- Miscellaneous

Sheet metal work included in this division is limited to that used on roofs or sidewalls of buildings, usually on the exterior exposed to the weather. Many of the items covered are wholly or partially prefabricated with labor added for installation. Several are materials that require labor added for on-site fabrication; this cost must be estimated separately.

Pricing shop-made items such as downspouts, drip edges, expansion joints, gravel stops, gutters, reglets, and termite shields requires that the estimator determine the material, size, and shape of the fabricated section, and the linear feet of the item. From this data, an accurate unit can be selected and multiplied by the linear footage in order to obtain a total cost.

The cost of items like copper roofing and metal flashing is estimated in a similar manner, except that unit costs are per square foot. Some roofing systems, particularly single-ply, require flashing materials that are unique to that roofing system.

Roofing materials like monel, stainless steel, and zinc copper alloy are also estimated by the same method, except that the unit costs are per square (100 square feet). Prefabricated items like strainers and louvers are priced on a cost-per-unit basis. Adhesives are priced by the gallon. The installed cost of roofing adhesives depends on the cost per gallon and the coverage per gallon. With trowel grade adhesive, the coverage will vary from a light coating at 25 S.F. per gallon to a heavy coating at 10 S.F. per gallon. With most flashing work, the asphalt adhesive will

Single-Ply Roofing Membrane Installation Guide

	Generic Materials (Classification)	Compatible Substrates						Attachment Method				Sealing Method				
		Slip-Sheet Req'd.	Concrete	Exist. Asphalt Memb.	Insulation Board	Plywood	Spray Urethane Foam	Adhesive	Fully Adhered	Loose Laid/Ballast	Partially-Adhered	Adhesive	Hot Air Gun	Self-Sealing	Solvent	Torch Heating
Thermo Setting	EPDM (Ethylene, propylene diene monomer)	X	X	X	X	X	X	X	X		X	X	X		X	X
	Neoprene (synthetic rubber)	X	X		X	X		X	X	X		X				
	PIB (Polyisobutylene)	X	X	X	X	X	X	X		X		X	X		X	
Thermo Plastic	CSPE (Chlorosulfenated polyethyene)	X	X		X	X	X	X	X	X	X	X	X			
	CPE (Chlorinated polyethylene)	X	X		X	X			X	X	X	X				
	PVC (Polyvinyl chloride)	X	X		X	X	X			X	X	X			X	
Composites	Glass reinforced EPDM/neoprene	X	X		X	X	X				X	X				
	Modified bitumen/polyester	X		X	X	X			X			X	X			X
	Modified bitumen/polyethylene & aluminum	X	X		X	X		X	X			X				X
	Modified bitumen/polyethylene sheet	X	X		X	X					X			X		X
	Modified CPE				X	X			X			X				
	Non-woven glass reinforced PVC							X	X	X		X				
	Nylon reinforced PVC		X		X	X					X			X	X	
	Nylon reinforced/butyl or neoprene	X							X					X	X	
	Polyester reinforced CPE	X	X	X	X	X	X			X	X	X	X			
	Polyester reinforced PVC	X	X		X	X	X			X	X	X	X		X	
	Rubber asphalt/plastic sheet	X	X	X	X	X			X					X		

Figure 8.81

cover an average of 15 S.F. for each layer or course. In many specifications the coverage of special materials like adhesives will be stated and should be used as the basis for the estimate.

Roof Accessories
- Hatches
- Skylights
- Vents
- Snow Guards

Roof accessories must be considered as part of the complete weatherproofing system. Standard size accessories, such as ceiling, roof and smoke vents or hatches, and snow guards, are priced per installed unit. Accessories that must be fabricated to meet project specifications may be priced per square foot, per linear foot or per unit. Skylight costs, for example, are listed by the square foot with unit costs decreasing in steps as the nominal size of individual units increases.

Skyroofs are priced on the same basis, but due to the many variations in the shape and construction of these units, costs are per square foot of surface area. These costs will vary with the size and type of unit, and in many cases, maximum and minimum costs give the estimator a range of prices for various design variations. Because there are many types and styles, the estimator must determine the exact specifications for the skyroof being priced. The accuracy of the total cost figure will depend entirely on the selection of the proper unit cost and calculation of the skyroof area. Skyroofs are becoming widely used in the industry and the work is growing more and more specialized. Often a particular manufacturer is specified. Specialty installing subcontractors are often factory authorized and required to perform the installation to maintain warranties and waterproof integrity.

Accessories such as roof drains, plumbing vents and duct penetrations are usually installed by other appropriate subcontractors. However, costs for flashing and sealing these items are often included by the roofing subcontractor.

When estimating Division 7, associated costs must be included for items that may not be directly stated in the specifications. Placement of materials, for example, may require the use of a crane or conveyors. Pitch pockets, sleepers, pads and walkways may be required for rooftop equipment. Blocking and cant strips and items associated with different trades must also be coordinated. Once again, the estimator must visualize the construction process.

Sample Estimate: Division 7

The moisture and thermal protection portion of the sample building project is to be done partially by crews of the general contractor and partially by a subcontractor. The estimate sheets are shown in Figures 8.82 and 8.83. It is important to verify that the "units" used for takeoff are the same as those used for pricing. Note in Figure 8.84, the polyethylene vapor barrier is priced by the square (sq.). It could be an easy mistake to enter 20,800 (18,900 square feet of floor area plus 10% overlap) on the estimate sheet (Figure 8.82). Even, if one person performs the takeoff and another the pricing, such an error could possibly occur in haste. Ideally time should be allowed for someone to always crosscheck the work and calculations of another.

MEANS CONSOLIDATED ESTIMATE

Division 7
SHEET NO. 1 of 2

PROJECT Office Building — CLASSIFICATION — ESTIMATE NO. 86-1

LOCATION — ARCHITECT — DATE 1986

TAKE OFF BY EBW — QUANTITIES BY EBW — PRICES BY RSM — EXTENSIONS BY SLM — CHECKED JDM

DESCRIPTION	SOURCE/DIMENSIONS			QUANTITY	UNIT	MATERIAL UNIT COST	MATERIAL TOTAL	LABOR UNIT COST	LABOR TOTAL	EQUIPMENT UNIT COST	EQUIPMENT TOTAL	SUBCONTRACT UNIT COST	SUBCONTRACT TOTAL
Division 7: Moisture & Thermal Protection													
Water Proofing													
Asphalt Coating	7.1	10	060	3000	SF	.50	1500	.30	900				
Protective Board 1/4"	7.1	10	400	3000	SF	.38	1140	.33	990				
Vapor Barrier - 6 mil poly	7.1	15	090	208	SQ	2.70	562	4.32	899				
Insulation													
3½" Fiberglass Ext.	7.2	85	042	17,600	SF	.22	3872	.10	1760				
3½" Fiberglass Int.	7.2	85	082	7620	SF	.18	1372	.12	914				
Roof Deck (Incl. Penthouse) 2 5/8" Urethane/fiberglass	7.2	50	130	18,900	SF		SUB CONTRACT					1.23	23247
Roofing													
4-ply Built-Up	7.4	15	050	189	SQ							125	23625
4x4 Cant	7.4	18	001	800	LF							1.92	1536
Sub Totals							8446		5463				48408

Figure 8.82

MEANS CONSOLIDATED ESTIMATE

Division 7

SHEET NO. 2 of 2

PROJECT Office Building | CLASSIFICATION | ESTIMATE NO. 86-1

LOCATION | ARCHITECT | DATE 1986

TAKE OFF BY EBW | QUANTITIES BY EBW | PRICES BY RSM | EXTENSIONS BY SLM | CHECKED JDM

DESCRIPTION	SOURCE/DIMENSIONS			QUANTITY	UNIT	MATERIAL UNIT COST	MATERIAL TOTAL	LABOR UNIT COST	LABOR TOTAL	EQUIPMENT UNIT COST	EQUIPMENT TOTAL	SUBCONTRACT UNIT COST	SUBCONTRACT TOTAL
Division 7: (Cont'd)													
Sheet Metal													
Gravel Stop	7.6	30	035	800	LF		SUBCONTRACT					7.45	5960
Alum. Flashing	7.6	25	010	200	SF							2.68	536
Accessories													
Smoke Hatches (Stairs)	7.8	20 55	120 030	3	Ea.							1235	3705
Smoke Vent (Elevator)	7.8	60	020	1	Ea.							1075	1075
Sub Total													11276
Sheet 1							8446		5463				48408
Sheet 2													11276
Division 7 Totals							8446		5463				59684

Figure 8.83

7.1 Waterproofing	CREW	DAILY OUTPUT	UNIT	BARE COSTS MAT.	BARE COSTS INST.	BARE COSTS TOTAL	TOTAL INCL O&P
05-001 BENTONITE Panels, 4' x 4', for walls, 3/16" thick	1 Rofc	625	S.F.	.65	.24	.89	1.08
010 Under slabs, 5/8" thick	"	900	"	.85	.17	1.02	1.19
030 Granular bentonite, 50 lb. bags (.625 C.F.)			Bag	9.50		9.50	10.45M
040 3/8" thick, troweled on	1 Rofc	475	S.F.	.69	.32	1.01	1.24
050 Drain board, expanded polystyrene, binder encapsulated, 1" thick		600		.49	.25	.74	.92
051 2" thick		600		.98	.25	1.23	1.46
052 3" thick		600		1.43	.25	1.68	1.96
053 4" thick	↓	600		1.90	.25	2.15	2.47
060 Filter fabric, minimum				.08		.08	.08M
061 Maximum				.10		.10	.11M
070 Vapor retarder, 4 mil polyethelene			↓	.05		.05	.05M
10-001 BITUMINOUS ASPHALT COATING For foundation							
002							
003 Brushed on, below grade, 1 coat	1 Rofc	665	S.F.	.08	.23	.31	.43
010 2 coat		500		.15	.30	.45	.63
030 Sprayed on, below grade, 1 coat, 25.6 S.F./gal.		830		.12	.18	.30	.41
040 2 coat, 20.5 S.F./gal.	↓	500	↓	.15	.30	.45	.63
050 Asphalt coating, with fibers			Gal.	15.60		15.60	17.15M
060 Troweled on, asphalt with fibers, 1/16" thick	1 Rofc	500	S.F.	.50	.30	.80	1.01
070 1/8" thick		400		1	.38	1.38	1.68
100 1/2" thick	↓	350	↓	4.30	.43	4.73	5.40
300 Asphalt roof coating			Gal.	9.75		9.75	10.70M
320 Asphalt base, fibered aluminum coating				10		10	11M
330 Asphalt primer, 5 gallon				9		9	9.90M
340 Glass fibered roof & patching cement, 5 gallon			↓	12.50		12.50	13.75M
345 Reinforcing glass membrane, 450 S.F./roll			Ea.	72		72	79M
347							
350 Neoprene roof coating, 5 gal., 2 gal./sq.			Gal.	24		24	26M
370 Roof patch & flashing cement, 5 gallon			"	35		35	39M
400 Protective board, asphalt coated, in mastic, 1/4" thick	1 Rofc	450	S.F.	.38	.33	.71	.93
500							
600 Roof resaturant, glass fibered, 3 gal./sq.			Gal.	11		11	12.10M
620 Mineral rubber, 3 gal./sq.			"	10		10	11M
15-001 BUILDING PAPER Aluminum and kraft laminated, foil 1 side	1 Carp	19	Sq.	3.20	8.40	11.60	15.70
010 Foil 2 sides		19		6.40	8.40	14.80	19.25
030 Asphalt, two ply, #30, for subfloors		37		6.60	4.32	10.92	13.55
040 Asphalt felt sheathing paper, #15		37		3	4.32	7.32	9.55
060 Polyethylene vapor barrier, standard, .002" thick		37		1.50	4.32	5.82	7.90
070 .004" thick		37		1.80	4.32	6.12	8.25
090 .006" thick		37		2.70	4.32	7.02	9.25
100 .008" thick		37		3.60	4.32	7.92	10.25
120 .010" thick		37		4.27	4.32	8.59	10.95
130 Clear reinforced, fire retardant, .008" thick		37		7.55	4.32	11.87	14.55
135 Cross laminated type, .003" thick		37		6.40	4.32	10.72	13.30
140 .004" thick		37		7.75	4.32	12.07	14.80
150 Red rosin paper, 5 sq. rolls, 4 lbs. per square		37		1.75	4.32	6.07	8.20
160 5 lbs. per square		37		2	4.32	6.32	8.45
180 Reinf. waterproof, .002" polyethylene backing, 1 side		37		6.25	4.32	10.57	13.15
190 2 sides	↓	37		7.50	4.32	11.82	14.50
210 Roof deck vapor barrier, class 1 metal decks	1 Rofc	37		5.30	4.06	9.36	12.05
220 For all other decks	"	37		3.25	4.06	7.31	9.80
240 Waterproofed kraft with sisal or fiberglass fibers, minimum	1 Carp	37		4.80	4.32	9.12	11.55
250 Maximum	"	37	↓	12	4.32	16.32	19.45
20-001 CAULKING AND SEALANTS							
002 Acoustical sealant, elastomeric			Gal.	19		19	21M
003 Backer rod, polyethylene, 1/4" diameter	1 Bric	4.60	C.L.F.	3.65	36	39.65	55
005 1/2" diameter		4.60		6.25	36	42.25	58
007 3/4" diameter		4.60		9.35	36	45.35	61
009 1" diameter	↓	4.60	↓	18.35	36	54.35	71

Figure 8.84

226

Smoke hatches are specified to be installed at the tops of the stair towers. Costs for smoke hatches in *Building Construction Cost Data* are given only as percentages to be added to the *bare costs* of roof hatches. See Figures 8.85 and 8.86. Calculations to add the percentages are shown in Figure 8.87. The bare costs are increased before overhead and profit are added. 10% is added to the bare material cost for handling. In Figure 8.85, the installing crew for the roof hatches is G-3 (see Figure 8.88). The crews consists of sheet metal workers and laborers. The percentage added to the labor costs, for overhead and profit, is the average of the percentages for the two trades from Figure 8.89 – 46.1% and 44.9%.

The development and application of these percentages for overhead and profit are discussed in Chapter 4 and Chapter 7 of this book.

Division 8: Doors, Windows and Glass

Any one door assembly (door, frame, hardware) can be one of hundreds of combinations of many variable features:

Door:	Frame:	Hardware:
Size	Size	Lockset
Thickness	Throat	Passage set
Wood-type	Wood-type	Panic bar
Metal-gauge	Metal-gauge	Closer
Laminate	Casing	Hinges
Hollow-core type	Stops	Stops
Solid-core material	Fire rating	Bolts
Fire rating	Knock down	Finish
Finish	Welded	Plates

Most architectural plans and specifications include door, window, and hardware schedules to tabulate these combinations. The estimator should use these schedules, and details in conjunction with the plans, to avoid duplication or omission of units when determining the quantities. The schedules should identify the location, size, and type of each unit. Schedules should also include information regarding the frame, fire-rating, hardware, and special notes. If no such schedules are included, the estimator should prepare them in order to provide an accurate quantity takeoff. Figure 8.90 is an example of a schedule that may be prepared by the estimator. Most suppliers will prepare separate schedules for approval by the architect or owner.

Metal Doors and Frames

A proper door schedule on the architectural drawings identifies each opening in detail. Define each opening in accordance with the items in the schedule and any other pertinent data. Installation information should be carefully reviewed in the specifications.

For the quantity survey, combine all similar door and frames, checking each off as you go to ensure none has been left out. An easy and obvious check is to count the total number of openings, making certain that two doors and only one frame have been included where double doors are used. Important details to check for both door and frame are:

- Material
- Gauge
- Size
- Core Material
- Fire Rating Label
- Finish
- Style

7.6	Sheet Metal Work	CREW	DAILY OUTPUT	UNIT	BARE COSTS			TOTAL INCL O&P
					MAT.	INST.	TOTAL	
020	For standing seam construction, deduct			Sq.	2%			
050	For flat seam construction, deduct				3%			
080	For lead or terne coated stainless, 28 gauge, add				70		70	77M
090	For 26 gauge, add				79		79	87M
60-001	TERMITE Shields, zinc, 10" wide, .012" thick	1 Carp	350	L.F.	1	.46	1.46	1.76
010	.020" thick	"	350	"	.70	.46	1.16	1.43
63-001	ZINC Copper alloy roofing, batten seam, .020" thick	1 Shee	1.20	Sq.	360	150	510	615
010	.027" thick		1.15		445	160	605	720
030	.032" thick		1.10		525	165	690	820
040	.040" thick		1.05		670	175	845	990
060	For standing seam construction, deduct				2%			
070	For flat seam construction, deduct				3%			

7.8	Roof Accessories	CREW	DAILY OUTPUT	UNIT	BARE COSTS			TOTAL INCL O&P
					MAT.	INST.	TOTAL	
10-001	CEILING HATCHES 2'-6" x 2'-6", single leaf, steel frame & cover	G-3	11	Ea.	268	59	327	380
010	Aluminum cover		11		288	59	347	400
030	2'-6" x 3'-0", single leaf, steel frame & steel cover		11		288	59	347	400
040	Aluminum cover		11		326	59	385	445
15-001	ROOF DRAINS See division 15.1-16							
20-001	ROOF HATCHES With curb, 1" fiberglass insulation, 2'-6" x 3'-0"							
050	Aluminum curb and cover	G-3	10	Ea.	361	64	425	490
052	Galvanized steel		10		340	64	404	465
054	Plain steel, primed		10		304	64	368	425
060	2'-6" x 4'-6", aluminum curb & cover		9		517	72	589	670
080	Galvanized steel		9		489	72	561	640
090	Plain steel, primed		9		430	72	502	575
120	2'-6" x 8'-0", aluminum curb and cover		6.60		897	98	995	1,125
140	Galvanized steel		6.60		850	98	948	1,075
150	Plain steel, primed		6.60		742	98	840	955
180	For plexiglass panels, add to above				200		200	220M
200	For galv. curb and alum. cover, deduct from aluminum				14		14	15.40M
30-001	ROOF VENTS Mushroom for built-up roofs, aluminum	1 Rofc	30		17.10	5	22.10	26
010	PVC, 6" high	"	30		20.90	5	25.90	31
40-001	SKYLIGHT Plastic roof domes, flush or curb mounted, ten or							
010	more units, curb not included, "L" frames							
030	Nominal size under 10 S.F., double	G-3	130	S.F.	17	4.96	21.96	26
040	Single		160		13	4.03	17.03	20
060	10 S.F. to 20 S.F., double		315		14	2.05	16.05	18.35
070	Single		395		10	1.63	11.63	13.35
090	20 S.F. to 30 S.F., double		395		12	1.63	13.63	15.55
100	Single		465		9	1.39	10.39	11.90
120	30 S.F. to 65 S.F., double		465		10	1.39	11.39	13
130	Single		610		8	1.06	9.06	10.30
150	For insulated 4" curbs, double, add				15%			
160	Single, add				30%			
180	For integral insulated 9" curbs, double, add				30%			
190	Single, add				45%			
210	Ceiling plastic domes compared with single roof domes				95%	100%		
211								
212	Ventilating insulated plexiglass dome with							
213	curb mounting, 36" x 36"	G-3	12	Ea.	332	54	386	445
215	52" x 52"		12		445	54	499	565
216	28" x 52"		10		368	64	432	500

Figure 8.85

7.8	Roof Accessories	CREW	DAILY OUTPUT	UNIT	BARE COSTS			TOTAL INCL O&P
					MAT.	INST.	TOTAL	
217	36" x 52"	G-3	10	Ea.	390	64	454	520
218	For electric opening system, add			"	200		200	220M
220	Field fabricated, factory type, aluminum and wire glass	G-3	120	S.F.	10.15	5.35	15.50	18.90
230	Insulated safety glass with aluminum frame		160		69	4.03	73.03	82
240	Sandwich panels, fiberglass, for walls, 1-9/16" thick, to 250 S.F.		200		12	3.22	15.22	17.85
250	250 S.F. and up		265		9.75	2.43	12.18	14.25
270	As above, but for roofs, 2-3/4" thick, to 250 S.F.		295		18	2.19	20.19	23
280	250 S.F. and up		330		14.50	1.95	16.45	18.75
300	Prefabricated glass block with metal frame, minimum		265		49	2.43	51.43	57
310	Maximum	▼	160		61	4.03	65.03	73
320	With precast concrete structural frame, minimum	C-11	1,500		43	1.71	44.71	50
330	Maximum	"	1,000	▼	55	2.57	57.57	64
50-001	SKYROOFS Translucent panels, 2-3/4" thick, under 5000 S.F.	G-3	395	S.F.Hor.	14.30	1.63	15.93	18.10
010	Over 5000 S.F.		465		12.70	1.39	14.09	15.95
030	Continuous vaulted, semi-circular, to 8' wide, double glazed		145		28	4.45	32.45	37
040	Single glazed		160		18	4.03	22.03	26
060	To 20' wide, single glazed		175		24	3.68	27.68	32
070	Over 20' wide, single glazed		200		25	3.22	28.22	32
090	Motorized opening type, single glazed, 1/3 opening		145		30	4.45	34.45	39
100	Full opening	▼	130	▼	37	4.96	41.96	48
120	Pyramid type units, self-supporting, to 30' clear opening,							
130	square or circular, single glazed, minimum	G-3	200	S.F.Hor.	22	3.22	25.22	29
131	Average		165		25	3.91	28.91	33
140	Maximum		130		27	4.96	31.96	37
150	Grid type, 4' to 10' modules, single glass glazed, minimum		200		21	3.22	24.22	28
155	Maximum		128		28	5.05	33.05	38
160	Preformed acrylic, minimum		300		14.20	2.15	16.35	18.70
165	Maximum	▼	175	▼	26	3.68	29.68	34
180	Dome type units, self-supporting, to 100' clear opening, circular ,							
190	rise to span ratio = 0.20							
192	Minimum	G-3	197	S.F.Hor.	15	3.27	18.27	21
195	Maximum		113		37	5.70	42.70	49
210	Rise to span ratio = 0.33, minimum		169		25	3.81	28.81	33
215	Maximum		101		40	6.40	46.40	53
220	Rise to span ratio = 0.50, minimum		148		38	4.36	42.36	48
225	Maximum		87		44	7.40	51.40	59
240	Ridge units, continuous, to 8' wide, double		130		89	4.96	93.96	105
250	Single		200		58	3.22	61.22	68
270	Ridge and furrow units, over 4' O.C., double, minimum		200		18.05	3.22	21.27	25
275	Maximum		120		35	5.35	40.35	46
280	Single, minimum		214		17.70	3.01	20.71	24
285	Maximum		153	▼	27	4.21	31.21	36
300	Rolling roof, translucent panels, flat roof, residential, minimun		253	S.F.	15.75	2.55	18.30	21
303	Maximum		160		25	4.03	29.03	33
310	Lean-to skyroof, long span, double, minimum		197		18.90	3.27	22.17	26
315	Maximum		101		35	6.40	41.40	48
330	Single, minimum		321		13.20	2.01	15.21	17.40
335	Maximum	▼	160	▼	23	4.03	27.03	31
55-001	SMOKE HATCHES Unlabeled, not including hand winch operator							
010								
020	For 3'-0" long, add to roof hatches from division 7.8-20			Ea.	25%	5%		
030	For 8'-0" long, add to roof hatches from division 7.8-20			"	10%	5%		
60-001	SMOKE VENTS Metal cover, heavy duty, low profile, 4' x 4'							
010	Aluminum	G-3	13	Ea.	1,015	50	1,065	1,200
020	Galvanized steel	"	13	"	910	50	960	1,075
025								
030	4' x 8' aluminum	G-3	8	Ea.	1,310	81	1,391	1,550
040	Galvanized steel	"	8		1,215	81	1,296	1,450
050	Sloped cover style, deduct			▼	10%			

Figure 8.86

229

Wood and Plastic Doors

The quantity survey for wood and plastic laminated doors is identical to that of metal doors. Where local work rules permit, prehung doors and windows are becoming prevalent in the industry. For these, locksets and interior casings are usually extra. As these may be standard for a number of doors in any particular building, they need only be counted. Remember that exterior prehung doors need casings on the interior.

Leave a space in the tabulation on the Quantity Sheet for casings, stops, grounds, and hardware. This can be done either on the same sheet or on separate sheets.

Special Doors

There are many types of specialty doors that may be included — for example, sliding glass doors, overhead garage doors and bulkhead doors. These items should be taken off individually. The estimator should thoroughly examine the plans and specifications to be sure to include all hardware, operating mechanisms, fire ratings, finishes, and any special installation requirements.

Fire Doors

The estimator must pay particular attention to fire doors when performing the quantity takeoff. It is important to determine the exact type of door required. Figure 8.91 is a table describing various types of fire doors. Please note that a "B" label door can be one of four types. If the plans or door schedule do not specify exactly which temperature rise is required, the estimator should consult the architect or local building inspector. Many building and fire codes also require that frames and hardware at fire doors be fire rated and labelled as such. When determining quantities, the estimator must also include any glass (usually wired) or special inserts to be installed in fire doors (or in any doors).

Line Number	Bare Costs		Total Including O&P
	Material	Installation	
7.8-20-120	$ 897	$ 98	
7.8-55-030	(10%) 90	(5%) 5	
	987	103	
Overhead & Profit	(10%) 98	(45.5%) 47	$1,235
	$1,085	$ 150	

Figure 8.87

CREWS

Crew No.	Bare Costs		Incl. Subs O & P		Cost Per Man-hour	
Crew E-15	Hr.	Daily	Hr.	Daily	Bare Costs	Incl. O&P
2 Painters, Struc. Steel	$20.00	$320.00	$32.35	$517.60	$20.00	$32.35
1 Paint Sprayer, 17 C.F.M.		27.00		29.70	1.68	1.85
16 M.H., Daily Totals		$347.00		$547.30	$21.68	$34.20
Crew F-1	Hr.	Daily	Hr.	Daily	Bare Costs	Incl. O&P
1 Carpenter	$20.00	$160.00	$29.00	$232.00	$20.00	$29.00
Power Tools		8.60		9.45	1.07	1.18
8 M.H., Daily Totals		$168.60		$241.45	$21.07	$30.18
Crew F-2	Hr.	Daily	Hr.	Daily	Bare Costs	Incl. O&P
2 Carpenters	$20.00	$320.00	$29.00	$464.00	$20.00	$29.00
Power Tools		17.20		18.90	1.07	1.18
16 M.H., Daily Totals		$337.20		$482.90	$21.07	$30.18
Crew F-3	Hr.	Daily	Hr.	Daily	Bare Costs	Incl. O&P
4 Carpenters	$20.00	$640.00	$29.00	$928.00	$20.21	$29.30
1 Equip. Oper. (crane)	21.05	168.40	30.50	244.00		
1 Hyd. Crane, 12 Ton		235.00		258.50		
Power Tools		17.20		18.90	6.30	6.93
40 M.H., Daily Totals		$1060.60		$1449.40	$26.51	$36.23
Crew F-4	Hr.	Daily	Hr.	Daily	Bare Costs	Incl. O&P
4 Carpenters	$20.00	$640.00	$29.00	$928.00	$19.75	$28.65
1 Equip. Oper. (crane)	21.05	168.40	30.50	244.00		
1 Equip. Oper. Oiler	17.50	140.00	25.40	203.20		
1 Hyd. Crane, 55 Ton		527.60		580.35		
Power Tools		17.20		18.90	11.35	12.48
48 M.H., Daily Totals		$1493.20		$1974.45	$31.10	$41.13
Crew F-5	Hr.	Daily	Hr.	Daily	Bare Costs	Incl. O&P
1 Carpenter Foreman	$22.00	$176.00	$31.90	$255.20	$20.50	$29.72
3 Carpenters	20.00	480.00	29.00	696.00		
Power Tools		17.20		18.90	.53	.59
32 M.H., Daily Totals		$673.20		$970.10	$21.03	$30.31
Crew F-6	Hr.	Daily	Hr.	Daily	Bare Costs	Incl. O&P
2 Carpenters	$20.00	$320.00	$29.00	$464.00	$18.57	$26.92
2 Building Laborers	15.90	254.40	23.05	368.80		
1 Equip. Oper. (crane)	21.05	168.40	30.50	244.00		
1 Hyd. Crane, 12 Ton		235.00		258.50		
Power Tools		17.20		18.90	6.30	6.93
40 M.H., Daily Totals		$995.00		$1354.20	$24.87	$33.85
Crew F-7	Hr.	Daily	Hr.	Daily	Bare Costs	Incl. O&P
2 Carpenters	$20.00	$320.00	$29.00	$464.00	$17.95	$26.02
2 Building Laborers	15.90	254.40	23.05	368.80		
Power Tools		17.20		18.90	.53	.59
32 M.H., Daily Totals		$591.60		$851.70	$18.48	$26.61
Crew G-1	Hr.	Daily	Hr.	Daily	Bare Costs	Incl. O&P
1 Roofer Foreman	$20.80	$166.40	$31.80	$254.40	$17.64	$26.98
4 Roofers, Composition	18.80	601.60	28.75	920.00		
2 Roofer Helpers	13.75	220.00	21.05	336.80		
Application Equipment		101.35		111.50	1.80	1.99
56 M.H., Daily Totals		$1089.35		$1622.70	$19.44	$28.97

Crew No.	Bare Costs		Incl. Subs O & P		Cost Per Man-hour	
Crew G-2	Hr.	Daily	Hr.	Daily	Bare Costs	Incl. O&P
1 Plasterer	$19.90	$159.20	$28.35	$226.80	$17.43	$24.96
1 Plasterer Helper	16.50	132.00	23.50	188.00		
1 Building Laborer	15.90	127.20	23.05	184.40		
Grouting Equipment		107.25		118.00	4.46	4.91
24 M.H., Daily Totals		$525.65		$717.20	$21.89	$29.87
Crew G-3	Hr.	Daily	Hr.	Daily	Bare Costs	Incl. O&P
2 Sheet Metal Workers	$22.70	$363.20	$33.15	$530.40	$19.30	$28.10
2 Building Laborers	15.90	254.40	23.05	368.80		
Power Tools		27.00		29.70	.84	.92
32 M.H., Daily Totals		$644.60		$928.90	$20.14	$29.02
Crew G-4	Hr.	Daily	Hr.	Daily	Bare Costs	Incl. O&P
1 Labor Foreman (outside)	$17.90	$143.20	$25.95	$207.60	$16.56	$24.01
2 Building Laborers	15.90	254.40	23.05	368.80		
1 Light Truck, 1.5 Ton		57.40		63.15		
1 Air Compr., 160 C.F.M.		70.25		77.30	5.31	5.85
24 M.H., Daily Totals		$525.25		$716.85	$21.87	$29.86
Crew G-5	Hr.	Daily	Hr.	Daily	Bare Costs	Incl. O&P
1 Roofer Foreman	$20.80	$166.40	$31.80	$254.40	$17.18	$26.28
2 Roofers, Composition	18.80	300.80	28.75	460.00		
2 Roofer Helpers	13.75	220.00	21.05	336.80		
Application Equipment		101.35		111.50	2.53	2.78
40 M.H., Daily Totals		$788.55		$1162.70	$19.71	$29.06
Crew H-1	Hr.	Daily	Hr.	Daily	Bare Costs	Incl. O&P
2 Glaziers	$20.15	$322.40	$28.75	$460.00	$20.92	$31.42
2 Struc. Steel Workers	21.70	347.20	34.10	545.60		
32 M.H., Daily Totals		$669.60		$1005.60	$20.92	$31.42
Crew H-2	Hr.	Daily	Hr.	Daily	Bare Costs	Incl. O&P
2 Glaziers	$20.15	$322.40	$28.75	$460.00	$18.73	$26.85
1 Building Laborer	15.90	127.20	23.05	184.40		
24 M.H., Daily Totals		$449.60		$644.40	$18.73	$26.85
Crew J-1	Hr.	Daily	Hr.	Daily	Bare Costs	Incl. O&P
3 Plasterers	$19.90	$477.60	$28.35	$680.40	$18.54	$26.41
2 Plasterer Helpers	16.50	264.00	23.50	376.00		
1 Mixing Machine, 6 C.F.		37.80		41.60	.94	1.04
40 M.H., Daily Totals		$779.40		$1098.00	$19.48	$27.45
Crew J-2	Hr.	Daily	Hr.	Daily	Bare Costs	Incl. O&P
3 Plasterers	$19.90	$477.60	$28.35	$680.40	$18.80	$26.73
2 Plasterer Helpers	16.50	264.00	23.50	376.00		
1 Lather	20.10	160.80	28.35	226.80		
1 Mixing Machine, 6 C.F.		37.80		41.60	.78	.86
48 M.H., Daily Totals		$940.20		$1324.80	$19.58	$27.59
Crew J-3	Hr.	Daily	Hr.	Daily	Bare Costs	Incl. O&P
1 Terrazzo Worker	$19.90	$159.20	$27.90	$223.20	$17.92	$25.12
1 Terrazzo Helper	15.95	127.60	22.35	178.80		
1 Mixing Mach. & Grinder		31.20		34.30		
Appropriate Fixtures		87.20		95.90	7.40	8.13
16 M.H., Daily Totals		$405.20		$532.20	$25.32	$33.25
Crew J-4	Hr.	Daily	Hr.	Daily	Bare Costs	Incl. O&P
1 Tile Layer	$19.75	$158.00	$27.70	$221.60	$17.67	$24.77
1 Tile Layer Helper	15.60	124.80	21.85	174.80		
16 M.H., Daily Totals		$282.80		$396.40	$17.67	$24.77

Figure 8.88

Abbr.	Trade	Base Rate Incl. Fringes		Workers' Comp. Ins.	Average Fixed Over-head	Subs Over-head	Subs Profit	Subs Total Overhead & Profit		Rate with Subs O & P	
		Hourly	Daily					%	Amount	Hourly	Daily
Skwk	Skilled Workers Average (35 trades)	$20.50	$164.00	9.3%	13.8%	12.8%	10%	45.9%	$ 9.40	$29.90	$239.20
	Helpers Average (5 trades)	15.55	124.40	9.8		13.0		46.6	7.25	22.80	182.40
	Foremen Average, Inside (50¢ over trade)	21.00	168.00	9.3		12.8		45.9	9.65	30.65	245.20
	Foremen Average, Outside ($2.00 over trade)	22.50	180.00	9.3		12.8		45.9	10.35	32.85	262.80
Clab	Common Building Laborers	15.90	127.20	10.1		11.0		44.9	7.15	23.05	184.40
Asbe	Asbestos Workers	22.75	182.00	7.7		16.0		47.5	10.80	33.55	268.40
Boil	Boilermakers	22.75	182.00	6.6		16.0		46.4	10.55	33.30	266.40
Bric	Bricklayers	20.50	164.00	7.6		11.0		42.4	8.70	29.20	233.60
Brhe	Bricklayer Helpers	16.00	128.00	7.6		11.0		42.4	6.80	22.80	182.40
Carp	Carpenters	20.00	160.00	10.1		11.0		44.9	9.00	29.00	232.00
Cefi	Cement Finishers	19.20	153.60	5.9		11.0		40.7	7.80	27.00	216.00
Elec	Electricians	22.40	179.20	4.0		16.0		43.8	9.80	32.20	257.60
Elev	Elevator Constructors	22.65	181.20	5.5		16.0		45.3	10.25	32.90	263.20
Eqhv	Equipment Operators, Crane or Shovel	21.05	168.40	7.2		14.0		45.0	9.45	30.50	244.00
Eqmd	Equipment Operators, Medium Equipment	20.60	164.80	7.2		14.0		45.0	9.25	29.85	238.80
Eqlt	Equipment Operators, Light Equipment	19.45	155.60	7.2		14.0		45.0	8.75	28.20	225.60
Eqol	Equipment Operators, Oilers	17.50	140.00	7.2		14.0		45.0	7.90	25.40	203.20
Eqmm	Equipment Operators, Master Mechanics	21.80	174.40	7.2		14.0		45.0	9.80	31.60	252.80
Glaz	Glaziers	20.15	161.20	7.9		11.0		42.7	8.60	28.75	230.00
Lath	Lathers	20.10	160.80	6.3		11.0		41.1	8.25	28.35	226.80
Marb	Marble Setters	20.10	160.80	7.6		11.0		42.4	8.50	28.60	228.80
Mill	Millwrights	20.75	166.00	6.6		11.0		41.4	8.60	29.35	234.80
Mstz	Mosaic and Terrazzo Workers	19.90	159.20	5.4		11.0		40.2	8.00	27.90	223.20
Pord	Painters, Ordinary	19.25	154.00	7.7		11.0		42.5	8.20	27.45	219.60
Psst	Painters, Structural Steel	20.00	160.00	27.0		11.0		61.8	12.35	32.35	258.80
Pape	Paper Hangers	19.50	156.00	7.7		11.0		42.5	8.30	27.80	222.40
Pile	Pile Drivers	20.10	160.80	17.0		16.0		56.8	11.40	31.50	252.00
Plas	Plasterers	19.90	159.20	7.7		11.0		42.5	8.45	28.35	226.80
Plah	Plasterer Helpers	16.50	132.00	7.7		11.0		42.5	7.00	23.50	188.00
Plum	Plumbers	22.55	180.40	4.8		16.0		44.6	10.05	32.60	260.80
Rodm	Rodmen (Reinforcing)	21.75	174.00	16.8		14.0		54.6	11.90	33.65	269.20
Rofc	Roofers, Composition	18.80	150.40	18.2		11.0		53.0	9.95	28.75	230.00
Rots	Roofers, Tile & Slate	18.95	151.60	18.2		11.0		53.0	10.05	29.00	232.00
Rohe	Roofer Helpers (Composition)	13.75	110.00	18.2		11.0		53.0	7.30	21.05	168.40
Shee	Sheet Metal Workers	22.70	181.60	6.3		16.0		46.1	10.45	33.15	265.20
Spri	Sprinkler Installers	23.25	186.00	5.5		16.0		45.3	10.55	33.80	270.40
Stpi	Steamfitters or Pipefitters	22.75	182.00	4.8		16.0		44.6	10.15	32.90	263.20
Ston	Stone Masons	20.30	162.40	7.6		11.0		42.4	8.60	28.90	231.20
Sswk	Structural Steel Workers	21.70	173.60	19.3		14.0		57.1	12.40	34.10	272.80
Tilf	Tile Layers (Floor)	19.75	158.00	5.4		11.0		40.2	7.95	27.70	221.60
Tilh	Tile Layer Helpers	15.60	124.80	5.4		11.0		40.2	6.30	21.90	175.20
Trlt	Truck Drivers, Light	16.35	130.80	8.6		11.0		43.4	7.10	23.45	187.60
Trhv	Truck Drivers, Heavy	16.60	132.80	8.6		11.0		43.4	7.20	23.80	190.40
Sswl	Welders, Structural Steel	21.70	173.60	19.3		14.0		57.1	12.40	34.10	272.80
Wrck	*Wrecking	15.90	127.20	20.7	▼	11.0	▼	55.5	8.80	24.70	197.60

*Not included in Averages.

Figure 8.89

232

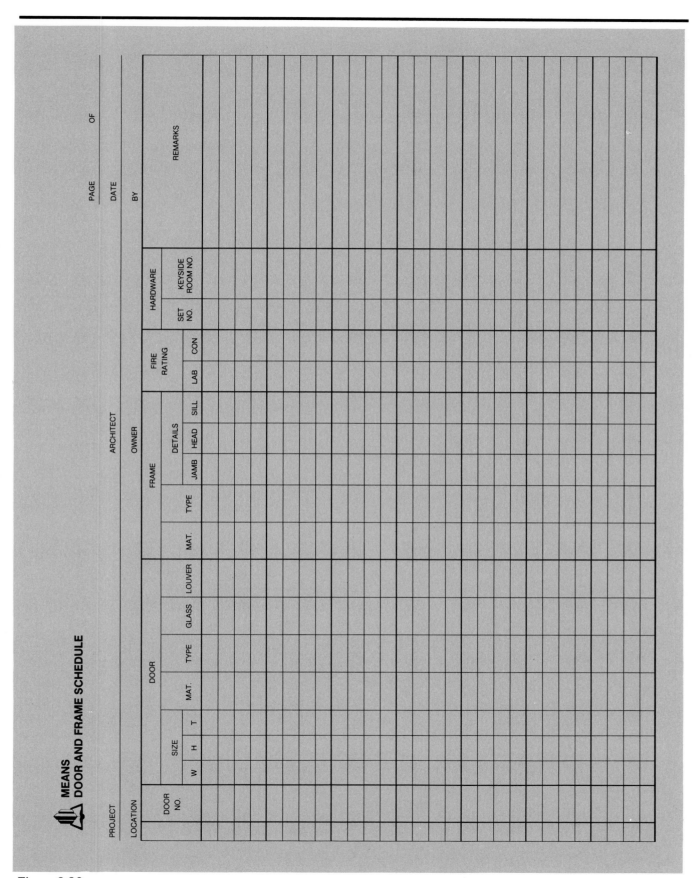

Figure 8.90

233

Entrances and Storefronts

Entrances and storefronts are almost all special designs and combinations of unit items to fit a unique situation. The estimator should submit the plans and specifications to a specialty installer for takeoff and pricing.

	Fire Door		
Classification	**Time Rating (as Shown on Label)**	**Temperature Rise (as Shown on Label)**	**Maximum Glass Area**
3 Hour fire doors (A) are for use in openings in walls separating buildings or dividing a single building into the areas.	3 Hr. (A) 3 Hr. (A) 3 Hr. (A) 3 Hr. (A)	30 Min. 250°F Max 30 Min. 450°F Max 30 Min. 650°F Max *	None
1-1/2 Hour fire doors (B) and (D) are for use in openings in 2 Hour enclosures of vertical communication through buildings (stairs, elevators, etc.) or in exterior walls which are subject to severe fire exposure from outside of the building. 1 Hour fire doors (B) are for use in openings in 1 Hour enclosures of vertical communication through buildings (stairs, elevators, etc.)	1-1/2 Hr. (B) 1-1/2 Hr. (B) 1-1/2 Hr. (B) 1-1/2 Hr. (B) 1 Hr. 1-1/2 Hr. (D) 1-1/2 Hr. (D) 1-1/2 Hr. (D) 1-1/2 Hr. (D)	30 Min. 250°F Max 30 Min. 450°F Max 30 Min. 650°F Max * 30 Min. 250°F Max 30 Min. 250°F Max 30 Min. 450°F Max 30 Min. 650°F Max *	100 square inches per door None
3/4 Hour fire doors (C) and (E) are for use in openings in corridor and room partitions or in exterior walls which are subject to moderate fire exposure from outside of the building.	3/4 Hr. (C) 3/4 Hr. (E)	** **	1296 Square 720 square inches per light
1/2 Hour fire doors and 1/3 Hour fire doors are for use where smoke controls is a primary consideration and are for the protection of openings in partitions between a habitable room and a corridor when the wall has a fire-resistance rating of not more than one hour.	1/2 Hr. 1/3 Hr.	** **	No limit

*The labels do not record any temperature rise limits. This means that the temperature rise on the unexposed face of the door at the end of 30 minutes of test is in excess of 650°F.
**Temperature rise is not recorded.

Figure 8.91

The general procedure for the installer's takeoff is:

For stationary units:

- Determine height and width of each like unit.
- Determine linear feet of intermediate, horizontal, and vertical members, rounded to next higher foot.
- Determine number of joints.

For entrance units:

- Determine number of joints.
- Determine special frame hardware per unit.
- Determine special door hardware per unit.
- Determine thresholds and closers.

Windows

As with doors, a window schedule should be included in the architectural drawings. Items that merit special attention are:

- Material
- Gauge/Thickness
- Screens
- Glazing (type of glass and setting specifications)
- Trim
- Hardware
- Special installation requirements

When using pre-hung units, be sure to add interior trim and stools.

Finish Hardware and Specialties

The estimator should list the hardware separately or on the door and window schedule. Remember that most pre-hung doors and windows do not include locksets. Some casement, awning, and jalousie windows include cranks and locks.

Be sure to check the specifications for:

- Base Metal
- Finish
- Service (Heavy, Light, Medium)
- Any other special detail

Also check the specifications and code for both handicap and exit requirements. Metal thresholds and astragals are also included in this division. Weatherstripping may or may not be included with pre-hung doors and windows.

Glass and Glazing

Glazing quantities are a function of the material, method, and length to be glazed. Therefore, quantities are measured in united inches or united feet (length + width). Many installers, however, figure all glass and glazing by the square foot. Be sure to read the specifications carefully, as there are many different grades, thicknesses, and other variables in glass.

The types of glass include tempered, plate, safety, insulated, tinted, and various combinations of the above.

Sample Estimate: Division 8

There are two basic ways that doors may be shown on a schedule. The first is to list each type of door (usually accompanied by elevations) that have common characteristics. An example of this method is shown for the sample project in Figure 8.92. Quantities of each type are not shown. The second method is to list each door individually by door number. An example of this method (for another project) is shown in Figure 8.93. In both cases, the information on the schedules provides parameters for takeoff. The specifications will provide much more detailed information that will be required before pricing.

The estimate sheets for Division 8 are shown in Figures 8.94 to 8.97. Note on Sheet 2 of the estimate (Figure 8.95) that costs for hinges are for material only. Labor costs for hinges are usually included in the installation costs for doors. To a carpenter, hanging a door and installing the hinges is one operation. The costs in *Building Construction Cost Data* are listed accordingly.

In Figure 8.98 a percentage is to be added to the aluminum entrances for black anodized finish. This percentage is applied to *bare* material cost. Subsequently, 10% for handling is added: Bare Material Cost: $14.50/SF

8.4-40-100

For black finish: add	20%	$2.90
8.4-40-160		
O & P (material handling): add	10%	.29
Total incl. O & P for black finish		$3.19/SF

Window/curtain walls are almost always custom fabricated for each project. Relatively few manufacturers supply and install these highly specialized systems, so architects will often design curtain walls based on the specifications of a particular system. These reasons dictate that a firm subcontractor quotation is required for estimating curtain walls. For budget purposes, historical costs or those in *Building Construction Cost Data* may be used. The telephone quotation (which would be followed by a detailed written quotation) for the sample project is shown in Figure 8.99.

Door and Frame Schedule								
	Door			Frame			Hardware Set	Remarks
	Size	Type	Rating	Type	Throat	Rating		
A	6⁰ x 7⁰	Alum.	—	Alum.	—	—	—	Double Door w/ 2⁰ x 6⁰ Transom
B	3⁰ x 7⁰	H.M. 18 ga.	—	H.M. 16 ga.	8"	—	4-1	Insulated
C	3⁰ x 7⁰	H.M. 18 ga.	"B" 1-1/2 hr.	H.M. 16 ga.	8"	"B" 1-1/2 hr.	4-1	10" x 10" Lites
D	3⁰ x 7⁰	Oak Veneer	"B" 1-1/2 hr.	H.M. 16 ga.	4-3/4"	"B" 1-1/2 hr.	4-2	10" x 10" Lites
E	3⁰ x 7⁰	Oak Veneer	"B" 1 hr.	H.M. 16 ga.	4-3/4"	"B" 1 hr.	4-3	
F	3⁰ x 7⁰	Oak Veneer	"B" 1 hr.	H.M. 16 ga.	4-3/4"	"B" 1 hr.	4-4	
G	3⁰ x 7⁰	H.M. 18 ga.	"B" 1 hr.	H.M. 16 ga.	8"	"B" 1 hr.	4-5	
H	6⁰ x 7⁰	H.M. 18 ga.	"B" 1 hr.	H.M. 16 ga.	8"	"B" 1 hr.	4-6	Double Door

Figure 8.92

Door Schedule								
Door	Size	Type	Rating	Frame	Depth	Rating	Hardware Set	Remarks
B01	3⁰ x 6⁸	Flush Steel 18 ga.	"B" 1-1/2 Hr.	Exist'g.	—	—	HW-1	10" x 10" Vision Lite Shop-Primed
B02	3⁰ x 6⁸	Flush Steel 18 ga.	"B" 1 Hr.	HMKD 16 ga.	4-7/8"	"B" 1 Hr.	HW-2	Shop-Primed
B03	3⁰ x 6⁸	Flush Steel 18 ga.	"B" 1 Hr.	H.M. Welded 16 ga.	8"	"B" 1 Hr.	HW-3	w/Masonry Anchors Shop-Primed
B04	3⁰ x 6⁸	Flush Steel 18 ga.	"B" 1-1/2 Hr.	H.M. Welded 16 ga.	8"	"B" 1-1/2 Hr.	HW-3	w/Masonry Anchors Shop-Primed
B05	3⁰ x 6⁸	Flush Steel 18 ga.	"B" 1-1/2 Hr.	H.M. Welded 16 ga.	8"	"B" 1-1/2 Hr.	HW-3	w/Masonry Anchors Shop-Primed
B06	3⁰ x 6⁸	Flush Steel 18 ga.	"B" 1 Hr.	HMKD 16 ga.	4-7/8"	"B" 1 Hr.	HW-2	Shop-Primed
101	3⁰ x 6⁸	Flush Steel 18 ga.	—	HMKD 16 ga.	4-7/8"	—	HW-4	Transom Frame Above w/Masonry Anchors
102	3⁰ x 6⁸	Flush Steel 18 ga.	"B" 1-1/2 Hr.	Exist'g.	—	—	HW-1	Shop-Primed
103	3⁰ x 6⁸	Flush Oak Face	"B" 1 Hr.	HMKD 16 ga.	4-7/8"	"B" 1 Hr.	HW-5	
104	2⁰ x 6⁸	Flush Oak Face SC	—	HMKD 16 ga.	4-5/8"	—	HW-6	
105	3⁰ x 6⁸	Flush Oak Face	"B" 1 Hr.	HMKD 16 ga.	4-7/8"	"B" 1 Hr.	HW-5	

Figure 8.93

MEANS CONSOLIDATED ESTIMATE

Division 8

SHEET NO. 1 of 4

PROJECT Office Building | CLASSIFICATION | ESTIMATE NO. 86-1

LOCATION | ARCHITECT | DATE 1986

TAKE OFF BY EBW | QUANTITIES BY EBW | PRICES BY RSM | EXTENSIONS BY SLM | CHECKED JDM

DESCRIPTION	SOURCE/DIMENSIONS			QUANTITY	UNIT	MATERIAL UNIT COST	MATERIAL TOTAL	LABOR UNIT COST	LABOR TOTAL	EQUIPMENT UNIT COST	EQUIPMENT TOTAL	SUBCONTRACT UNIT COST	SUBCONTRACT TOTAL
Division 8: Doors, Windows & Glass													
H.M.													
Frames 16 ga. 3°x7°													
8"	8.1	10	440	2	Ea.	84	168	22	44				
8" "B"	8.1	10	620	10	Ea.	87	870	22	220				
4¾" "B"	8.1	10	540	21	Ea.	76	1596	22	462				
6°x7°													
8" "B"	8.1	10	624	1	Ea.	105	105	28	28				
Metal Doors 18 ga.													
3°x7°	8.1	21	116	2	Ea.	160	320	21	42				
3°x7° "B"	8.1	23	018	12	Ea.	200	2400	21	252				
10"x10" Lites	8.1	23	024	12	Ea.	75	900						
Wood Doors Flush Oak													
3°x7° "B" 1½ Hr.	8.2	23	089	9	Ea.	155	1395	28	252				
3°x7° "B" 1 Hr.	8.2	23	019	12	Ea.	140	1680	28	336				
Sub Totals							9434		1636				

Figure 8.94

MEANS CONSOLIDATED ESTIMATE

PROJECT Office Building

LOCATION

TAKE OFF BY EBW   QUANTITIES BY EBW   PRICES BY RSM   EXTENSIONS BY SLM

CLASSIFICATION

ARCHITECT

DESCRIPTION	SOURCE/DIMENSIONS		QUANTITY	UNIT	MATERIAL		LABOR		EQUIPMENT		SUBCONTRACT	
					UNIT COST	TOTAL	UNIT COST	TOTAL	UNIT COST	TOTAL	UNIT COST	TOTAL
Division 8: (Cont'd)												
Hardware												
Locksets	8.7	40 140	8	Ea.	115	920	16	128				
Panic Hardware	8.7	45 002	17	Ea.	245	4165	32	544				
Closers	8.7	15 240	35	Ea.	54	1890	27	945				
Push/Pull	8.7	50 001	9	Ea.	30	270	13.35	120				
Kickplates	8.7	35 001	9	Ea.	12.75	115	10.65	96				
Hinges	8.7	33 140	52.5	Pr.	71	3727						
Sub Totals						(11087)		(1833)				

Figure 8.95

240

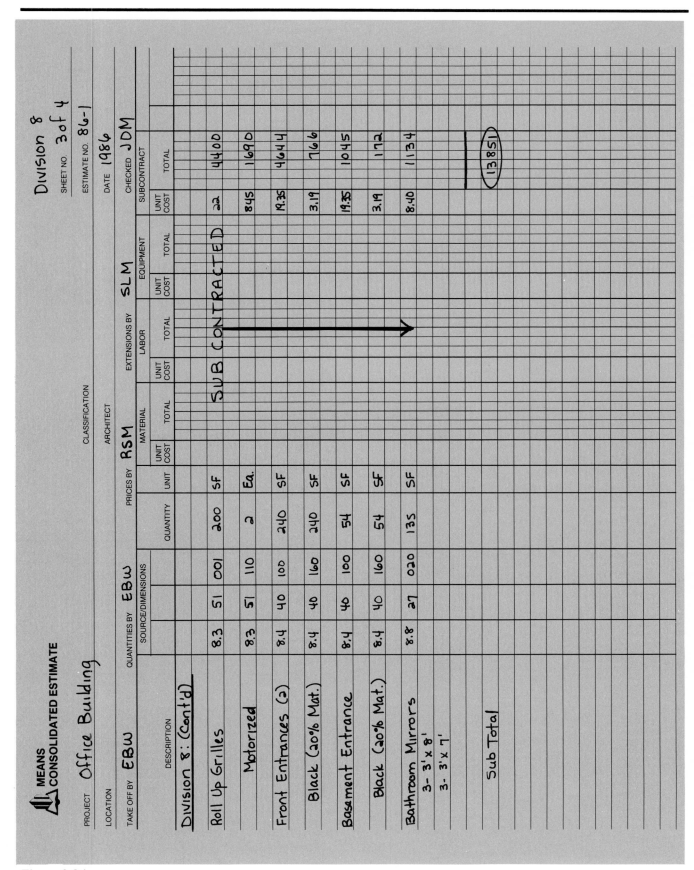

MEANS
CONSOLIDATED ESTIMATE

PROJECT Office Building

LOCATION

TAKE OFF BY EBW   QUANTITIES BY EBW   PRICES BY RSM   EXTENSIONS BY SLM   CLASSIFICATION   ARCHITECT

DESCRIPTION	SOURCE/DIMENSIONS			QUANTITY	UNIT	MATERIAL UNIT COST	MATERIAL TOTAL	LABOR UNIT COST	LABOR TOTAL	EQUIPMENT UNIT COST	EQUIPMENT TOTAL	SUBCONTRACT UNIT COST	SUBCONTRACT TOTAL
Division 8: (Cont'd)													
Roll Up Grilles	8.3	51	001	200	SF							22	4400
Motorized	8.3	51	110	2	Ea.		SUB CONTRACTED					845	1690
Front Entrances (2)	8.4	40	100	240	SF							19.35	4644
Black (20% Mat.)	8.4	40	160	240	SF							3.19	766
Basement Entrance	8.4	40	100	54	SF							19.35	1045
Black (20% Mat.)	8.4	40	160	54	SF							3.19	172
Bathroom Mirrors	8.8	27	020	135	SF							8.40	1134
3- 3' x 8'													
3- 3' x 7'													
Sub Total													(13851)

Figure 8.96

241

MEANS CONSOLIDATED ESTIMATE

Division 8
SHEET NO. 4 of 4

PROJECT Office Building — CLASSIFICATION — ESTIMATE NO. 86-1

LOCATION — ARCHITECT — DATE 1986

TAKE OFF BY EBW — QUANTITIES BY EBW — PRICES BY RSM — EXTENSIONS BY SLM — CHECKED JDM

DESCRIPTION	SOURCE/DIMENSIONS	QUANTITY	UNIT	MATERIAL UNIT COST	MATERIAL TOTAL	LABOR UNIT COST	LABOR TOTAL	EQUIPMENT UNIT COST	EQUIPMENT TOTAL	SUBCONTRACT UNIT COST	SUBCONTRACT TOTAL
Division 8: (Cont'd)											
Window/Curtain Wall	Telephone Quote	25,060	SF								982038
Sheet 1: Doors & Frames					9434		1636				
Sheet 2: Hardware					11087		1833				
Sheet 3: Grilles & Glazing											13851
Sheet 4: Curtain Wall											982038
Division 8 Totals					20521		3469				995889

Figure 8.97

8.3	Special Doors	CREW	DAILY OUTPUT	UNIT	BARE COSTS			TOTAL INCL O&P
					MAT.	INST.	TOTAL	
080	Day gate, painted, wire mesh, 32" wide	2 Sswk	1.50	Ea.	900	230	1,130	1,350
085	40" wide		1.40		1,100	250	1,350	1,600
090	Aluminum, 32" wide		1.50		1,325	230	1,555	1,825
095	40" wide	↓	1.40	↓	1,550	250	1,800	2,100
205	Security vault door, 3-1/2" thick, class 5R, minimum		.40	Opng.	15,500	870	16,370	18,400
210	Maximum		.30		24,000	1,150	25,150	28,200
215	7" thick, class 9R, minimum		.40		21,500	870	22,370	25,000
220	Maximum	↓	.30	↓	31,000	1,150	32,150	35,900
225	For Western states, add				5%			
230								
78-001	VERTICAL LIFT Doors, motor operator, incl. frame, 16' x 16' high	E-3	.50	Ea.	11,500	1,275	12,775	14,600
010	32' x 24' high	E-2	.75	"	21,200	2,650	23,850	26,900

8.4	Entrances & Storefronts	CREW	DAILY OUTPUT	UNIT	BARE COSTS			TOTAL INCL O&P
					MAT.	INST.	TOTAL	
05-001	ALUMINUM & GLASS DOORS See division 8.1-40							
10-001	BALANCED DOORS Incl. hdwre & frame, alum. & glass, 3' x 7', economy	2 Sswk	.90	Ea.	2,225	385	2,610	3,050
015	Premium		.70		3,750	495	4,245	4,900
050	Stainless steel and glass, 3' x 7', economy		.90		3,525	385	3,910	4,475
060	Premium	↓	.70	↓	6,000	495	6,495	7,375
20-001	REVOLVING DOORS 6'-6" to 7'-0" diameter							
002	6'-10" to 7' high, stock units, minimum	4 Sswk	.75	Opng.	15,000	925	15,925	18,000
005	Average		.60		19,000	1,150	20,150	22,700
010	Maximum		.45		23,000	1,550	24,550	27,700
100	Stainless steel		.30		28,000	2,325	30,325	34,400
110	Solid bronze	↓	.15		35,000	4,625	39,625	45,800
150	For automatic controls, add	2 Elec	2	↓	3,000	180	3,180	3,550
25-001	SLIDING ENTRANCE 12' x 7'-6" opening, 5' x 7' door, two way traffic,							
002	mat activated, panic pushout, incl. operator & hardware,							
003	not incl. glass or glazing	2 Glaz	.70	Opng.	7,000	460	7,460	8,350
30-001	SLIDING PANEL Mall fronts, aluminum & glass, 15' x 9' high	2 Glaz	1.30	Opng.	1,700	250	1,950	2,225
010	24' x 9' high		.70		2,700	460	3,160	3,625
020	48' x 9' high, with fixed panels	↓	.90		5,200	360	5,560	6,225
050	For bronze finish, add			↓	15%			
35-001	STAINLESS STEEL and glass entrance unit, narrow stiles							
002	3' x 7' opening, including hardware, minimum	2 Sswk	1.60	Opng.	1,350	215	1,565	1,825
005	Average		1.40		2,500	250	2,750	3,150
010	Maximum	↓	1.20		3,450	290	3,740	4,250
100	For solid bronze entrance units, statuary finish, add				60%			
110	Without statuary finish, add			↓	45%			
40-001	STOREFRONT SYSTEMS Aluminum frame, clear 3/8" plate glass,							
002	incl. 3' x 7' door with hardware (400 sq. ft. max. wall)							
050	Wall height to 12' high, commercial grade	2 Glaz	150	S.F.	11.55	2.15	13.70	15.75
060	Institutional grade		130		13.50	2.48	15.98	18.40
070	Monumental grade	↓	115	↓	18.20	2.80	21	24
090								
100	6' x 7' door with hardware, commercial grade	2 Glaz	135	S.F.	14.50	2.39	16.89	19.35
110	Institutional grade		115		17.50	2.80	20.30	23
120	Monumental grade	↓	100		24	3.22	27.22	31
150	For bronze anodized finish, add				15%			
160	For black anodized finish, add			↓	20%			
170	For stainless steel framing, add to monumental			↓	75%			

Figure 8.98

MEANS TELEPHONE QUOTATION

PROJECT Office Building	DATE 1986
FIRM QUOTING	TIME
ADDRESS	PHONE ( )
ITEM QUOTED	BY
	RECEIVED BY EBW

WORK INCLUDED	AMOUNT OF QUOTATION
Window / Curtain Wall	939750
25,060 S.F. @ 37.50	
Tax	42288

DELIVERY TIME 18 weeks	TOTAL BID	982038

DOES QUOTATION INCLUDE THE FOLLOWING: If ☐ NO is checked, determine the following:

STATE & LOCAL SALES TAXES	☒ YES	☐ NO	MATERIAL VALUE
DELIVERY TO THE JOB SITE	☒ YES	☐ NO	WEIGHT
COMPLETE INSTALLATION	☒ YES	☐ NO	QUANTITY
COMPLETE SECTION AS PER PLANS & SPECIFICATIONS	☒ YES	☐ NO	DESCRIBE BELOW

EXCLUSIONS AND QUALIFICATIONS

ADDENDA ACKNOWLEDGEMENT	TOTAL ADJUSTMENTS	
	ADJUSTED TOTAL BID	

ALTERNATES

ALTERNATE NO. 1 — Custom color	58700
ALTERNATE NO. 2 — Grid texture	102350
ALTERNATE NO.	
ALTERNATE NO.	
ALTERNATE NO.	
ALTERNATE NO.	
ALTERNATE NO.	
ALTERNATE NO.	

Figure 8.99

Division 9: Finishes

Many buildings today are built "on spec" or speculatively, before they are partially or fully tenanted. In this case, interior work (primarily finishes, and electrical and mechanical distribution) is not usually completed until a tenant is secured. "Interior contractors" are becoming more prevalent in the industry. This type of firm may perform or subcontract all work in Division 9, and may or may not be a builder of structures from the ground up — a conventional general contractor. Because of the skills involved and the quality required, subcontractors usually specialize in only one type of finish. Hence, most finish work is subcontracted.

In today's fireproof and fire resistant types of construction, some finish materials may be the only combustibles used in a building project. Most building codes (and specifications) require strict adherence to maximum fire, flame spread, and smoke generation characteristics. The estimator must be sure that all materials meet the specified requirements. Materials may have to be treated for fire retardancy, at an additional cost.

Lathing and Plastering

The different types of plaster work require varied pricing strategies. Large open areas of continuous walls or ceilings will require considerably less labor per unit of area than small areas or intricate work, such as archways, curved walls, cornices and at window returns. Gypsum and metal lath are most often used as subbases, however plaster may be applied directly on masonry, concrete, and, in some restoration work, wood. In the latter cases, a bonding agent may be specified.

The number of coats of plaster may also vary. Traditionally, a scratch coat is applied to the substrate. A brown coat is then applied two days later, and the finish, smooth coat seven days after the brown coat. Currently, the systems most often used are two-coat and one-coat (imperial plaster on "blueboard"). Textured surfaces, with and without patterns, may be required. All of these variables in plaster work make it difficult to develop "system" prices. Each project, and even areas within each project, must be examined individually.

The quantity takeoff should proceed in the normal construction sequence — furring (or studs), lath, plaster and accessories. Studs, furring and/or ceiling suspension systems, whether wood or steel, should be taken off separately. Responsibility for the installation of these items should be made clear. Depending upon local work practices, lathers may or may not install studs or furring. These materials are usually estimated by the piece or linear foot, and sometimes by the square foot. Lath is traditionally estimated by the square yard for both gypsum and metal lath and is done more recently by the square foot. Usually, a 5% allowance for waste is included. Casing bead, corner bead, and other accessories are measured by the linear foot. An extra foot of surface area should be allowed for each linear foot of corner or stop. Although wood plaster grounds are usually installed by carpenters, they should be measured when taking off the plaster requirements.

Plastering is also traditionally measured by the square yard. Deductions for openings vary by preference — from zero deduction to 50% of all openings over 2 feet in width. Some estimators deduct a percentage of the total yardage for openings. The estimator should allow one extra square foot of wall area for each linear foot of inside or outside corner located below the ceiling level. Also, double the areas of small radius work. Quantities are determined by measuring surface areas (walls, ceilings). The estimator must consider both the complexity and the intricacy of the work, and in pricing plaster work, should also consider quality. Basically, there are two quality categories:

1. Ordinary — for commercial purposes, and with waves 1/8" to 3/16" in 10 feet, angles and corners fairly true.
2. First quality with variations less than 1/16" in 10 feet. Labor costs for first quality work are approximately 20% more than that for ordinary plastering.

Drywall

With the advent of light gauge metal framing, tin snips are as important to the carpenter as the circular saw. Metal studs and framing are usually installed and included by the drywall subcontractor. The estimator should make sure that studs (and other framing — whether metal or wood) are not included twice by different subcontractors. In some drywall systems, such as shaftwall, the framing is integral and installed simultaneously with the drywall panels.

Metal studs are manufactured in various widths (1-5/8", 2-1/2", 3-5/8", 4" and 6") and in various gauges, or metal thicknesses. They may be used for both load-bearing and non-load-bearing partitions, depending on design criteria and code requirements. Metal framing is particularly useful due to the prohibitive use of structural wood (combustible) materials in new building construction. Metal studs, track and accessories are purchased by the linear foot, and usually stocked in 8' to 16' lengths, by 2' increments. For large orders, metal studs can be purchased in any length up to 20'.

For estimating, light gauge metal framing is taken off by the linear foot or by the square foot of wall area of each type. Different wall types — with different stud widths, stud spacing, or dry wall requirements — should each be taken off separately, especially if estimating by the square foot.

Metal studs can be installed very quickly. Depending upon the specification, metal studs may have to be fastened to the track with self-tapping screws, tack welds or clips, or may not have to be prefastened. Each condition will affect the labor costs. Fasteners, such as screws, clips and powder-actuated studs are very expensive, though labor-saving. These costs must be included.

Drywall may be purchased in various thicknesses — 1/4" to 1" — and in various sizes — 2' x 8' to 4' x 20'. Different types include standard, fire resistant, water resistant, blueboard, coreboard and pre-finished. There are many variables and possible combinations of sizes and types. While the installation cost of 5/8" standard drywall may be the same as that of 5/8" fire resistant drywall, the two types (and all other types) should be taken off separately. The takeoff will be used for purchasing and material costs will vary.

Because drywall is used in such large quantities, current, local prices should always be checked. A variation of a few cents per square foot can become many thousands of dollars over a whole project.

Fire resistant drywall provides an excellent design advantage in creating relatively lightweight, easy to install firewalls (as opposed to masonry walls). As with any type of drywall partition, the variations are numerous. The estimator must be very careful to take off the appropriate firewalls exactly as specified. (Even more important, the contractor must *build* the firewalls exactly as specified. Liabilities can be great.) For example, a metal stud partition with two layers of 1/2" fire resistant drywall on each side may constitute a two-hour partition (when all other requirements such as staggered joints, taping, sealing openings, etc. are met). If a one-hour partition is called for, the estimator cannot assume that one layer of 1/2" fire resistant drywall on each side of a metal stud partition will suffice. Alone, it does not. When left to choose the appropriate assembly (given the rating required), the estimator must be sure that the system has been tested and *approved* for use — by Underwriters Laboratory as well as local building and fire codes and responsible authorities. In all cases, the drywall (and studs) for firewalls must extend completely from the deck below to the underside of the deck above, covering the area above and around any and all obstructions. All penetrations must be protected.

In the past, structural members — such as beams or columns — to be fireproofed had to be "wrapped" with a specified number of layers of fire resistant dry wall — a very labor intensive and expensive task. With the advent of spray-on fireproofing, structural members can be much more easily protected. This type of work is usually performed by a specialty subcontractor. Takeoff and pricing are done by square foot of surface area.

When walls are specified for minimal sound transfer, the same continuous, unbroken construction is required. Sound proofing specifications may include additional accessories and related work. Resilient channels attached to studs, mineral fiber batts and staggered studs may all be used. In order to develop high noise reduction coefficients, double stud walls may be required with sheet lead between double or triple layers of drywall. (Sheet lead may also be required at X-ray installations.) Caulking is required at all joints and seams. All openings must be specially framed with double, "broken" door and window jambs.

Shaftwall, developed for a distinct design advantage, is another drywall assembly which should be estimated separately. Firewalls require protection from both sides of the partition, and hence drywall installation from both sides. Shaftwall, used at vertical openings (elevators, utility chases) can be installed completely from one side. Special track, studs (C-H or double E type) and drywall (usually 1" thick and 2' wide coreboard) are used and should be priced separately from other drywall partition components.

Because of the size and weight of drywall, costs for material handling and loading should be included. Using larger sheets (manufactured up to 4' x 20') may require less taping and finishing, but these sheets may each weigh well in excess of 100 pounds and are awkward to handle. The weight of drywall must also be considered (and distributed) when loading a job on elevated slabs, so that allowable floor loads are not exceeded. All material handling involves costs that must be included.

As with plaster work, open spans of drywall should be priced differently from small, intricate areas that require much cutting and piecing. Similarly, areas with many corners or curves will require higher finishing costs than open walls or ceilings. Corners, both inside and outside, should be estimated by the linear foot, in addition to the square feet of surface area.

Although difficult because of variations, the estimator may be able to develop historical systems or assemblies prices for metal studs, drywall, taping and finishing. When using systems, whether complete or partial, the estimator must be sure that the system, as specified, is exactly the same as the system for which the costs are developed. For example, a cost is developed for 5/8" fire resistant drywall, taped and finished. The project specifications require a firewall with two layers of the 5/8" drywall on each side of the studs. It could be easy to use the "system" cost for each layer, when only one of the two layers is to be taped and finished. The more detailed the breakdown and delineation, the less chance for error.

Tile and Terrazzo

Tile, terrazzo and other hard surface floor and wall finishes are most often estimated by the square foot. Linear features such as bullnose and cove base are taken off in linear feet. Small areas and individually laid tile patterns should be separately estimated, apart from large, open expanses, and installations of pre-attached tile sheets which are taken off by the square foot.

In addition to the considerable variation in material prices, the installation method of tile will also have a significant impact on the total cost. Two basic methods are used — "thin" set, with an epoxy-type adhesive, and "mud" set, using a fine-grained mortar. Mud set is approximately 30% more expensive than thin set, but provides a harder and more durable treatment. Hard, cement-like backer board can be used as a base for thin set tile. The more commonly used types of ceramic wall tile are now manufactured in pre-grouted sheets which require less labor expense.

Currently, most terrazzo installed is in the form of manufactured tiles. However, the traditional method of pouring, grinding and rubbing the terrazzo over a concrete base slab is still used. In such cases, an experienced subcontractor should estimate this very labor intensive work. Accessories, such as embedded decorative strips and grounds must be included.

In all tile work, surface preparation may be the responsibility of the installer. Especially in renovation, this preparation may be very involved and costly.

Acoustical Treatment

Acoustical treatments may involve sound absorbing panels on walls, sheet lead within walls or floors, suspended or "dropped" ceilings, or sound attenuation blankets in wall cavities. While sound deadening is primary, it does not have to be the only function.

Most applications of acoustical treatments are for ceilings, whether suspended or attached to the structure above, or concealed spline or lay-in. In most cases, acoustical ceilings are estimated by the square foot. Suspension systems or furring can be estimated by linear feet of pieces or by square feet of surface area. The installation and leveling of suspension grids can be very labor intensive. The estimator must be sure that adequate points of support are available, spaced often enough to meet specified requirements. If not, attachments for support — such as anchors, toggle bolts, and carrier channels — will be required and the costs included. Invariably, a duct or other obstruction runs just above a main support "T", or runner. Design modification of the grid (or duct) system may be necessary, and the architect should be notified.

In small areas and rooms, leveling a suspension grid may be relatively easy. In large open areas, a laser may be necessary for leveling. Especially for large open areas, the cost of installing a ceiling (whether acoustical or drywall) will depend on how clear and clean the floor space is. Most ceilings are installed from rolling platforms. If the workers are only able to work in certain areas, or if the platform must be hand lifted over material and debris, installation costs will increase significantly. When developing the preliminary schedule, good planning will help to assure minimum installation costs for ceilings. Costs for equipment, such as lasers and rolling scaffolding, should be listed separately. For very high installations, scissors or telescoping lifts may be required.

Tile for acoustical ceilings may consist of mineral fiber, wood fiber, fiberglass or metal, and might be cloth covered, colored, textured and/or patterned. There is little waste when installing grid systems (usually less than 5%), because pieces can be butted and joined. Waste for tile, however, can be as low as 5% for large open areas, to as high as 30%-40% for small areas and rooms. Waste for tile may depend on grid layout as well as room dimensions. Figure 8.100 demonstrates that for the same size room, the layout of a typical 2' x 4' grid has a significant effect on generated waste of ceiling tile. Since most textures and patterns on ceiling tile are aligned in one direction, pieces cannot be turned 90 degrees (to the specified alignment) to try to reduce waste.

Certain tile types, such as tegular (recessed) require extra labor for cutting and fabrication at edge moldings. Soffits, facias and "boxouts" should be estimated separately due to extra labor, material waste and special attachment techniques. Costs should also be added for unusually high numbers of tiles to be specially cut for items such as sprinkler heads, diffusers or telepoles.

While the weight of ceiling tile is not the primary consideration, that it is with drywall, some material handling and storage costs will still be incurred and must be included. Acoustical tile is very bulky and cumbersome, as well as fragile; and must be protected from damage before installation.

Flooring

Finish floor coverings include carpet, resilient sheet goods and tile, rubber and vinyl stair treads and risers, and wood finish flooring. When estimating all types of finish flooring, the condition and required preparation of the subfloor must be considered.

Resilient Flooring: Resilient materials are vinyl, rubber and linoleum products in the form of tiles, sheet goods and base. The most commonly used is vinyl composition tile — mistakenly referred to as vinyl asbestos tile. Resilient flooring is taken off and priced by the square foot. Most resilient flooring is directionally patterned. The construction documents will most likely specify a particular laying pattern. Because of the size of resilient tiles (12" x 12" or 9" x 9"), waste is not necessarily dependent upon room configuration. However, depending upon seam requirements, sheet goods may involve a great deal of waste. Each application should be viewed individually. Cove base and straight base are measured by the linear foot. If the specifications are not clear, the estimator must determine whether the base is to be wrapped around corners, or if premolded corners are required.

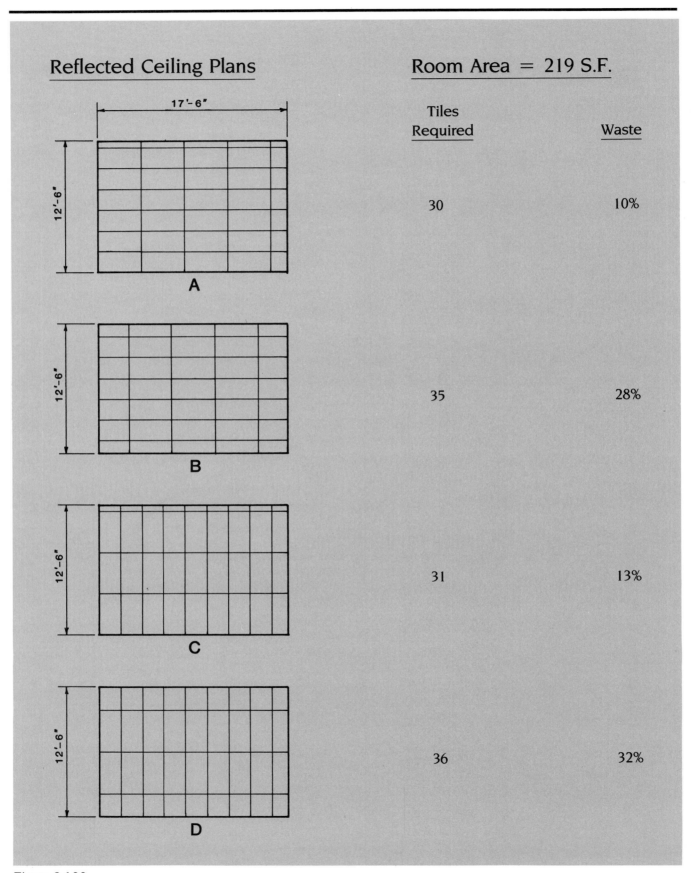

Figure 8.100

250

Due to the thinness and flexibility of resilient goods, defects in the subfloor easily "telegraph" through the material. Consequently, the subfloor material and the quality of surface preparation are very important. Subcontractors will often make contracts conditional on a smooth, level subfloor. Surface preparation, which can involve chipping and patching, grinding or washing, is often an "extra". Costs should be included to account for some surface preparation which will invariably be required. This is especially true in renovation where, in extreme cases, the floor may have to be leveled with a complete application of special lightweight leveling concrete.

Carpet: There are hundreds of carpeting manufacturers, each with hundreds of products. The specifications for a project will usually include a generic description of the carpeting and a recommended manufacturer. The description will include items such as pile type and weight, backing requirements and smoke and flame characteristics. Usually this description is so generically specific that, even if an approved equal is allowed, no such equal exists. It is best to estimate the carpeting exactly as specified.

Carpeting and padding is manufactured most commonly in 12´ widths (sometimes 9´ or 15´), and is taken off by the square yard. Costs for installation will vary depending upon the specified method — direct cement (without pad) or stretched (with pad and perimeter tack strips).

The specifications may also require and define the location of seams. Often, butt seams — roll end to roll end — are not allowed. Where seams do occur, costs for sewing (by hand) and gluing will differ. When a carpeting subcontractor estimates a job, the whole job is drawn on a floor plan based upon the seaming requirements to determine the quantity of carpet to be purchased. Depending upon the requirements and the configuration of the installation, waste can be high.

Where carpet base is specified, costs must be included for binding, priced by the linear foot. Carpet base may or may not be the same material used on the floor. The specifications should be carefully checked. Carpet tile systems have been developed for ease of repairing damaged areas and for use with under-carpet power and telecommunication systems. Tiles are available in various sizes from 18" to 36" square and are normally taken off and priced by the square foot.

All resilient materials and direct cement carpeting are installed with adhesive. If adhesive materials are estimated separately, costs are per gallon. Coverage depends upon the flooring material and the type of adhesive. Prices developed or quoted for direct glue-down flooring usually include the adhesive.

Wood flooring: Everyone loves to see a wood floor specified and installed, except for the estimator who has not included all requirements. Wood flooring can be deceptively expensive.

Wood flooring is available in strip, parquet, or block configuration. All types are estimated by the square foot. There are three basic grades of wood flooring: first, second, and third, plus combination grades of "second and better" and "third and better" There are also color grades and special grade labels for different kinds of lumber, such as oak, maple, walnut, pecan, or beech. The estimator should be acquainted with these classifications and the associated price differences. The laying pattern will influence both labor costs and material waste.

Strip wood floors may be used for applications from residences to gymnasiums and large sports complexes. While the wood may be the same, installation methods vary considerably. For residential work, the strips are nailed to wood joist/subfloor systems. For commercial applications, installation is usually over concrete. The strips may be nailed to wood sleepers or attached to steel channels with steel clips. In most cases, resilient materials, pads and/or sheets, are used between wood and concrete in addition to a continuous vapor barrier. Wood expands and contracts considerably with variations in temperature and humidity. Precautions must, therefore, be taken. Since expansion joints are not aesthetically pleasing within wood floors, gaps are used at the perimeter. Costs for hiding this gap, with a wood base or metal angles, must be included. Since large, commercial wood floors are usually installed by a specialty subcontractor, the estimator must be sure that all associated work is taken into account.

Parquet floors are currently made of prefinished, manufactured tiles, installed with adhesive. Durable synthetic finishes make this type of wood flooring suitable for commercial uses and public spaces.

Wood end grain block flooring is still commonly used for industrial applications. Set in, and filled with epoxy or asphalt, this type of flooring is installed by specialty subcontractors using specialized equipment. The estimator must check with all such subcontractors who are familiar with methods and materials, to ensure that all requirements are met, and the costs included.

For all types of finish flooring, surface treatments may be required after installation. For wood flooring (unless prefinished), sanding and finishing will be necessary. If the wood is prefinished, as with most resilient goods, waxing and buffing is an additional expense that must be included. Carpeting should be installed after *all* other work is completed. This is rarely the case, however, and invariably, the brand new carpet gets dirty quickly. A minimum of vacuuming and spot cleaning should be anticipated. In extreme cases, steam cleaning of the entire carpet may be necessary. Stretched carpet may require restretching after steam cleaning. The estimator must try to anticipate such items, all of which involve extra cost.

In many projects, and most often with flooring, the architect or designer may not select the final finish material until the project is underway. In such cases, a specified allowance is usually carried in the estimate. The allowance is most often for material *only*, and is specified per unit (square foot for resilient and wood flooring, square yard for carpet), but must be carried in the estimate as a lump sum. The estimator must still determine quantities of materials and installation costs.

Painting

As with most finishes, architects and designers will be particularly insistent about adherence to specifications and specified colors for painting. This is not an area in which to cut corners, in estimating, or performance of the work. The specifications usually will clearly define acceptable materials, manufacturers, preparation and application methods for *each* different type of surface to be painted. Samples may be required for approval by the architect or owner. Quarts of various paint colors may be required before the final color decision is made.

When estimating painting, the materials and methods are included in the specifications. Areas to be painted are usually defined on a Room Finish

Schedule and taken off from the plans and elevations in square feet of surface area. Odd shaped and special items can be converted to an equivalent wall area. The following table includes suggested conversion factors for various types of surfaces:

Balustrades:		1 Side x 4
Blinds:	Plain	Actual area x 2
	Slotted	Actual area x 4
Cabinets:	Including interior	Front area x 5
Downspouts and Gutters:		Actual area x 2
Drop Siding:		Actual area x 1.1
Cornices:	1 Story	Actual area x 2
	2 Story	Actual area x 3
	1 Story Ornamental	Actual area x 4
	2 Story Ornamental	Actual area x 6
Doors:	Flush	Actual area x 1.5
	Two Panel	Actual area x 1.75
	Four Panel	Actual area x 2.0
	Six Panel	Actual area x 2.25
Door Trim:		LF x 0.5
Fences:	Chain Link	1 side x 3 for both sides
	Picket	1 side x 4 for both sides
Gratings:		1 side x 0.66
Grilles:	Plain	1 side x 2.0
	Lattice	Actual area x 2.0
Moldings:	Under 12" Wide	1 SF/LF
Open Trusses:		Length x Depth x 2.5
Pipes:	Up to 4"	1 SF per LF
	4" to 8"	2 SF per LF
	8" to 12"	3 SF per LF
	12" to 16"	4 SF per LF
	Hangers Extra	
Radiators:		Face area x 7
Sanding and Puttying:	Quality Work	Actual area x 2
	Average Work	Actual area x 0.5%
	Industrial	Actual area x 0.25%
Shingle Siding:		Actual Area x 1.5
Stairs:		No. of risers x 8 widths
Tie Rods:		2 SF per LF
Wainscoting, Paneled:		Actual area x 2
Walls and Ceilings:		Length x Width no deducts for less than 100 SF
Window Sash:		1 LF of part = 1 SF

While the above factors are used to determine quantities of equivalent wall surface areas, the appropriate, specified application method must be used for pricing.

The choice of application method will have a significant effect on the final cost. Spraying is very fast, but the costs of masking the areas to be protected may offset the savings. Oversized rollers may be used to increase production. Brushwork, on the other hand, is labor intensive. The specifications often include (or restrict) certain application methods. Typical coverage and man-hour rates are shown in Figure 8.101 for different application methods.

Depending upon local work rules, some unions require that painters be paid higher rates for spraying, and even for roller work. In some cases, paint is applied to walls and surfaces with a brush and then rolled for the desired finish. Higher rates also tend to apply for structural steel painting, for high work and for the application of fire retardant paints. The estimator should determine which restrictions may be encountered.

The surface preparation of walls, as in the case of floor finishes, may represent a significant cost. Invariably, the painter claims that the walls were not finished properly, and the general contractor contends that a certain amount of wall prep is included in the painting subcontract. This conflict should be resolved at the estimate stage. Also, caulking at door frames and windows — the responsibility similarly argued — must be included.

Painting

Item	Coat	One Gallon Covers			In 8 Hrs. Man Covers			Man Hours per 100 S.F.		
		Brush	Roller	Spray	Brush	Roller	Spray	Brush	Roller	Spray
Paint wood siding	prime	275 S.F.	250 S.F.	325 S.F.	1150 S.F.	1400 S.F.	4000 S.F.	.695	.571	.200
	others	300	275	325	1600	2200	4000	.500	.364	.200
Paint exterior trim	prime	450	—	—	650	—	—	1.230	—	—
	1st	525	—	—	700	—	—	1.143	—	—
	2nd	575	—	—	750	—	—	1.067	—	—
Paint shingle siding	prime	300	285	335	1050	1700	2800	.763	.470	.286
	others	400	375	425	1200	2000	3200	.667	.400	.250
Stain shingle siding	1st	200	190	220	1200	1400	3200	.667	.571	.250
	2nd	300	275	325	1300	1700	4000	.615	.471	.200
Paint brick masonry	prime	200	150	175	850	1700	4000	.941	.471	.200
	1st	300	250	320	1200	2200	4400	.364	.364	.182
	2nd	375	340	400	1300	2400	4400	.615	.333	.182
Paint interior plaster or drywall	prime	450	425	550	1600	2500	4000	.500	.320	.200
	others	500	475	550	1400	3000	4000	.571	.267	.200
Paint interior doors and windows	prime	450	—	—	1300	—	—	.333	—	—
	1st	475	—	—	1150	—	—	.696	—	—
	2nd	500	—	—	1000	—	—	.800	—	—

Figure 8.101

Wallcovering

Wall coverings are usually estimated by the number of rolls. Single rolls contain approximately 36 S.F.; this figure forms the basis for determining the number of rolls required. Wall coverings are, however, usually sold in double or triple roll bolts.

The area to be covered is measured, length times height of wall above baseboards in order to get the square footage of each wall. This figure is divided by 30 to obtain the number of single rolls, allowing 6 S.F. of waste per roll. Deduct one roll for every two door openings. Two pounds of dry paste makes about three gallons of ready-to-use adhesive and hangs about 36 single rolls of light to medium weight paper, or 14 rolls of heavyweight paper. Application labor costs vary with the quality, pattern, and type of joint required.

With vinyls and grass cloths requiring no pattern match, a waste allowance of 10% is normal — approximately 3.5 S.F. per roll. Wall coverings that require a pattern match may have about 25% – 30% waste, or 9 – 11 S.F. per roll. Waste can run as high as 50% – 60% on wall coverings with a large, bold, or intricate pattern repeat.

Commercial wallcoverings are available in widths from 21" to 54", and in lengths from 5-1/3 yards (single roll) to 100 yard bolts. To determine quantities, independent of width, measure the linear (perimeter) footage of walls to be covered. Divide the linear footage by the width of the goods, to determine the number of "strips" or drops. Then determine the number of strips per bolt or package by dividing the length per bolt by the ceiling height.

$$\frac{\text{Linear Footage of Walls}}{\text{Width of goods}} = \text{No. of Strips}$$

$$\frac{\text{Length of Bolt roll}}{\text{Ceiling height}} = \frac{\text{No. of Strips (whole no.)}}{\text{Bolt (roll)}}$$

Finally, divide the quantity of strips required by the number of strips per bolt (roll) in order to determine the required amount of material. Use the same waste allowance as above.

Surface preparation costs for wallcovering must also be included. If the wallcovering is to be installed over new surfaces, the walls must treated with a wall sizing, shellac or primer coat for proper adhesion. For existing surfaces, scraping, patching and sanding may be necessary. Requirements will be included in the specifications.

Sample Estimate: Division 9

Most of the finishes for the sample project involve large quantities in wide open areas. For an interior space broken up into many rooms or suites, the estimate would be much more involved, and a detailed Room Finish Schedule should be provided. The estimate sheets for the sample project are shown in Figures 8.102 to 8.105. On all the estimate sheets for the project, items are entered on every other line. Many more sheets are used this way, but paper is cheap. Invariably, omitted items must be inserted at the last minute and sheet subtotals and division totals will be recalculated as a result. If the sheets are concise, neat and organized, recalculation can be easy, and will involve less chance of error.

Particularly when estimating drywall, the same dimensions can be used to calculate the quantities of different items − in this case, drywall, metal studs, and accessories. When an opening (to be finished with drywall) is deducted from the drywall surface area, perimeter dimensions are used to calculate corner bead. Similarly, at joints with items such as windows, the same dimensions are used for J-bead. The quantity sheet for drywall and associated items is shown in Figure 8.106. Types, sizes and different applications of drywall and studs are listed (and priced) separately. The square foot quantities of studs and drywall can be used for comparison to check for possible errors. When such a method is used, the estimator must be aware of those partitions which receive drywall only on one side, as opposed to both sides, and those with more than one layer. A comparison for the sample project is performed as follows:

Framing	Stud Area	No. of Sides	No. of Layers	Drywall Area
6″	300 S.F.	2	1	600 S.F.
3-5/8″	3,560 S.F.	2	1	7,120 S.F.
3-5/8″	10,104 S.F.	1	1	10,104 S.F.
1-5/8″	5,640 S.F.	1	2	11,280 S.F.
1-5/8″	1,704 S.F.	1	1	1,704 S.F.
Furring	4,200 S.F.	1	1	4,200 S.F.
	25,508 S.F.			35,008 S.F.

$$25,508 \text{ S.F.} = 35,008 - (300 + 3560 + 5640) = 25,508 \text{ S.F.}$$

Note that furring is included in the above crosscheck calculations as square feet. The estimator must always be aware of units during *any* calculations. When deductions are made from the drywall totals for two-side application and double layers, the drywall and stud quantities should equate.

MEANS CONSOLIDATED ESTIMATE

PROJECT: Office Building
LOCATION:
TAKE OFF BY: EBW QUANTITIES BY: EBW PRICES BY: RSM EXTENSIONS BY: SLM
CLASSIFICATION: ARCHITECT:

Division 9
SHEET NO. 1 of 4
ESTIMATE NO. 86-1
DATE 1986
CHECKED JDM

DESCRIPTION	SOURCE/DIMENSIONS			QUANTITY	UNIT	MATERIAL UNIT COST	MATERIAL TOTAL	LABOR UNIT COST	LABOR TOTAL	EQUIPMENT UNIT COST	EQUIPMENT TOTAL	SUBCONTRACT UNIT COST	SUBCONTRACT TOTAL
Division 9: Finishes													
Framing: Metal Studs													
6" – 25 ga.	9.2	20	250	300	SF	.35	105.44	.44	132				
3 5/8" – 25 ga.	9.2	20	230	13,664	SF	.23	3143	.40	5466				
1 5/8" – 25 ga.	9.2	20	200	7,344	SF	.17	1248.38	.38	2791				
Accessories:													
7/8" Furring	9.2	02	090	31.5	CLF	15.50	488	62	1953				
J-Bead	9.2	02	112	34.1	CLF	12.50	426	54	1841				
Corner Bead	9.2	02	030	58.4	CLF	8	467	55	3212				
Drywall:													
5/8" F.R. @ Columns	9.2	07	405	5640	SF	.42	2369	1.07	6035				
5/8" F.R. @ Core	9.2	07	215	7720	SF	.27	2084	.38	2934				
5/8" Standard	9.2	07	205	16,008	SF	.26	4162	.38	6083				
Shaftwall:@ Elevator	9.2	45	003	2,040	SF	1.44	2938	1.94	3958				
Subtotals							(17430)		(34405)				

Figure 8.102

MEANS CONSOLIDATED ESTIMATE

Division 9

SHEET NO. 2 of 4

PROJECT Office Building

CLASSIFICATION

ESTIMATE NO. 86-1

LOCATION

ARCHITECT

DATE 1986

TAKE OFF BY EBW | QUANTITIES BY EBW | PRICES BY RSM | EXTENSIONS BY SLM | CHECKED JDM

DESCRIPTION	SOURCE/DIMENSIONS			QUANTITY	UNIT	MATERIAL UNIT COST	MATERIAL TOTAL	LABOR UNIT COST	LABOR TOTAL	EQUIPMENT UNIT COST	EQUIPMENT TOTAL	SUBCONTRACT UNIT COST	SUBCONTRACT TOTAL
Division 9: (Cont'd)													
Fireproofing: @ Beams	9.1	50	040	40,500	SF							.81	32805
Total Fireproofing													(32805)
Ceramic Tile:													
Walls	9.3	05	540	1584	SF							3.43	5433
Bull nose	9.3	05	250	396	LF							4.25	1683
Cove base	9.3	05	070	396	LF							4.66	1845
Floors	9.3	05	330	960	SF							4.15	3984
Total Ceramic Tile													(12945)
Acoustical Ceilings:													
Grid	9.5	20	005	56,700	SF	.36	20412	.20	11340				
Tile	9.5	15	374	53,735	SF	.66	35465	.28	15046				
Total Ceiling							(55877)		(26386)				

Figure 8.103

MEANS CONSOLIDATED ESTIMATE

Division 9
SHEET NO. 3 of 4

PROJECT Office Building | CLASSIFICATION | ESTIMATE NO. 86-1

LOCATION | ARCHITECT | DATE 1986

TAKE OFF BY EBW | QUANTITIES BY EBW | PRICES BY RSM | EXTENSIONS BY SLM | CHECKED JDM

DESCRIPTION	SOURCE/DIMENSIONS			QUANTITY	UNIT	MATERIAL		LABOR		EQUIPMENT		SUBCONTRACT	
						UNIT COST	TOTAL	UNIT COST	TOTAL	UNIT COST	TOTAL	UNIT COST	TOTAL
Division 9: (Cont'd)													
Flooring:													
Carpet	9.6	05	320	5850	SY							16.70	97695
Cove base	9.6	20	115	2530	LF							1.20	3036
Parquet @ lobby & elevators	9.6	40	650	1800	SF							4.86	8748
Total Flooring													109479
Painting:													
Walls (Drywall)	9.8	21	084	27,784	SF							.29	8057
Wood Doors	9.8	17	180	21	Ea.							47	987
Metal Doors (Primed)	9.8	17	100	14	Ea.							10.20	143
Block Walls	9.8	21	288	9846	SF							.21	2068
Total Painting													11255

Figure 8.104

MEANS CONSOLIDATED ESTIMATE

Division 9
SHEET NO. 4 of 4

PROJECT Office Building | CLASSIFICATION | ESTIMATE NO. 86-1

LOCATION | ARCHITECT | DATE 1986

TAKE OFF BY EBW | QUANTITIES BY EBW | PRICES BY RSM | EXTENSIONS BY SLM | CHECKED JDM

DESCRIPTION	SOURCE/DIMENSIONS	QUANTITY	UNIT	MATERIAL UNIT COST	MATERIAL TOTAL	LABOR UNIT COST	LABOR TOTAL	EQUIPMENT UNIT COST	EQUIPMENT TOTAL	SUBCONTRACT UNIT COST	SUBCONTRACT TOTAL
Division 9: (Cont'd)											
Drywall & Framing	Sheet 1				17430		34405				
Fireproofing	Sheet 2										32805
Ceramic Tile	Sheet 2										12945
Acoustical Ceiling	Sheet 2				55877		26386				
Flooring	Sheet 3										109479
Painting	Sheet 3										11255
Division 9 Totals					73307		60791				166484

Figure 8.105

MEANS QUANTITY SHEET

Division 9

SHEET NO. 1 of 1

PROJECT Office Building

ESTIMATE NO. 86-1

LOCATION

ARCHITECT

DATE 1986

TAKE OFF BY EBW

EXTENSIONS BY: EBW

CHECKED BY: JDM

DESCRIPTION	NO.	DIMENSIONS L	W	H	Studs	UNIT	5/8" Std. Drywall	UNIT	5/8" F.R. Drywall	UNIT	Accessories	UNIT
Partitions - 25 ga.												
Bath Chase 6"	3	10'		10'	300	SF			600	SF		
Interior 3 5/8"												
Lobby	1	86'		10'	860	SF			1720	SF		
Core	3	90'		10'	2700	SF			5400	SF		
Corner Bead	27			10'							270	LF
Furring 16" o.c.	3	140'		10'			4200	SF			3151	LF
Exterior 3 5/8"	3	560'		10'	10104	SF	10104	SF				
Deduct Windows	3	496'		4.5"								
Corner bead	6	496'									3408	LF
	96	4.5'										
J-Bead	6	496'									3408	LF
	96	4.5'										
Window Returns 1 5/8" Studs		3,408'	0.5'		1704	SF	1704	SF				
Columns 1 5/8"	3	188'		10'	5640	SF						
Unfinished									5640	SF		
Taped									5640	SF		
Corner bead	3	72'		10'							2160	LF
Quantity Summary												
Studs: 6"					300	SF						
3 5/8"					13664	SF						
1 5/8"					7344	SF						
Drywall: 5/8" F.R.									13360	SF		
Unfinished 5/8" F.R.									5640	SF		
5/8" Std.							16008	SF				
Corner bead											5838	
J-Bead											3408	
Furring											3151	

Figure 8.106

For the ceiling grid, because of the large, open areas, no allowance for waste is included. Note, however, that the dimensions used are for the exterior of the building (210 ' x 90' x 3 floors). This includes a small overage. For purchasing purposes, all ceiling perimeter dimensions would be measured separately for edge moldings. A 5% allowance is added to the ceiling tile. The large quantity of light fixtures must be considered and is deducted from the total. Deductions for light fixtures should be based on experience. Carpeting quantities are also derived from the building perimeter measurements, with appropriate deductions for the building core.

Division 10: Specialties

Division 10 includes prefinished, manufactured items that are usually installed at the end of a project when other finish work is complete. Following is a partial list of items that may be included in Division 10:

- Bathroom accessories
- Bulletin and chalkboards
- Flagpoles
- Lockers
- Mail boxes
- Partitions
  - Toilet
  - Office
  - Accordion
  - Woven Wire

Items as listed in *Building Construction Cost Data* provide a good checklist to help assure that all appropriate work is included. The prices shown in *Building Construction Cost Data* are national averages and do not reflect any particular manufacturer's product or prices.

A thorough review of the drawings and specifications is necessary to be sure that all items are accounted for. The estimator should list each type of item and the recommended manufacturers. Often, no substitutes are allowed. Each type of item is then counted. Takeoff units will vary with different items.

Quotations and bids should be solicited from local suppliers and specialty subcontractors. The estimator must include all appropriate shipping and handling costs. If no historical costs for installation are available, then costs for labor may be taken from data books, such as *Building Construction Cost Data*, or estimated from scratch. When a specialty item is particularly large, job-site equipment may be needed for placement or installation.

The estimator should pay particular attention to the construction requirements which are necessary to Division 10 work but are included in other divisions. Almost all items in Division 10 require some form of base or backing for proper installation. These requirements may or may not be included in the construction documents, but are usually listed in the manufacturers' recommendations for installation. It is often stated in the General Conditions of the specifications that "the contractor shall install all products according to manufacturers' recommendations" — another catch-all phrase that places responsibility on the contractor (and estimator).

Examples of such items are concrete bases for lockers and supports for ceiling-hung toilet partitions. Concrete bases for lockers cannot be installed until partitions are erected, or at least accurately laid out. The specific locker must be approved by the architect before the exact size of the base is determined. Installation of the concrete often requires a small truckload (hence an extra charge for a minimum order) and hand placement with wheelbarrow and shovel. Similarly, supports for toilet partitions cannot be installed until precise locations are determined. Such supports can be small steel beams, or large angles that must be welded in place. For a room-dividing accordion, folding or telescoping partitions, supports must be strong enough so that no deflection is allowed.

Preparation costs prior to the installation of specialty items may, in some cases, exceed the costs of the items themselves. The estimator must visualize the installation in order to anticipate all of the work and costs.

Sample Estimate: Division 10

The estimate sheet for Division 10 is shown in Figure 8.107. The takeoff and pricing involve a simple counting process. If not included on a schedule, these items should be counted a few times to ensure that all items are included, and in the proper quantities. When estimating for Division 10, it is important to be sure that all backing, supports and blocking are included, usually elsewhere in the estimate. Accessories attached only to drywall with toggles or plastic anchors will work loose very quickly. Installing backing after a wall is finished is very expensive.

There are a few specific manufacturers that are usually specified for bathroom accessories and toilet partitions. A good estimator will find that there are many less expensive but "equal" products (almost exact copies) on the market, and these may be approved by the architects. Smart shopping for such costly items can help to lower the bid.

Division 11: Architectural Equipment

Architectural equipment includes permanent fixtures that cause the space to function as designed — book stacks for libraries, vaults for banks. Often leaving this division until the end of the estimate, the estimator can use the average costs shown in *Building Construction Cost Data* for budget pricing purposes. *Building Construction Cost Data* can also serve as a checklist to ensure that items have not been omitted.

The construction documents may specify that the owner will purchase architectural equipment directly, and that the contractor will install it. In such cases, the daily output shown in the cost book can be used to complete the labor portion of the estimate. If architectural equipment is furnished by the owner, it is common practice to add about 10% of the materials cost into the estimate. This procedure protects the contractor from the risks, and covers handling costs associated with the materials. Often the contractor is responsible for receipt, storage and protection of these owner-purchased items until they are installed.

As with specialties in Division 10, architectural equipment must also be evaluated to determine what is required from other divisions for its successful installation. Some possibilities are:
- Concrete
- Miscellaneous Metals
- Rough Carpentry
- Mechanical Coordination
- Electrical Requirements

MEANS CONSOLIDATED ESTIMATE

PROJECT: Office Building
LOCATION:
TAKE OFF BY: EBW QUANTITIES BY: EBW PRICES BY: RSM EXTENSIONS BY: SLM
CLASSIFICATION:
ARCHITECT:
CHECKED: JDM

DESCRIPTION	SOURCE/DIMENSIONS	QUANTITY	UNIT	MATERIAL UNIT COST	MATERIAL TOTAL	LABOR UNIT COST	LABOR TOTAL	EQUIPMENT UNIT COST	EQUIPMENT TOTAL	SUBCONTRACT UNIT COST	SUBCONTRACT TOTAL
Division 10: Specialties											
Bathroom Accessories:											
Towel/Waste	10.1 02 061	9	Ea.	295	2655	16	144				
Grab Bar	10.1 02 110	6	Ea.	23	138	8	48				
Napkin Dispenser	10.1 02 420	6	Ea.	255	1530	10.65	64				
Mirrors (Handicapped)	10.1 02 300	3	Ea.	59	177	8	24				
Soap Dispenser	10.1 02 460	15	Ea.	52	780	8	120				
S.S. Shelves	10.1 02 570	6	Ea.	60	360	10	60				
T.P. Holder	10.1 02 610	18	Ea.	17.50	315	5.35	96				
Ash Trays	10.1 02 780	12	Ea.	45	540	8.90	107				
Toilet Partitions:											
Floor Mounted, Headrail	10.1 60 250	15	Ea.	195	2925	53	795				
Urinal Screens	10.1 60 470	3	Ea.	115	345	40	120				
Division 10 Totals					9765		1578				

Figure 8.107

Division 11 includes equipment that can be packaged and delivered complete or partially assembled by the factory. Also, some items can or must be purchased and installed by an authorized factory representative. The estimator must investigate these variables in order to include adequate costs.

Division 12: Furnishings

Division 12, Furnishings, is best defined as furniture designed for specific uses, such as for dormitories, hospitals, hotels, offices and restaurants. Window treatments are also included in Division 12. These important furnishings may be listed in the budget estimate to help determine the total financial investment, though they are usually not a part of the actual construction contract. If the furnishings are built-in, then additional man-hours for unpacking, installing, and clean-up are necessary and must be calculated. In most cases, architects will separately specify and arrange for the purchase and installation of furnishings.

Division 13: Special Construction

The items in this division are specialized subsystems that are usually manufactured or constructed, and installed by specialty subcontractors. The costs shown in *Building Construction Cost Data* are for budget purposes only. Final cost figures should be furnished by the appropriate subcontractor after the exact requirements of the project have been specified.

It is a good idea to review this portion of the project with the subcontractor to determine both the exact scope of the work and those items that are not covered by the quotation. If the subcontractor requires services such as excavation, unloading, or other temporary work, then these otherwise excluded items must be included elsewhere in the estimate.

The specialty subcontractor will have more detailed information at hand concerning the system. The more detailed the estimator's knowledge of a system, the easier it will be to subdivide that system into cost components. Each component can be further subdivided into material, labor, and equipment costs that will fully identify the direct cost of the specialty item for future purposes.

Division 14: Conveying Systems

The following systems may be included in this division:
- Correspondence lifts
- Dumbwaiters
- Elevators
- Escalators and Moving ramps
- Material Handling systems
- Pneumatic Tube Systems
- Handicapped Lifts

Because of the specialized construction of the above units, it is almost impossible for the general estimator to price most of this equipment, except in a preliminary, budgetary capacity. Sometimes the plans specify package units that carry standard prices. For general budget pricing, refer to *Building Construction Cost Data*. When quotations on specific equipment are received, they should be checked against the specifications to verify that all requirements are met. All required inspections, tests and permits, as well as the responsibility for their costs, should be included in the installed price of each system.

Many of the costs associated with conveying systems are not included in the subcontract bid. When drilling for hydraulic pistons, for example, the preliminary project schedule must be adjusted so that the work can be performed prior to the erection of the superstructure. Drill tailings must also be disposed of, and if ledge or boulders are encountered, drilling costs will increase substantially. Contracts for elevator installations often have more exclusions than inclusions. The estimator must be sure that all associated costs are taken into account.

One of the most commonly underestimated or unanticipated costs is that for the installation of elevator door frames and sills. Typically, frames and sills are supplied by the elevator subcontractor and installed by the general contractor when constructing the elevator shaft walls. At this stage, shop drawings for the elevator usually not have yet been approved. The resulting late installation often involves the cutting and patching of other completed work (concrete floors and block walls). Even if shop drawings are approved, the materials often arrive late. Good planning and proper estimating can help to alleviate or lessen these problems.

Even when determining budget costs for elevators, many variables must be considered. Circle Reference Number 123 from *Building Construction Cost Data*, shown in Figures 8.108 and 8.109, indicates the complexity of estimating for elevators.

Sample Estimate: Division 14

The architect's design criteria is apt to be based on the standard elevator "packages" of certain manufacturers. In such cases, firm subcontract bids would be received. For the sample estimate, a budget price is developed and shown in Figure 8.110. The costs would be based on project specifications and are derived from Figures 8.108 and 8.109. If a budget price for elevators is carried in an estimate for bidding, a qualification should be included that the bid may change upon receipt of subcontract prices. Budget prices should be carried *only* if no specifications are available or obtainable.

Division 15: Mechanical

Unit price estimates for the mechanical and electrical portions of a project should always be performed by the installing subcontractors. Each field requires specialized experience and expertise. Nevertheless, the estimator for the general contractor often requires costs to compare to subcontract bids. In most cases, adjusted square foot costs based on previous, similar projects will suffice. A Systems Estimate may be used if more accuracy is needed. It is essential to understand both the work and the estimating process in order to properly interpret and analyze subcontract costs, and to ensure that all requirements are met. Following are brief discussions of the estimating process — for mechanical and electrical work.

⑫③ Elevator Selective Costs (Div. 14.1-20)

	Passenger		Freight		Hospital	
A. Base Unit	Hydraulic	Electric	Hydraulic	Electric	Hydraulic	Electric
Capacity	1500 Lb.	2000 Lb.	2000 Lb.	4000 Lb.	3500 Lb.	3500 Lb.
Speed	50 F.P.M.	100 F.P.M.	25 F.P.M.	50 F.P.M.	50 F.P.M.	100 F.P.M.
#Stops/Travel Ft.	2/10	4/40	2/10	4/40	2/10	4/40
Push Button Oper.	Yes	Yes	Yes	Yes	Yes	Yes
Telephone Box & Wire	"	"	"	"	"	"
Emergency Lighting	"	"	No	No	"	"
Cab	Painted Steel	Painted Steel	Painted Steel	Painted Steel	S.S. Wainscot, Baked	Enamel Above
Cove Lighting	Yes	Yes	No	No	Yes	Yes
Floor	V.A.T.	V.A.T.	Wood w/Safety Treads	Wood w/Safety Treads	V.A.T.	V.A.T.
Doors, & Speedside Slide	Yes	Yes	No	No	Yes	Yes
Gates, Manual	No	No	Yes	Yes	No	No
Signals, Lighted Buttons	Car Only	Car Only	In Use Light	In Use Light	Car and Hall	Car and Hall
O.H. Geared Machine	N.A.	Yes	N.A.	Yes	N.A.	Yes
Variable Voltage Contr.	"	"	"	"	"	"
Emergency Alarm	"	"	"	"	"	"
Class "A" Loading	"	N.A.	Yes	"	"	N.A.
Base Cost	$37,500	$49,000	$29,900	$47,500	$41,700	$58,500
B. Capacity Adjustment						
2,000 Lb.	$ 2,350					
2,500	4,500	$ 2,350	$ 2,150			
3,000	5,000	2,800	3,500			
3,500	6,200	4,000	4,000			
4,000	6,600	4,600	5,200		$ 4,200	$ 2,925
4,500	7,800	5,700	5,600		4,850	3,350
5,000	9,000	7,000	6,800	$ 2,350	7,000	4,600
6,000			8,000	2,800		
7,000			9,600	4,000		
8,000			12,800	12,000		
10,000			15,000	15,000		
12,000			19,250	19,250		
16,000			22,500	22,500		
20,000			25,000	27,600		
C. Travel Over Base	$ 535 V.L.F.	$ 185 V.L.F.	$ 640 V.L.F.	$ 185 V.L.F.	$ 640 V.L.F.	$ 185 V.L.F.
D. Additional Stops	$ 5,025 Ea.	$ 5,025 Ea.	$ 4,300 Ea.	$ 4,300 Ea.	$ 5,200 Ea.	$ 5,025 Ea.
E. Speed Adjustment						
50 F.P.M.			$ 535			
75	535		750	$ 1,875	$ 590	
100	940		1,500	2,975	965	
125	1,300		2,375	4,100	1,400	
150	3,575		3,200	5,100	2,450	
175				6,000	3,000	
200		$ 4,800		6,800		$ 5,800
Geared 250		6,950		7,800		7,950
4 Flrs. 300		8,550		10,200		9,550
Min. 350		9,600		11,700		10,600
400		10,700		12,800		11,700
500		25,700		16,400		26,700
Gearless 600		28,900		18,000		29,900
10 Flrs. 700		29,900		21,000		30,900
Min. 800		37,500		23,500		38,500
1,000		Spec. Applic.		Spec. Applic.		Spec. Applic.
1,200		"		"		"
F. Other Than Class "A" Loading						
"B"			$ 1,225	$ 1,225		
"C-1"			2,150	2,150		
"C-2"			1,350	1,350		
"C-3"			2,780	2,780		

Figure 8.108

(123) Elevator Selective Costs (cont.)

	Passenger	Freight	Hospital
G. Options			
1. Controls			
Automatic, 2 car group	$ 3,200		$ 3,200
3 car group	5,500		5,500
4 car group	6,950		6,950
5 car group	8,550		8,550
6 car group	12,800		12,800
Emergency, fireman service	2,000		2,000
Intercom service	1,500		1,500
Selective collective, single car	2,350		2,350
Duplex car	3,850		3,850
2. Doors			
Center opening, 1 speed	$ 750		$ 750
2 speed	800		800
Rear opening-opposite front	—		5,350
Side opening, 2 speed	800		800
Freight, bi-parting	—	$3,000	—
Power operated door and gate	—	6,900	—
3. Emergency power switching, automatic	$ 2,125		$ 2,125
Manual	1,075		1,075
4. Finishes based on 3500# cab			
Ceilings, acrylic panel	$ 225		—
Aluminum egg crate	275		$ 215
Doors, stainless steel	325		215
Floors, carpet, class "A"	80		—
Epoxy	215		215
Quarry tile	125		215
Slate	140		—
Steel plate	—	$ 535	—
Textured rubber	65		54
Walls, plastic laminate	300		215
Stainless steel	765		535
Return at door	430		430
Steel plate, 1/4" x 4' high, 14 ga. above	—	1,175	—
Entrance, doors, baked enamel	250		180
Stainless steel	430		430
Frames, baked enamel	250		180
Stainless steel	535		535
5. Maintenance contract - 12 months	$ 2,600	$1,650	$ 2,850
6. Signal devices			
Hall lantern, each	$ 375	$ 375	$ 375
Position indicator, car or lobby	270	270	270
Add for over three each	65	65	65
7. Specialties			
High speed, heavy duty door opener	$ 450		$ 450
Variable voltage, O.H. gearless machine	26,700 - 53,400		26,700 - 53,400
Basement installed geared machine	6,000	$6,000	6,000

Figure 8.109

MEANS CONSOLIDATED ESTIMATE

Division 14

SHEET NO. 1 of 1

PROJECT Office Building | CLASSIFICATION | ESTIMATE NO. 86-1

LOCATION | ARCHITECT | DATE 1986

TAKE OFF BY EBW | QUANTITIES BY EBW | PRICES BY RSM | EXTENSIONS BY SLM | CHECKED JDM

DESCRIPTION	SOURCE/DIMENSIONS	QUANTITY	UNIT	MATERIAL UNIT COST	MATERIAL TOTAL	LABOR UNIT COST	LABOR TOTAL	EQUIPMENT UNIT COST	EQUIPMENT TOTAL	SUBCONTRACT UNIT COST	SUBCONTRACT TOTAL
Division 14: Conveying Systems											
Pass. Hydraulic- base	$ 37,500										
2500 lbs. capacity	4,500										
Travel - 37'	14,445										
Stops (plus 2)	10,050										
Speed - 75 fpm	535										
S.S. Doors	325										
Carpet	80										
P.L. Walls	300										
S.S. Entrance - Doors	430										
- Frame	535										
Each Elevator	$ 68,700	2	Ea.								137400
Automatic Controls		1	Ea.								3200
Fire Service		1	Ea.								2000
Hall Lanterns		8	Ea.								3000
Position Indicators		4	Ea.								875
Maintenance		1	Ea.								2600
Division 14 Total											149075

Figure 8.110

When a complete set of mechanical plans and specifications is available, the first step in preparing an estimate is to review all information, making notes on any special or unique requirements. Also, while it is not unusual to see an item on the plans that is not reflected in the specifications, or vice versa, the estimator should make careful note of any contradictions. Such inconsistencies will require resolution before a meaningful estimate can be put together. A review of the other drawings is also advised to determine how the building structure, site layout and other work will affect the mechanical installation. The scales of architectural and engineering drawings should be compared. Plumbing, sprinkler and HVAC designs are frequently prepared by consulting engineers who are not associated with the architects. In these cases, inconsistencies in scale, location, and terminology may result.

One basic feature of almost all mechanical designs is the fact that their different elements can be separated into systems, such as hot water, cold water, fire protection, and heating and/or cooling. Some of these systems may be interconnected or have some common parts, but they are nevertheless distinct. Most systems can be broken down into the following categories: source, conductor or connector, and a terminal unit; for example, water meter – copper tubing – sink faucet. Note that while the sink with faucet or a water closet may be terminal units for the cold water system, they are a source for the drain-waste-vent (DWV) system.

Pre-printed forms are especially useful for preparing the mechanical portion of the estimate. While careful measurements and a count of components are important, they will not compensate for omissions such as forgetting to include pipe insulation. A well designed form acts as a checklist, a guide for standardization, and a permanent record.

Plumbing

The first step in preparing a plumbing estimate is to visualize the scope of the job by scanning all of the drawings and specifications. The next step is to make a list of the types of materials on a takeoff sheet. This process will help the estimator to remember the various components as they are located on the drawings. For major items, pieces of equipment and fixtures, the quantity sheet can serve as a checklist. The estimator must be sure to include the required labor-only items, such as cleaning, adjusting, purifying, testing, and balancing, since these will not show up on the drawings and have little, if any, material costs.

The easiest way to do a material takeoff is by system, as most of the pipe components of a system will tend to be related as a group – of the same material, class weight, and grade. For example, a waste system could consist of pipe varying from 3″ to 8″ in diameter, but would probably be all service weight cast iron, DWV copper, or PVC up to a specified size – and then cast iron for the larger sizes.

Fixtures: Fixture takeoff is usually nothing more than counting the various types, sizes and styles, and then entering them on a fixture form. It is important, however, that each fixture be fully identified. A common error occurs when parts that must be purchased separately are overlooked; examples are trim, carriers, and flush valves. Equipment like pumps, water heaters, water softeners, and all items not previously counted are also listed at this time. The order in which the takeoff proceeds is not as important as the development of a consistent method. With consistency, the estimator can speed up the process while minimizing the chances of overlooking any item or class of items. Taking off fixtures and equipment before the piping is best for several reasons. Done in this order, the fixture and equipment lists can be given to suppliers for pricing while the estimator is performing the more arduous and time consuming piping takeoff. Taking off the fixtures and equipment first also gives the estimator a good perspective on the building and its systems. The next step is transferring these figures to the estimate sheet. Figure 8.111 shows relative installation times for different types of fixtures.

Piping: Fixture costs in *Building Construction Cost Data* (Figure 8.112) are based on the cost per fixture set in place. The rough-in piping cost, which must be added for each fixture, includes a carrier, if required, some supply, waste and vent pipe, connecting fittings and stops. The lengths of rough-in pipe are nominal runs which would connect to the larger runs and stacks (to within 10'). The supply runs and DWV runs and stacks must be accounted for in separate entries.

Pipe runs for any type of system consist of straight sections and fittings of various shapes and styles, for various purposes. Depending on the required detail, pipe and fittings can be itemized or included as a percentage of the fixtures. If detail is required, the estimator should measure and record the lengths of each size of pipe. When a fitting is crossed, a list of all fitting types and sizes can be used for counting. Colored pencils can be used to mark runs that have been completed, and to note termination points on the main line where measurements are stopped so that a branch may be taken off. Care must be taken to note changes in pipe material. Since different materials can only meet at a joint, it should become an automatic habit to see that the piping material going into a joint is the same as that leaving the joint.

Plumbing Fixture Installation Time

Item	Rough-In	Set	Total Hours	Item	Rough-In	Set	Total Hours
Bathtub	5	5	10	Shower head only	2	1	3
Bathtub and shower, cast iron	6	6	12	Shower drain	3	1	4
Fire hose reel and cabinet	4	2	6	Shower stall, slate		15	15
Floor drain to 4" diameter	3	1	4	Slop sink	5	3	8
Grease trap, single, cast iron	5	3	8	Test six fixtures			14
Kitchen gas range		4	4	Urinal, wall	6	2	8
Kitchen sink, single	4	4	8	Urinal, pedestal or floor	6	4	10
Kitchen sink, double	6	6	12	Water closet and tank	4	3	7
Laundry tubs	4	2	6	Water closet and tank, wall hung	5	3	8
Lavatory wall hung	5	3	8	Water heater, 45 gals. gas, automatic	5	2	7
Lavatory pedestal	5	3	8	Water heaters, 65 gals. gas, automatic	5	2	7
Shower and stall	6	4	10	Water heaters, electric, plumbing only	4	2	6

Figure 8.111

15.2 Plumbing Fixtures	CREW	DAILY OUTPUT	UNIT	BARE COSTS MAT.	INST.	TOTAL	TOTAL INCL O&P
60-001 **SINKS** With faucets and drain							
200 Kitchen, counter top, P.E. on C.I., 24" x 21" single bowl	Q-1	3.20	Ea.	113	100	213	270
210 30" x 21" single bowl		3.20		134	100	234	295
220 32" x 21" double bowl		2.60		148	125	273	345
230 42" x 21" double bowl	↓	2.60	↓	255	125	380	460
260							
300 Stainless steel, self rimming, 19" x 18" single bowl	Q-1	3.20	Ea.	205	100	305	370
310 25" x 22" single bowl		3.20		228	100	328	400
400 Steel, enameled, with ledge, 24" x 21" single bowl		3.20		59	100	159	210
410 32" x 21" double bowl	↓	2.60		67	125	192	255
496 For color sinks except stainless steel, add			↓	10%			
498 For rough-in, supply, waste and vent, counter top sinks	Q-1	1.85		58.30	175	233.30	320
500 Kitchen, raised deck, P.E. on C.I.							
510 32" x 21", dual level, double bowl	Q-1	1.60	Ea.	205	205	410	520
570 For color, add				30%			
579 For rough-in, supply, waste & vent, sinks	Q-1	1.85		58.30	175	233.30	320
665 Service, floor, corner, P.E. on C.I., 28" x 28"		4		305	81	386	455
679 For rough-in, supply, waste & vent, floor service sinks		1.30		87.70	250	337.70	460
700 Service, wall, P.E. on C.I., roll rim, 22" x 18"		3		230	110	340	410
710 24" x 20"		3		255	110	365	435
860 Vitreous china, 22" x 20"	↓	3		260	110	370	445
896 For stainless steel rim guard, front or side, add				18		18	19.80M
898 For rough-in, supply, waste & vent, wall service sinks	Q-1	1.30	↓	145.22	250	395.22	520
68-001 **URINALS**							
002							
300 Wall hung, vitreous china, with hanger & self-closing valve	Q-1	3	Ea.	290	110	400	475
330 Rough-in, supply, waste & vent		1.99		53.01	165	218.01	295
500 Stall type, vitreous china, includes valve		2.50		360	130	490	585
510 3" seam cover, add		12		90	27	117	140
520 6" seam cover, add		12		125	27	152	175
698 Rough-in, supply, waste and vent	↓	1.99	↓	67.47	165	232.47	310
76-001 **WASH FOUNTAINS** Rigging not included							
190 Group, foot control							
200 Precast terrazzo, circular, 36" diam., 5 or 6 persons	Q-2	3	Ea.	880	170	1,050	1,200
210 54" diameter for 8 or 10 persons		2.50		1,025	200	1,225	1,425
240 Semi-circular, 36" diam. for 3 persons		3		800	170	970	1,125
250 54" diam. for 4 or 5 persons		2.50		985	200	1,185	1,375
270 Quarter circle (corner), 54" for 3 persons	↓	3.50	↓	1,045	145	1,190	1,350
285							
300 Stainless steel, circular, 36" diameter	Q-2	3.50	Ea.	1,050	145	1,195	1,375
310 54" diameter		2.80		1,360	180	1,540	1,750
340 Semi-circular, 36" diameter		3.50		905	145	1,050	1,200
350 54" diameter	↓	2.80		1,180	180	1,360	1,550
570 Rough-in, supply, waste and vent for above wash fountains	Q-1	1.38	↓	187.85	235	422.85	545
590							
620 Duo for small washrooms, stainless steel	Q-1	2	Ea.	485	160	645	770
650 Rough-in, supply, waste & vent for duo fountains	"	2.02	"	28.71	160	188.71	265
80-001 **WATER CLOSETS**							
015 Tank type, vitreous china, including seat, supply pipe with stop							
020 Wall hung, one piece	Q-1	5.30	Ea.	465	61	526	600
040 Two piece, close coupled		5.30		290	61	351	410
096 For rough-in, supply, waste, vent and carrier		2.24		121.66	145	266.66	345
100 Floor mounted, one piece		5.30		360	61	421	485
110 Two piece, close coupled, water saver	↓	5.30		100	61	161	200
196 For color, add				30%			
198 For rough-in, supply, waste and vent	Q-1	1.94	↓	83.25	165	248.25	335
200							
300 Bowl only, with flush valve, seat							
310 Wall hung	Q-1	5.80	Ea.	230	56	286	335

Figure 8.112

When summarizing quantities of piping for estimate or purchase, it is good practice to round the totals of each size up to the lengths normally available from the supply house or mill. This method is even more appropriate in larger projects where rounding might be done to the nearest hundred or thousand feet. With this approach, a built-in percentage for scrap or waste is allowed. Rigid copper tubing and rigid plastic pipe are normally supplied in 20' lengths, cast iron soil pipe in either 5' or 10' sections. Steel pipe of 2" diameter or less is furnished in 21' lengths, and pipe of a larger diameter is available in single random lengths ranging from 16' to 22'.

Apart from counting and pricing every pipe and fitting, there are other ways to determine budget costs for plumbing. *Building Construction Cost Data* provides costs for fixtures, as well as the associated costs for rough-in of the supply, waste and vent piping as shown in Figure 8.112. The rough-in costs include piping within 10' of the fixture. If these prices are used, further costs must be added for the stacks and mains. Another method involves adding percentages to the cost of the fixtures. Recommended percentages are shown in Figure 8.113. Using information such as that provided in Figures 8.112 and 8.113, the estimator can develop "systems" to be used for budget pricing.

Plumbing Approximations for Quick Estimating

Water Control
Water Meter; Backflow Preventer;
Shock Absorbers; Vacuum Breakers; .... 10 to 15% of Fixtures
Mixer.
Pipe And Fittings: .... 30 to 60% of Fixtures
    Note: Lower percentage for compact buildings or larger buildings with plumbing in one area.
           Larger percentage for large buildings with plumbing spread out.
           In extreme cases pipe may be more than 100% of fixtures.
           Percentages **do not** include special purpose or process piping.

Plumbing Labor:
1 & 2 Story Residential .... Rough-in Labor = 80% of Materials
Apartment Buildings .... Rough-in Labor = 90 to 100% of Materials
Labor for handling and placing fixtures is approximately 25 to 30% of fixtures.

Quality/Complexity Multiplier (For all installations)
Economy installation, add .... 0 to 5%
Good quality, medium complexity, add .... 5 to 15%
Above average quality and complexity, add .... 15 to 25%

Figure 8.113

In addition to the cost of pipe installation, the estimator must also consider any associated costs. In many cases, mechanical and electrical subcontractors must dig, by hand, their own underslab trenches. Site utility excavation (and backfill) may also be included, if required. Underground piping may require special wrapping. For interior piping, the estimator must visualize the installation in order to to determine how — and to what — the pipe hangers are attached. Overhead installations will require rolling scaffolding. For installations higher than an average of 15', labor costs may be increased by the following suggested percentages:

Ceiling Height	Labor Increase
15' to 20'	10%
20' to 25'	20%
25' to 30'	30%
30' to 35'	40%
35' to 40'	50%
Over 40'	60%

Fire Protection

The takeoff of fire protection systems (sprinklers and standpipes) is very much like that of other plumbing — the estimator should measure the pipe loops and count fittings, valves, sprinkler heads, alarms, and other components. The estimator then makes note of special requirements, as well as any conditions that would affect job performance and cost.

There are many different types of sprinkler systems; examples are wet pipe, dry pipe, pre-action, and chemical. Each of these types involves a different set of requirements and costs. Figure 8.114, from *Means Mechanical Cost Data*, 1986, provides descriptions of various sprinkler systems.

Most sprinkler systems must be approved by Factory Mutual for insurance purposes *before* installation. This requirement means that shop drawings must be produced and submitted for approval. The shop drawings take time and the approval process takes more time. This process can cause serious delays and added expense if it is not anticipated and given adequate consideration at the estimating and scheduling phase.

Square foot historical costs for fire protection systems may be developed for budget purposes. These costs may be based on the relative hazard of occupancy — light, ordinary and extra. A comparison of some requirements of the different hazards is shown in Figure 8.115. Consideration must also be given to special or unusual requirements. For example, many architects specify that sprinkler heads must be located in the center of ceiling tiles. Each head may require extra elbows and nipples for precise location. Recessed heads are more expensive. Special dry pendant heads are required in areas subject to freezing. When installing a sprinkler system in an existing structure, a completely new water service may be required in addition to the existing domestic water service. These are just a few examples of requirements which may necessitate an adjustment of square foot costs.

Table 8.2-101   Sprinkler Systems (Automatic)

Sprinkler systems may be classified by type as follows:

1. **Wet Pipe System.** A system employing automatic sprinklers attached to a piping system containing water and connected to a water supply so that water discharges immediately from sprinklers opened by a fire.

2. **Dry Pipe System.** A system employing automatic sprinklers attached to a piping system containing air under pressure, the release of which as from the opening of sprinklers permits the water pressure to open a valve known as a "dry pipe valve". The water then flows into the piping system and out the opened sprinklers.

3. **Pre-Action System.** A system employing automatic sprinklers attached to a piping system containing air that may or may not be under pressure, with a supplemental heat responsive system of generally more sensitive characteristics than the automatic sprinklers themselves, installed in the same areas as the sprinklers; actuation of the heat responsive system, as from a fire, opens a valve which permits water to flow into the sprinkler piping system and to be discharged from any sprinklers which may be open.

4. **Deluge System.** A system employing open sprinklers attached to a piping system connected to a water supply through a valve which is opened by the operation of a heat responsive system installed in the same areas as the sprinklers. When this valve opens, water flows into the piping system and discharges from all sprinklers attached thereto.

5. **Combined Dry Pipe and Pre-Action Sprinkler System.** A system employing automatic sprinklers attached to a piping system containing air under pressure with a supplemental heat responsive system of generally more sensitive characteristics than the automatic sprinklers themselves, installed in the same areas as the sprinklers; operation of the heat responsive system, as from a fire, actuates tripping devices which open dry pipe valves simultaneously and without loss of air pressure in the system. Operation of the heat responsive system also opens approved air exhaust valves at the end of the feed main which facilitates the filling of the system with water which usually procedes the opening of sprinklers. The heat responsive system also serves an an automatic fire alarm system.

6. **Limited Water Supply System.** A system employing automatic sprinklers and conforming to these standards but supplied by a pressure tank of limited capacity.

7. **Chemical Systems.** Systems using halon, carbon dioxide, dry chemical or high expansion foam as selected for special requirements. Agent may extinguish flames by chemically inhibiting flame propagation, suffocate flames by excluding oxygen, interrupting chemical action of oxygen uniting with fuel or sealing and cooling the combustion center.

8. **Firecycle System.** Firecycle is a fixed fire protection sprinkler system utilizing water as its extinguishing agent. It is a time delayed, recycling, preaction type which automatically shuts the water off when heat is reduced below the detector operating temperature and turns the water back on when that temperature is exceeded. The system senses a fire condition through a closed circuit electrical detector system which controls water flow to the fire automatically. Batteries supply up to 90 hour emergency power supply for system operation. The piping system is dry (until water is required) and is monitored with pressurized air. Should any leak in the system piping occur, an alarm will sound, but water will not enter the system until heat is sensed by a Firecycle detector.

Area coverage sprinkler systems may be laid out and fed from the supply in any one of several patterns as shown in Figure 8.2-101. It is desirable, if possible, to utilize a central feed and achieve a shorter flow path from the riser to the furthest sprinkler. This permits use of the smallest sizes of pipe possible with resulting savings.

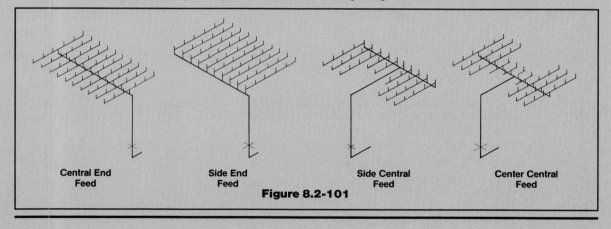

Central End Feed   Side End Feed   Side Central Feed   Center Central Feed

Figure 8.2-101

Figure 8.114

275

Heating, Ventilation, and Air Conditioning

As with plumbing, equipment for HVAC should be taken off first so that the estimator is familiarized with the various systems and layouts. While actual pieces of equipment must be counted at this time, it is also necessary to note sizes, capacities, controls, special characteristics and features. The weight and size of equipment may be important if the unit is especially large or is going into comparatively close quarters. If hoisting or rigging is not included in the subcontract price, then costs for placing the equipment must be figured and listed. From the equipment totals, other important items, such as motor starters, valves, strainers, gauges, thermometers, traps, and air vents can also be counted.

Sheet metal ductwork for heating, ventilation and air conditioning is usually estimated by weight. The lengths of the various sizes are measured and recorded on a worksheet. The weight per foot of length is then determined. Figure 8.116 is a conversion chart for determining the weight of ductwork based on size and material. A count must also be made of all duct-associated accessories, such as fire dampers, diffusers, and registers. This count may be done during the duct takeoff. It is usually less confusing, however, to make a separate count. For budget purposes, duct work, insulation, diffusers and registers may be estimated using the information in Figure 8.117.

Sprinkler Quantities for Various Size and Types of Pipe

Sprinkler Quantities: The table below lists the usual maximum number of sprinkler heads for each size of copper and steel pipe for both wet and dry systems. These quantities may be adjusted to meet individual structural needs or local code requirements. Maximum area on any one floor for one system is: light hazard and ordinary hazard 52,000 S.F., extra hazardous 25,000 S.F.

Pipe Size	Light Hazard Occupancy		Ordinary Hazard Occupancy		Extra Hazard Occupancy	
Diameter	Steel Pipe	Copper Pipe	Steel Pipe	Copper Pipe	Steel Pipe	Copper Pipe
1"	2 sprinklers	2 sprinklers	2 sprinklers	2 sprinklers	1 sprinklers	1 sprinklers
1-1/4"	3	3	3	3	2	2
1-1/2"	5	5	5	5	5	5
2"	10	12	10	12	8	8
2-1/2"	30	40	20	25	15	20
3"	60	65	40	45	27	30
3-1/2"	100	115	65	75	40	45
4"			100	115	55	65
5"			160	180	90	100
6"			275	300	150	170

Figure 8.115

The takeoff of heating, ventilation and air conditioning pipe and fittings is accomplished in a manner similar to that of plumbing. In addition to the general, miscellaneous items noted during the review of plans and specifications, the heating, ventilation and air conditioning estimate usually includes the work of subcontractors. All material suppliers and appropriate subcontractors should be notified as soon as possible to verify material availability and pricing and to ensure timely submission of bids. Typical subcontract work includes:

- Balancing
- Controls
- Insulation
- Water Treatment
- Sheet Metal
- Core Drilling

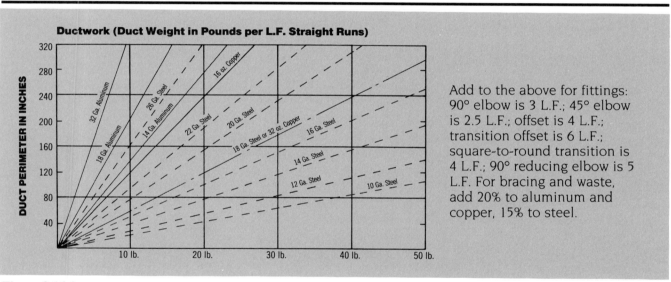

Add to the above for fittings: 90° elbow is 3 L.F.; 45° elbow is 2.5 L.F.; offset is 4 L.F.; transition offset is 6 L.F.; square-to-round transition is 4 L.F.; 90° reducing elbow is 5 L.F. For bracing and waste, add 20% to aluminum and copper, 15% to steel.

Figure 8.116

Ductwork Packages (per ton of cooling)

System	Sheet Metal	Insulation	Diffusers	Return Register
Roof top Unit Single Zone	120 Lbs.	52 S.F.	1	1
Roof top Unit Multizone	240 Lbs.	104 S.F.	2	1
Self-contained Air or Water Cooled	108 Lbs.	—	2	—
Split System Air Cooled	102 Lbs.	—	2	—

Figure 8.117

If similar systems are used repeatedly, it is easy to develop historical square foot costs for budget and comparison purposes. However, with variation in the types and size of HVAC systems, the estimator must use caution when using square foot prices. A way to adjust such relative prices can be to adjust costs based on the quality or complexity of the installation:

Quality/Complexity	Adjustment
Economy/Low	0 to 5%
Good/Medium	5 to 15%
Above average/High	15 to 25%

Sample Estimate: Division 15

For bidding purposes, firm subcontract prices should always be solicited for all phases of mechanical work. However, the estimator should still be familiar with the project requirements and the basics of mechanical estimating. Only with an understanding of what is involved will the estimator be able to judge the validity of a subcontract quote.

For the purposes of this sample estimate, Figures 8.118 through 8.123 are included to show how a subcontractor might prepare a bid for the HVAC work. Unit prices are from *Means Mechanical Cost Data, 1986*. Different types of ductwork installations are separated on the quantity sheet in Figure 8.118. The weight (pounds per linear foot) for each size of duct is derived from the table in Figure 8.124 from *Means Mechanical Cost Data, 1986*. The detail of the HVAC estimate reflects the precision required for proper mechanical estimating.

Overhead and profit are added to the bare cost totals using the methods described in Chapters 4 and 7. Ten percent is added to each — material, equipment and subcontracts — for handling and supervision. To labor, 46.1% is added. This includes employer-paid taxes and insurance, office overhead, and profit.

While usually only one subcontractor will handle the complete mechanical portion of the project, different subcontractors may separately bid and perform the plumbing, fire protection and HVAC portions of the estimate. When soliciting quotes, the estimator for the general contractor should try to obtain detailed breakdowns of each. The estimator will be able to use these breakdowns for comparing bids if the quote is not as expected, and can thereby discover which areas are "out of line". While subcontractors are often reluctant to provide detailed information, it is to their own benefit if possible errors or omissions which exist in their prices are discovered.

A summary of the subcontract prices is shown in Figure 8.125. Separation and breakdowns as shown can be used to help develop historical costs for future projects, whether they are done by system or square foot.

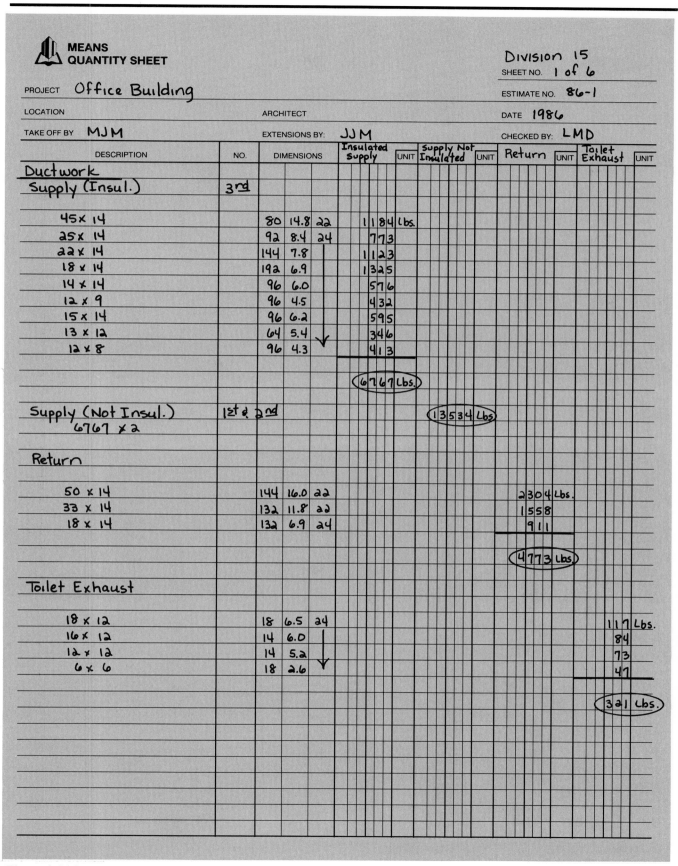

MEANS QUANTITY SHEET

PROJECT: Office Building

LOCATION: _____ ARCHITECT: _____

TAKE OFF BY: MJM   EXTENSIONS BY: JJM   CHECKED BY: LMD

Division 15
SHEET NO. 1 of 6
ESTIMATE NO. 86-1
DATE: 1986

DESCRIPTION	NO.	DIMENSIONS			Insulated Supply	UNIT	Supply Not Insulated	UNIT	Return	UNIT	Toilet Exhaust	UNIT
Ductwork												
Supply (Insul.)	3rd											
45 × 14	80	14.8	22		1184	Lbs.						
25 × 14	92	8.4	24		773							
22 × 14	144	7.8			1123							
18 × 14	192	6.9			1325							
14 × 14	96	6.0			576							
12 × 9	96	4.5			432							
15 × 14	96	6.2			595							
13 × 12	64	5.4	↓		346							
12 × 8	96	4.3			413							
					6767 Lbs.							
Supply (Not Insul.)	1st & 2nd						13534	Lbs				
6767 × 2												
Return												
50 × 14	144	16.0	22						2304	Lbs.		
33 × 14	132	11.8	22						1558			
18 × 14	132	6.9	24						911			
									4773	Lbs.		
Toilet Exhaust												
18 × 12	18	6.5	24								117	Lbs.
16 × 12	14	6.0	↓								84	
12 × 12	14	5.2									73	
6 × 6	18	2.6									47	
											321	Lbs.

Figure 8.118

279

MEANS CONSOLIDATED ESTIMATE

Division 15: HVAC

SHEET NO. 1 of 5

PROJECT Office Building | CLASSIFICATION | ESTIMATE NO. 86-1

LOCATION | ARCHITECT | DATE 1986

TAKE OFF BY MJM | QUANTITIES BY MJM | PRICES BY JJM | EXTENSIONS BY SLM | CHECKED LMD

DESCRIPTION	SOURCE/DIMENSIONS			QUANTITY	UNIT	MATERIAL UNIT COST	MATERIAL TOTAL	LABOR UNIT COST	LABOR TOTAL	EQUIPMENT UNIT COST	EQUIPMENT TOTAL	SUBCONTRACT UNIT COST	SUBCONTRACT TOTAL
HVAC Sheet Metal Duct Work													
Supply Duct 3^D Floor (Insul.)				6800	Lb.								
Supply Duct (Not Insulated)				14000	Lb.								
Return Duct (Not Insulated)				4800	Lb.								
Toilet Exhaust Duct Work				325	Lb.								
Total Duct Work	15.7	64	058	25,925	Lb.	.53	13740	1.69	43813				
9"x9" Supply Diffusers	15.7	52	202	3	Ea.	57.75	173	12.95	39				
15"x15" Supply Diffusers	15.7	52	206	132	Ea.	96.25	12705	16.50	2178				
24"x24" Framed Eggcrate	15.7	55	404	19	Ea.	46.50	884	12.10	230				
Splitter Damper, 1 Foot Rod	15.7	61	700	12	Ea.	8.60	103	7.55	91				
6" Flexible Toilet Exhaust Duct	15.7	64	156	200	LF	.41	82	1.17	234				
4" Flexible Toilet Exhaust Duct	15.7	64	152	90	LF	.31	28	.91	82				
8"x6" Exhaust Register	15.7	58	504	3	Ea.	10.40	31	7.55	23				
8"x4" Exhaust Register	15.7	58	502	1	Ea.		10		7				
Roof Exhaust Fan 4600 CFM	15.7	70	724	1	Ea.		895		105				
24" Double Wall Galv. Chimney	15.5	92	034	12	LF	77.75	933	15.90	191				
24" Roof Flashing Collar	15.5	92	117	1	Ea.		129		42				
24" Double Wall Tee	15.5	92	133	1	Ea.		380		42				
24" Tee Cap	15.5	92	159	1	Ea.		25		24				
24" Rain Cap & Screen	15.5	92	188	1	Ea.		355		25				
Subtotals							30473		47126				

Figure 8.119

MEANS CONSOLIDATED ESTIMATE

PROJECT Office Building

Division 15: HVAC
SHEET NO. 2 of 5
ESTIMATE NO. 86-1
DATE 1986

						CLASSIFICATION								
LOCATION							ARCHITECT							
TAKE OFF BY MJM	QUANTITIES BY MJM		PRICES BY JJM			EXTENSIONS BY SLM							CHECKED LMD	

DESCRIPTION	SOURCE/DIMENSIONS		QUANTITY	UNIT	MATERIAL		LABOR		EQUIPMENT		SUBCONTRACT	
					UNIT COST	TOTAL	UNIT COST	TOTAL	UNIT COST	TOTAL	UNIT COST	TOTAL
Air Conditioning												
Chiller, 175 Tons	15.7	98	160	1	Ea.		61500		1900			
30 Ton Fan Coil Unit	15.7	73	026	6	Ea.	4250	25500	850	5100			
175 Ton Tower	15.7	49	190	175	Ton	39.25	6869	23	4025			
6" Thermometer 30° to 140°F	15.7	40	450	4	Ea.	24	96	5.70	23			
3½" Dial Pressure Gauge	15.7	40	230	6	Ea.	12.65	76	5.70	34			
7½ H.P. Condenser Water Pump	15.2	41	442	1	Ea.		1150		205			
5 H.P. Chill Water Pump	15.2	41	441	2	Ea.	985	1970	205	410			
4" Steel Pipe, Bevel End	15.1	55	211	180	LF	6.88	1238	9.30	1674			
2" Steel Pipe, Thread & Coupled	15.1	55	061	340	LF	2.76	938	5.05	1717			
4" Weld Tee	15.1	57	344	15	Ea.	41	615	115	1725			
4" Weld Elbow	15.1	57	313	20	Ea.	21.25	425	69	1380			
4" Weld Neck Flange	15.1	57	650	14	Ea.	30	420	34	476			
4" Sets Bolts, Nuts & Gaskets	15.1	57	067	30	Ea.	8.35	250	6.70	201			
2" Cast Iron Tee	15.1	56	058	12	Ea.	5.95	71	30	360			
2" Cast Iron Elbow	15.1	56	014	24	Ea.	4.40	106	18.05	433			
4" OS & Y Gate Valve IB	15.1	82	368	8	Ea.	160	1280	110	880			
4" Wafer, Check Valve	15.1	82	667	3	Ea.	100	300	110	330			
2" Bronze Gate Valve	15.1	80	348	6	Ea.	39.25	236	16.40	98			
4" Balancing Valve, Flanged	15.1	93	705	3	Ea.	237	711	110	330			
2" Stop and Balance Valve	15.1	93	108	6	Ea.	123	738	23	138			
4" Flanged Y Strainer	15.6	75	106	3	Ea.	157	471	110	330			
ASME 31 Gal. Expansion Tank	15.5	89	302	1	Ea.		700		27			
Subtotals							(105660)		(31796)			

Figure 8.120

MEANS CONSOLIDATED ESTIMATE

PROJECT: Office Building
LOCATION:
TAKE OFF BY: MJM | QUANTITIES BY: MJM | PRICES BY: JJM | EXTENSIONS BY: SLM | CHECKED: LMD
CLASSIFICATION
ARCHITECT

DESCRIPTION	SOURCE/DIMENSIONS		QUANTITY	UNIT	MATERIAL UNIT COST	MATERIAL TOTAL	LABOR UNIT COST	LABOR TOTAL	EQUIPMENT UNIT COST	EQUIPMENT TOTAL	SUBCONTRACT UNIT COST	SUBCONTRACT TOTAL
Heating												
3500 MBH, Gas, CI Water Boiler	15.5	08 340	1	Ea.		21550		2675				
Electric Duct Heater	15.5	29 106	1	Ea.		262		42				
79 Gal. ASME Expansion Tank	15.5	89 306	1	Ea.		1210		41				
3" Steel Pipe, Bevel End	15.1	55 209	120	LF	4.72	566	8	960				
1½" Steel Pipe, Thread & Coupled	15.1	55 060	320	LF	2.01	643	4.06	1299				
3" Weld Tee	15.1	57 343	15	Ea.	33.50	503	86	1290				
3" Weld Elbow	15.1	57 312	12	Ea.	13.10	157	49	588				
3" Weld Neck Flange	15.1	57 648	8	Ea.	23	184	25	200				
3" Sets Bolts, Nuts & Gaskets	15.1	57 065	16	Ea.	4.06	65	6	96				
1½" Cast Iron Tee	15.1	56 067	12	Ea.	3.95	47	25	300				
1½" Cast Iron Elbow	15.1	56 014	24	Ea.	4.40	106	18.05	433				
3" OS&Y Iron Boot Gate Valve	15.1	82 366	4	Ea.	115	460	72	288				
3" Wafer Check Valve	15.1	82 666	2	Ea.	76.75	154	72	144				
1½" Bronze Gate Valve	15.1	80 347	6	Ea.	27.50	165	13.90	83				
3" Balancing Valve, Flanged	15.1	93 702	2	Ea.	174	348	72	144				
1½" Stop and Balance Valve	15.1	93 107	6	Ea.	104	624	16.40	98				
3" Iron Body, Flanged Strainer	15.6	75 104	2	Ea.	80.50	161	73	146				
3" Air Control Fitting	15.6	08 010	1	Ea.		495		82				
6" Thermometer, 40° to 240°F	15.7	46 450	2	Ea.	24	48	5.70	11				
3½" Dial Pressure Gauge	15.7	40 230	4	Ea.	12.65	51	5.70	23				
5 H.P. Hot Water Pump	15.2	41 430	2	Ea.	955	1910	180	360				
Subtotals						29709		9303				

Figure 8.121

282

Division 15: HVAC

SHEET NO. 4 of 5
ESTIMATE NO. 86-1
DATE 1986
CHECKED LMD

PROJECT: Office Building
LOCATION:
TAKE OFF BY: MJM
QUANTITIES BY: MJM
PRICES BY: RSM
EXTENSIONS BY: JJM
CLASSIFICATION:
ARCHITECT:

DESCRIPTION	SOURCE/DIMENSIONS	QUANTITY	UNIT	MATERIAL UNIT COST	MATERIAL TOTAL	LABOR UNIT COST	LABOR TOTAL	EQUIPMENT UNIT COST	EQUIPMENT TOTAL	SUBCONTRACT UNIT COST	SUBCONTRACT TOTAL
HVAC: Miscellaneous											
Record Drawings		8	Hr.								
Operating Instructions		8	Hr.								
Maintenance Manuals		4	Hr.								
Cleaning System		16	Hr.								
Total		32	Hr.			22.75	819				
Subcontracts											
Insulation											14430
Balancing											9190
Controls											31980
Crane									1000		
Sub totals							819		1000		55600

MEANS CONSOLIDATED ESTIMATE

PROJECT Office Building
LOCATION
TAKE OFF BY MJM QUANTITIES BY MJM PRICES BY RSM EXTENSIONS BY JJM CHECKED LMD

CLASSIFICATION
ARCHITECT

HVAC - Summary

DESCRIPTION	SOURCE/DIMENSIONS	QUANTITY	UNIT	MATERIAL UNIT COST	MATERIAL TOTAL	LABOR UNIT COST	LABOR TOTAL	EQUIP. UNIT COST	EQUIP. TOTAL	SUBCONTRACT UNIT COST	SUBCONTRACT TOTAL
Ductwork	Sheet 1				304973		471226				
Air Conditioning	Sheet 2				1056660		317796				
Heating	Sheet 3				29709		9303				
Miscellaneous	Sheet 4						819				
Subcontracts	Sheet 4								1000		55600
Material Subtotal					1658442						
Sales Tax				6%	9951						
Bare Cost Totals					1757993		890944		1000		55600
Overhead & Profit	10/46.1/10/10			10%	175799	46.1%	410499	10%	100	10%	5560
Totals					(1933792)		(1300093)		(1100)		(61160)
Total Bid											3857725

Table 8.4-009 Sheet Metal Calculator (Weight in Lb./Ft. of Length)

Gauge	26	24	22	20	18	16
Wt.-Lb./S.F.	.906	1.156	1.406	1.656	2.156	2.656
SMACNA Max. Dimension - Long Side		30"	54"	84"	85" Up	
Sum-2 Sides						
2	.3	.40	.50	.60	.80	.90
3	.5	.65	.80	.90	1.1	1.4
4	.7	.85	1.0	1.2	1.5	1.8
5	.8	1.1	1.3	1.5	1.9	2.3
6	1.	1.3	1.5	1.7	2.3	2.7
7	1.2	1.5	1.8	2.0	2.7	3.2
8	1.3	1.7	2.0	2.3	3.0	3.6
9	1.5	1.9	2.3	2.6	3.4	4.1
10	1.7	2.2	2.5	2.9	3.8	4.5
11	1.8	2.4	2.8	3.2	4.2	5.0
12	2.0	2.6	3.0	3.5	4.6	5.4
13	2.2	2.8	3.3	3.8	4.9	5.9
14	2.3	3.0	3.5	4.1	5.3	6.3
15	2.5	3.2	3.8	4.4	5.7	6.8
16	2.7	3.4	4.0	4.6	6.1	7.2
17	2.8	3.7	4.3	4.9	6.5	7.7
18	3.0	3.9	4.5	5.2	6.8	8.1
19	3.2	4.1	4.8	5.5	7.2	8.6
20	3.3	4.3	5.0	5.8	7.6	9.0
21	3.5	4.5	5.3	6.1	8.0	9.5
22	3.7	4.7	5.5	6.4	8.4	9.9
23	3.8	5.0	5.8	6.7	8.7	10.4
24	4.0	5.2	6.0	7.0	9.1	10.8
25	4.2	5.4	6.3	7.3	9.5	11.3
26	4.3	5.6	6.5	7.5	9.9	11.7
27	4.5	5.8	6.8	7.8	10.3	12.2
28	4.7	6.0	7.0	8.1	10.6	12.6
29	4.8	6.2	7.3	8.4	11.0	13.1
30	5.0	6.5	7.5	8.7	11.4	13.5
31	5.2	6.7	7.8	9.0	11.8	14.0
32	5.3	6.9	8.0	9.3	12.2	14.4
33	5.5	7.1	8.3	9.6	12.5	14.9
34	5.7	7.3	8.5	9.9	12.9	15.3
35	5.8	7.5	8.8	10.2	13.3	15.8
36	6.0	7.8	9.0	10.4	13.7	16.2
37	6.2	8.0	9.3	10.7	14.1	16.7
38	6.3	8.2	9.5	11.0	14.4	17.1
39	6.5	8.4	9.8	11.3	14.8	17.6
40	6.7	8.6	10.0	11.6	15.2	18.0
41	6.8	8.8	10.3	11.9	15.6	18.5
42	7.0	9.0	10.5	12.2	16.0	18.9
43	7.2	9.2	10.8	12.5	16.3	19.4
44	7.3	9.5	11.0	12.8	16.7	19.8
45	7.5	9.7	11.3	13.1	17.1	20.3
46	7.7	9.9	11.5	13.3	17.5	20.7
47	7.8	10.1	11.8	13.6	17.9	21.2
48	8.0	10.3	12.0	13.9	18.2	21.6
49	8.2	10.5	12.3	14.2	18.6	22.1
50	8.3	10.7	12.5	14.5	19.0	22.5
51	8.5	11.0	12.8	14.8	19.4	23.0
52	8.7	11.2	13.0	15.1	19.8	23.4
53	8.8	11.4	13.3	15.4	20.1	23.9
54	9.0	11.6	13.5	15.7	20.5	24.3
55	9.2	11.8	13.8	16.0	20.9	24.8

Gauge	26	24	22	20	18	16
Wt.-Lb./S.F.	.906	1.156	1.406	1.656	2.156	2.656
SMACNA Max. Dimension - Long Side		30"	54"	84"	85" Up	
Sum-2 Sides						
56	9.3	12.0	14.0	16.2	21.3	25.2
57	9.5	12.3	14.3	16.5	21.7	25.7
58	9.7	12.5	14.5	16.8	22.0	26.1
59	9.8	12.7	14.8	17.1	22.4	26.6
60	10.0	12.9	15.0	17.4	22.8	27.0
61	10.2	13.1	15.3	17.7	23.2	27.5
62	10.3	13.3	15.5	18.0	23.6	27.9
63	10.5	13.5	15.8	18.3	24.0	28.4
64	10.7	13.7	16.0	18.6	24.3	28.8
65	10.8	13.9	16.3	18.9	24.7	29.3
66	11.0	14.1	16.5	19.1	25.1	29.7
67	11.2	14.3	16.8	19.4	25.5	30.2
68	11.3	14.6	17.0	19.7	25.8	30.6
69	11.5	14.8	17.3	20.0	26.2	31.1
70	11.7	15.0	17.5	20.3	26.6	31.5
71	11.8	15.2	17.8	20.6	27.0	32.0
72	12.0	15.4	18.0	20.9	27.4	32.4
73	12.2	15.6	18.3	21.2	27.7	32.9
74	12.3	15.8	18.5	21.5	28.1	33.3
75	12.5	16.1	18.8	21.8	28.5	33.8
76	12.7	16.3	19.0	22.0	28.9	34.2
77	12.8	16.5	19.3	22.3	29.3	34.7
78	13.0	16.7	19.5	22.6	29.6	35.1
79	13.2	16.9	19.8	22.9	30.0	35.6
80	13.3	17.1	20.0	23.2	30.4	36.0
81	13.5	17.3	20.3	23.5	30.8	36.5
82	13.7	17.5	20.5	23.8	31.2	36.9
83	13.8	17.8	20.8	24.1	31.5	37.4
84	14.0	18.0	21.0	24.4	31.9	37.8
85	14.2	18.2	21.3	24.7	32.3	38.3
86	14.3	18.4	21.5	24.9	32.7	38.7
87	14.5	18.6	21.8	25.2	33.1	39.2
88	14.7	18.8	22.0	25.5	33.4	39.6
89	14.8	19.0	22.3	25.8	33.8	40.1
90	15.0	19.3	22.5	26.1	34.2	40.5
91	15.2	19.5	22.8	26.4	34.6	41.0
92	15.3	19.7	23.0	26.7	35.0	41.4
93	15.5	19.9	23.3	27.0	35.3	41.9
94	15.7	20.1	23.5	27.3	35.7	42.3
95	15.8	20.3	23.8	27.6	36.1	42.8
96	16.0	20.5	24.0	27.8	36.5	43.2
97	16.2	20.8	24.3	28.1	36.9	43.7
98	16.3	21.0	24.5	28.4	37.2	44.1
99	16.5	21.2	24.8	28.7	37.6	44.6
100	16.7	21.4	25.0	29.0	38.0	45.0
101	16.8	21.6	25.3	29.3	38.4	45.5
102	17.0	21.8	25.5	29.6	38.8	45.9
103	17.2	22.0	25.8	29.9	39.1	46.4
104	17.3	22.3	26.0	30.2	39.5	46.8
105	17.5	22.5	26.3	30.5	39.9	47.3
106	17.7	22.7	26.5	30.7	40.3	47.7
107	17.8	22.9	26.8	31.0	40.7	48.2
108	18.0	23.1	27.0	31.3	41.0	48.6
109	18.2	23.3	27.3	31.6	41.4	49.1
110	18.3	23.5	27.5	31.9	41.8	49.5

Example: If duct is 34" x 20" x 15' long, 34" is greater than 30" maximum, for 24 ga. so must be 22 ga. 34" + 20" = 54" going across from 54" find 13.5 lb. per foot. 13.5 x 15' = 202.5 lbs. For

S.F. of surface area 202.5 ÷ 1.406 = 144 S.F.
Note: figures include an allowance for scrap.

Figure 8.124

MEANS CONSOLIDATED ESTIMATE

PROJECT Office Building

LOCATION

TAKE OFF BY EBW QUANTITIES BY EBW PRICES BY RSM EXTENSIONS BY SLM CHECKED JDM

CLASSIFICATION ARCHITECT

Division 15 SHEET NO. 1 of 1 ESTIMATE NO. 86-1 DATE 1986

DESCRIPTION	SOURCE/DIMENSIONS	QUANTITY	UNIT	MATERIAL UNIT COST	MATERIAL TOTAL	LABOR UNIT COST	LABOR TOTAL	EQUIPMENT UNIT COST	EQUIPMENT TOTAL	SUBCONTRACT UNIT COST	SUBCONTRACT TOTAL
Division 15: Mechanical											
	SUBCONTRACTOR QUOTATIONS										
Plumbing:											
Base Price											92641
Pipe Insulation	(HW Only)										912
Total Plumbing											93553
Fire Protection:											
Standpipes											15075
Sprinklers											87718
Total Fire Protection											102793
HVAC:											
Base Price											323465
Insulation											15873
Balancing											10109
Controls											35178
Crane											1100
Total HVAC											385725
Division 15: Total											582071

Figure 8.125

Division 16: Electrical

A good estimator must be able to visualize the proposed electrical installation from source (service) to end use (fixtures or devices). This process helps to identify each component needed to make the system work. Before starting the takeoff, the estimator should follow some basic steps:

- Read the electrical specifications thoroughly.
- Scan the electrical plans. Check other sections of the plans and specifications for their potential effect on electrical work (special attention should be given to mechanical and site work).
- Check the architectural and structural plans for unique or atypical requirements.
- Check and become familiar with the fixture and power symbols.
- Clarify with the architect or engineer any unclear areas, making sure that the scope of work is understood. Addenda may be necessary to clarify certain items of work so that the responsibility for the performance of all work is defined.
- Immediately contact suppliers, manufacturers, and subsystem specialty contractors in order to get their quotations, sub-bids, and drawings.

Certain information should be taken from complete plans and specifications in order to properly estimate the electrical portion of the work. In addition to floor plans, other sources of information are:

- Power riser diagram
- Panelboard schedule
- Fixture schedule
- Electrical symbol legend
- Reflected ceiling plans
- Branch circuit plans
- Fire alarm and telephone riser diagrams
- Special systems

Performing a fixture and device takeoff can be a good way to become familiar with the proposed electrical installation. Take off one bay, section, or floor at a time. Mark each fixture and device with colored pencils and list them as you proceed. Check the site plans for exterior fixtures.

Fixtures should be taken off using the fixture schedule in conjunction with the reflected ceiling plan. Fixture counts should have outlet boxes, plaster rings, or Greenfield with connectors and fixture wire if needed. Include fixture supports as needed.

Separate quantity sheets should be used for each of the major categories of electrical work. By keeping each system on different sheets, the estimator will find it easy to isolate various costs. This format becomes a reference for purchasing and cost control. It also provides a breakdown of items that can be submitted to the general contractor when billing.

While making takeoffs of each category, identify all other required components of the systems. Determine the materials that will be part of a quotation or sub-bid from a supplier, including additional items to complete the vendor's package.

Switchgear

Material costs for large equipment such as switchgear, motor control centers and associated items should be obtained from suppliers or manufacturers. When determining the installation cost for large equipment (for any division) the estimator must consider a number of factors to be sure that all work is included:

- Access and placement
- Uncrating
- Rigging and setting
- Pads and anchors
- Leveling and shimming
- Assembly of components
- Connections
- Temporary protection requirements

While pads and anchors for large equipment may be well designated on the plans, supports for smaller equipment, such as panels and transformers, may not be well defined. For example, floor to ceiling steel supports may be required. The same consideration must be given to large cable troughs and conduits. Special support requirements may be necessary. If so, they must be included, whether they are the responsibility of the electrical or general contractor. For elevated installation of equipment, labor costs should be adjusted. Suggested adjustments follow:

Ceiling Height	Labor Adjustment
10' – 15'	+ 15%
15' – 25'	+ 30%
Over 25'	+ 35%

Ducts and Cable Trays

Bus ducts and cable trays should be estimated by component:

- Type and size of duct or tray
- Material (aluminum or galvanized)
- Hangers
- Fittings

The installation of under floor ducts systems (and conduit) must be scheduled after placement of any reinforcing at the bottom of slabs, but before installation of the upper steel. Without proper coordination, delays can occur. The estimate and preliminary schedule should reflect associated costs. Because of the high cost of tray and duct systems, the takeoff should be as accurate as possible. Fittings should not be deducted from straight lengths. In this way, an adequate allowance for waste should be provided. For high ceiling installations, labor costs for bus duct and cable trays should be adjusted accordingly. Suggested adjustments are:

Ceiling Height	Labor Adjustment
15' – 20'	+ 10%
20' – 25'	+ 20%
25' – 30'	+ 25%
30' – 35'	+ 30%
35' – 40'	+ 35%
Over 40'	+ 40%

Feeders

Feeder conduit and wire should be carefully taken off using a scale or printed dimensions. This is a more accurate method than the use of a rotometer. Large conduit and wire are expensive and require a considerable amount of labor. Accurate quantities are important. Switchboard locations should be marked on each floor before measuring horizontal runs. The distance between floors should be marked on riser plans and added to the horizontal for a complete feeder run. Conduits should be measured at right angles to the structure unless it has been determined that they can be routed directly. Elbows, terminations, bends, or expansion joints should also be taken off at this time. Under-slab and high ceiling installations should be treated the same as in the case of ducts and trays. The estimator should also consider the weight of material for high ceiling installations. Extra workers may be required for heavier components. Typical weights are shown in Figure 8.126. If standard feeder takeoff sheets are used, the wire column should reflect longer lengths than the conduit. This is because of added amounts of wire used in the panels and switchboard to make connections. If the added length is not shown on the plans, it can be determined by checking a manufacturer's catalog. Conduit, cable supports, and accessories should all be totaled at this time.

Branch Circuits

Branch circuits may be taken off using a rotometer. The estimator should take care to start and stop accurately at boxes. Start with two wire circuits and mark with colored pencil as items are taken off. Add about 5% to conduit quantities for normal waste. On wire, add 10% to 12% overage to make connections. Add conduit fittings, such as locknuts, bushings, couplings, expansion joints, and fasteners. Two conduit terminations per box are average. Figure 8.127 shows prices for conduit as presented in *Building Construction Cost Data*. Note that a minimum amount of fittings are included in the costs.

Wiring devices should be entered with plates, boxes, and plaster rings. Calculate stub ups or drops for wiring devices. Switches should be counted and multiplied by the distance from switch to ceiling.

Receptacles are handled similarly, depending on whether they are wired from the ceiling or floor. In many cases, there are two conduits going to a receptacle box as you feed in and out to the next outlet. Some estimators let rotometers overrun outlets purposely as an adjustment for vertical runs; this practice can, however, lead to inaccuracies.

In metal stud partitions, it is often acceptable to go horizontally from receptacle to receptacle. In wood partitions, horizontal runs are also the usual practice. In suspended ceilings, the specifications should be checked to see if straight runs are allowed. If the space above the ceiling is used as a return air plenum, conduit is usually required for all wiring.

Motors, safety switches, starters, and controls, should each include power lines, junction boxes, supports, wiring troughs, and wire terminations. Short runs of Greenfield or Sealtite with appropriate connectors and wire should be added for motor wiring.

Conduit Weight Comparisons (Lbs. per 100 ft.)

Type	1/2"	3/4"	1"	1-1/4"	1-1/2"	2"	2-1/2"	3"	3-1/2"	4"	5"	6"
Rigid Aluminum	28	37	55	72	89	119	188	246	296	350	479	630
Rigid Steel	79	105	153	201	249	332	527	683	831	972	1314	1745
Intermediate Steel (IMC)	60	82	116	150	182	242	401	493	573	638		
Electrical Metallic Tubing (EMT)	29	45	65	96	111	141	215	260	365	390		
Polyvinyl Chloride, Schedule 40	16	22	32	43	52	69	109	142	170	202	271	350
Polyvinyl Chloride Encased Burial						38		67	88	105	149	202
Fibre Duct Encased Burial						127		164	180	206	400	511
Fibre Duct Direct Burial						150		251	300	354		
Transite Encased Burial						160		240	290	330	450	550
Transite Direct Burial						220		310		400	540	640

Weight Comparisons of Common Size Cast Boxes in Lbs.

Size NEMA 4 or 9	Cast Iron	Cast Aluminum	Size NEMA 7	Cast Iron	Cast Aluminum
6" x 6" x 6"	17	7	6" x 6" x 6"	40	15
8" x 6" x 6"	21	8	8" x 6" x 6"	50	19
10" x 6" x 6"	23	9	10" x 6" x 6"	55	21
12" x 12" x 6"	52	20	12" x 6" x 6"	100	37
16" x 16" x 6"	97	36	16" x 16" x 6"	140	52
20" x 20" x 6"	133	50	20" x 20" x 6"	180	67
24" x 18" x 8"	149	56	24" x 18" x 8"	250	93
24" x 24" x 10"	238	88	24" x 24" x 10"	358	133
30" x 24" x 12"	324	120	30" x 24" x 10"	475	176
36" x 36" x 12"	500	185	30" x 24" x 12"	510	189

Size Required and Weight (Lbs./1000 L.F.) of Aluminum and Copper THW Wire by Ampere Load

Amperes	Copper Size	Aluminum Size	Copper Weight	Aluminum Weight
15	14	12	24	11
20	12	10	33	17
30	10	8	48	39
45	8	6	77	52
65	6	4	112	72
85	4	2	167	101
100	3	1	205	136
115	2	1/0	252	162
130	1	2/0	324	194
150	1/0	3/0	397	233
175	2/0	4/0	491	282
200	3/0	250	608	347
230	4/0	300	753	403
255	250	400	899	512
285	300	500	1068	620
310	350	500	1233	620
335	400	600	1396	772
380	500	750	1732	951

Weight (Lbs./L.F.) of 4 Pole Aluminum and Copper Bus Duct by Ampere Load

Amperes	Aluminum Feeder	Copper Feeder	Aluminum Plug-In	Copper Plug-In
225			7	7
400			8	13
600	10	10	11	14
800	10	19	13	18
1000	11	19	16	22
1350	14	24	20	30
1600	17	26	25	39
2000	19	30	29	46
2500	27	43	36	56
3000	30	48	42	73
4000	39	67		
5000		78		

Figure 8.126

16.0 Raceways	CREW	DAILY OUTPUT	UNIT	BARE COSTS MAT.	BARE COSTS INST.	BARE COSTS TOTAL	TOTAL INCL O&P
10-001 **CABLE TRAY** Ladder type with fittings and supports, 4" deep							
016 Galvanized steel tray							
017 4" rung spacing, 6" wide	1 Elec	49	L.F.	4.35	3.66	8.01	10.05
020 12" wide		43		5.30	4.17	9.47	11.80
040 18" wide		41		6.15	4.37	10.52	13.05
060 24" wide		39		7.15	4.59	11.74	14.45
320 Aluminum tray, 4" deep, 6" rung spacing, 6" wide		67		6.50	2.67	9.17	11
322 12" wide		62		7.30	2.89	10.19	12.20
324 24" wide	▼	53	▼	9	3.38	12.38	14.75
20-001 **CONDUIT TO 15' HIGH** Includes 2 terminations, 2 elbows and							
002 10 beam clamps per 100 L.F.							
030 (139) Aluminum, 1/2" diameter	1 Elec	100	L.F.	.50	1.79	2.29	3.13
050 3/4" diameter		90		.68	1.99	2.67	3.61
070 1" diameter		80		1	2.24	3.24	4.32
100 1-1/4" diameter		70		1.35	2.56	3.91	5.15
103 1-1/2" diameter		65		1.70	2.76	4.46	5.85
105 2" diameter		60		2.30	2.99	5.29	6.80
107 2-1/2" diameter		50		3.50	3.58	7.08	9
110 3" diameter		45		4.90	3.98	8.88	11.10
113 3-1/2" diameter		40		6.90	4.48	11.38	14.05
114 4" diameter		35		7.60	5.10	12.70	15.70
175 Rigid galvanized steel, 1/2" diameter		90		.54	1.99	2.53	3.46
177 3/4" diameter		80		.66	2.24	2.90	3.95
180 1" diameter		65		1	2.76	3.76	5.05
183 1-1/4" diameter		60		1.35	2.99	4.34	5.80
185 1-1/2" diameter		55		1.60	3.26	4.86	6.45
187 2" diameter		45		2.25	3.98	6.23	8.20
190 2-1/2" diameter		35		3.70	5.10	8.80	11.45
193 3" diameter		25		5.10	7.15	12.25	15.90
195 3-1/2" diameter		22		5.75	8.15	13.90	18.05
197 4" diameter		20		8	8.95	16.95	22
250 Steel, intermediate conduit (IMC), 1/2" diameter		100		.44	1.79	2.23	3.06
253 3/4" diameter		90		.54	1.99	2.53	3.46
255 1" diameter		70		.84	2.56	3.40	4.61
257 1-1/4" diameter		65		1.10	2.76	3.86	5.15
260 1-1/2" diameter		60		1.35	2.99	4.34	5.80
263 2" diameter		50		1.85	3.58	5.43	7.20
265 2-1/2" diameter		40		3.15	4.48	7.63	9.90
267 3" diameter		30		4.35	5.95	10.30	13.35
270 3-1/2" diameter		27		4.95	6.65	11.60	15
273 4" diameter		25		7.10	7.15	14.25	18.10
500 Electric metallic tubing (EMT), 1/2" diameter		170		.23	1.05	1.28	1.77
502 3/4" diameter		130		.33	1.38	1.71	2.35
504 1" diameter		115		.54	1.56	2.10	2.83
506 1-1/4" diameter		100		.84	1.79	2.63	3.50
508 1-1/2" diameter		90		1.06	1.99	3.05	4.03
510 2" diameter		80		1.40	2.24	3.64	4.76
512 2-1/2" diameter		60		2.97	2.99	5.96	7.55
514 3" diameter		50		3.70	3.58	7.28	9.20
516 3-1/2" diameter		45		4.67	3.98	8.65	10.85
518 4" diameter	▼	40	▼	5.50	4.48	9.98	12.50
990 Add to labor for higher elevated installation							
991 15' to 20' high, add					10%		
992 20' to 25' high, add					20%		
993 25' to 30' high, add					25%		
994 30' to 35' high, add					30%		
995 35' to 40' high, add					35%		
996 Over 40' high, add					40%		

Figure 8.127

For large installations, the economy of scale may have a definite impact on the electrical costs. If large quantities of a particular item are installed in the same general area certain deductions can be made for labor. Suggested deductions include:

	Quantity	Labor Deduction
Under floor ducts, bus ducts, conduit, cable systems:	150 to 250 LF	-10%
	250 to 350 LF	-15%
	350 to 500 LF	-20%
	Over 500 LF	-25%
Outlet boxes:	25 to 50	-15%
	50 to 75	-20%
	75 to 100	-25%
	Over 100	-30%
Wiring devices:	10 to 25	-20%
	25 to 50	-25%
	50 to 100	-30%
	Over 100	-35%
Lighting fixtures:	25 to 50	-15%
	50 to 75	-20%
	75 to 100	-25%
	Over 100	-30%

The estimator for the general contractor may require only a budget cost for the purpose of verifying subcontractor bids. As described in the section on mechanical estimating, square foot or systems costs developed from similar, past projects can also be useful for electrical estimating.

Sample Estimate: Division 16

While electrical work should be accurately estimated by a subcontractor for bidding purposes, the estimator for the general contractor should understand the work involved. Complete plans and specifications will include a number of schedules and diagrams that will help the estimator to determine quantities. Figures 8.128 and 8.129 are the lighting fixture and panelboard schedules, respectively, for the building project. While such schedules may not always provide quantities, they can serve as a check list to ensure that all types are counted.

Figure 8.130 is the quantity sheet for lighting. Note that associated boxes, devices and wiring are taken off at the same time as the fixtures and that the takeoff is done by floor. By performing the estimate in this way, quantities for purchase are easily determined and changes can be calculated quickly. For example, in a typical project, lighting fixtures are often changed or substituted, either because of aesthetic decisions or unavailability. If quantities and costs are isolated, adjustments are easily made.

Type	Manufacturer & Catalog #	Fixture	Type	Lamps Qty	Lamps Volts	Watts	Mounting	Remarks
A	Meansco #7054	2'x4' Troffer	F-40 CW	4	277	40	Recessed	Acrylic Lens
B	Meansco #7055	1'x4' Troffer	F-40 CW	2	277	40	Recessed	Acrylic Lens
C	Meansco #7709	6"x4'	F-40 CW	1	277	40	Surface	Acrylic Wrap
D	Meansco #7710	6"x8' Strip	F96T12 CW	1	277	40	Surface	
E	Meansco #7900A	6"x4'	F-40	1	277	40	Surface	Mirror Light
F	Kingston #100A	6"x4'	F-40	1	277	40	Surface	Acrylic Wrap
G	Kingston #110C	' Strip	F-40 CW	1	277	40	Surface	
H	Kingston #3752	Wallpack	HPS	1	277	150	Bracket	W/Photo Cell
J	Kingston #201-202	Floodlight	HPS	1	277	400	Surface	2' Below Fascia
K	Kingston #203		HPS	1	277	100	Wall Bracket	
L	Meansco #8100	Exit Light	1-13W 20W T6-1/2	1 2	120 6½	13 20	Surface	
M	Meansco #9000	Battery Unit	Sealed Beam	2	12	18	Wall Mount	12 Volt Unit

Figure 8.128

Panel	Main Breaker	Main	Lugs	Amps	Circ.	Breakers #	Breakers Type	Location	Volts
PP-1	No	3-P	Wire	100	20	(20)	1P 20 A	Basement	120/208
PP-2	No	3-P	4 Wire	225	42	(42)	1P 20 A	1st Floor	120/208
PP-3	No	3-P	4 Wire	225	42	(42)	1P 20 A	2nd Floor	120/208
PP-4	No	3-P	4 Wire	225	42	(42)	1P-20 A	3rd Floor	120/208
LP-1	No	3-P	4 Wire	225	42	(42)	1P-20 A	Basement	277/480
LP-2	No	3-P	4 Wire	225	42	(42)	1P-20 A	1st Floor	277/480
LP-3	No	3-P	4 Wire	225	42	(42)	1P-20 A	2nd Floor	277/480
LP-4	No	3-P	4 Wire	225	42	(42)	1P-20 A	3rd Floor	277/480

Figure 8.129

MEANSCO FORM F 180.0

QUANTITY SHEET

PROJECT: Office Building
LOCATION: OWNER: ARCHITECT:
SECTION: Lighting TAKE OFF BY: PHD DATE:
EXTENSIONS BY: CHECKED BY:
SHEET NO. ESTIMATE NO.

NO	DESCRIPTION / DIMENSIONS	Garage	UNIT	1st Flr	UNIT	2nd Flr	UNIT	3rd Flr	UNIT	Penthouse	UNIT	SubTotal	UNIT	Adjustments	UNIT	Total	UNIT
Fixtures																	
A	2'x4' Troffer, 4L	1		237		244		244				725	Ea.			725	Ea.
B	1'x4' Troffer, 2L	6		10		6		6				28				28	
C	6'x4' Acrylic	4		9		8		8				29				29	
D	6'x8' Strip	53										53				53	
E	6'x8' Mirror Lite			3		3		3				9				9	
G	4" Strip Surf	6						1		18		27				27	
H	150W Wall Pack	2		1								3				3	
J												0				0	
K	70W Wall Pack	1		1						1		3				3	
L	Exit Light	6		8		4		4		1		23				23	
N	Remote Head	1		1		1		1				4				4	
M	Emergency Lite	3		3		3		3		1		13				13	

Type F is deleted - Use Type C

NO	DESCRIPTION / DIMENSIONS	Garage	UNIT	1st Flr	UNIT	2nd Flr	UNIT	3rd Flr	UNIT	Penthouse	UNIT	SubTotal	UNIT	Adjustments	UNIT	Total	UNIT
Boxes & Devices																	
O	4" Round Junction Box, Steel	8		128		129		129				394	Ea.			394	Ea.
	4" Round Cover	8		128		129		129				394				394	
S₁	Switch Box, 1 Gang Steel	1		5		5		5		4		20				20	
S₁	S.P.Switch 20A, Single Pole Sw.	1		5		5		5		4		20				20	
	4" Sq. Box	6		8		4		4		1		23				23	
	Switch Cover	1		5		5		5		4		20				20	
	Plaster Rings 4"	6		8		4		4		1		23				23	

NO	DESCRIPTION / DIMENSIONS	Garage	UNIT	1st Flr	UNIT	2nd Flr	UNIT	3rd Flr	UNIT	Penthouse	UNIT	SubTotal	UNIT	Adjustments	UNIT	Total	UNIT
Raceways																	
	1/2" EMT	1460		2070		1880		1880		940		8250	LF	830 10%		9080	LF
	1/2" Conn. Set screw type	190		264		242		242		114		1052	Ea.			1052	Ea.
	1/2" Conn. Compression type	18		26		24		24		12		104	Ea.			104	Ea.
	3/8" Greenfield	70		1295		1330		1330				4025	LF	405 10%		4430	LF
	3/8" Greenfield Conn.	32		474		488		488				1482	Ea.			1482	Ea.

NO	DESCRIPTION / DIMENSIONS	Garage	UNIT	1st Flr	UNIT	2nd Flr	UNIT	3rd Flr	UNIT	Penthouse	UNIT	SubTotal	UNIT	Adjustments	UNIT	Total	UNIT
Conductors																	
	#12 THHN / Copper	9660		10095		9630		9630		2820		36035	LF	2683 LF =>		405	CLF

Figure 8.130

294

The estimate sheets for lighting — as might be prepared by an electrical subcontractor — are shown in Figures 8.131 and 8.132. Prices are from *Means Electrical Cost Data, 1986*. By including the associated costs for boxes, devices and wiring with the lighting fixtures and the other major components, the electrical estimator is able to develop system costs for comparison to other projects, and for crosschecking. Since this is only part of the electrical work, overhead and profit are not likely to be added until the end of the electrical estimate. However, if a breakdown of costs is provided as part of the quotation, each portion of that breakdown would include overhead and profit. Such is the case in the estimate sheet for Division 16 as prepared by the general contractor, in Figure 8.133. For each system, the associated costs for devices and wiring are included, in addition to overhead and profit.

Estimate Summary

At this point in the estimating process, the estimate is complete for Divisions 2 through 16. All vendor quotations and subcontractors' bids should be in hand (ideally, but not necessarily realistically); and all costs should be determined for the work to be done "in-house". All costs known at this time should be entered on the Estimate Summary sheet as shown in Figure 8.134. Based on the subtotal of these costs, the items in Division 1 which are dependent on job costs can then be calculated.

The Project Overhead Summary is shown in Figures 8.135 and 8.136. In addition to those items related to job costs, there are also certain project overhead items that depend on job duration. A preliminary schedule is required in order to calculate these time related costs. Using the procedure described in Chapter 5, a preliminary precedence schedule is prepared for the project as shown in Figure 8.137. Note that only those items that effect the project duration are calculated and included in the total time (247 working days). A more extensive and detailed project schedule is completed when the construction contract is awarded. The corresponding preliminary bar schedule is shown in Figure 8.138.

Throughout the estimate for all divisions, the estimator should note all items which should be included as project overhead as well as those which may affect the project schedule. The estimator must be especially aware of items which are implied but may not be directly stated in the specifications. Some of the "unspecified" costs which may be included are for the preparation of shop drawings, as-built drawings and the final project schedule. Costs for general job safety — such as railings, safety nets, fire extinguishers — must also be included if these items are required. If costs for job safety are not listed in the estimate, the items may not be installed on the job — until an OSHA fine, or worse, an accident.

Costs for shop drawings are mentioned above because the time involved in their preparation, submission and approval must also be considered when preparing the schedule. Construction delays are often blamed on the fact that shop drawings or "cuts" weren't submitted early enough, or approved in a timely fashion. The estimator must base such scheduling decisions on experience.

MEANS CONSOLIDATED ESTIMATE

PROJECT: Office Building
LOCATION:
TAKE OFF BY: PHD   QUANTITIES BY: PHD
CLASSIFICATION
ARCHITECT
PRICES BY: RSM   EXTENSIONS BY: SLM   CHECKED: JDM

DESCRIPTION	SOURCE/DIMENSIONS			QUANTITY	UNIT	MATERIAL		LABOR		EQUIPMENT		SUBCONTRACT	
						UNIT COST	TOTAL	UNIT COST	TOTAL	UNIT COST	TOTAL	UNIT COST	TOTAL
Lighting													
Fixtures:													
Type													
A 2'x4' w/4L	16.6	10	060	725	Ea.	49	35525	38	27550				
B 1'x4' w/2L	16.6	10	020	28	Ea.	35	980	31	868				
C 6"x4' w/1L	16.6	10	202	29	Ea.	32	928	22	638				
D 6"x8' w/1L	16.6	10	260	53	Ea.	32	1696	27	1431				
E 6"x4' Mirror Lt.	16.6	10	690	9	Ea.	39	351	22	198				
G 4' Surface Mt.	16.6	10	220	27	Ea.	18	468	21	567				
H 150 w HPS Wall Pk.	16.6	50	117	2	Ea.	280	560	45	90				
K 70 w HPS Wall Pk.	16.6	50	116	3	Ea.	265	795	45	135				
L Exit Single Face	16.6	25	008	23	Ea.	36	828	22	506				
M Remote Head	16.6	25	018	4	Ea.	16	64	6.70	27				
N Emerg. Battery Unit	16.6	25	050	13	Ea.	195	2535	45	585				
Raceways:													
1/2" EMT	16.0	20	500	9080	LF	.23	2088	1.05	9534				
Set Screw Conn.	16.0	20	650	1052	Ea.	.35	368	1.49	1567				
Com. Pr. Conn.	16.0	20	880	104	Ea.	.61	63	1.49	155				
Greenfield	16.0	60	005	4430	LF	.18	797.90	.90	3987				
Connectors	16.0	60	042	1482	Ea.	.20	296	1.79	2653				
Subtotals							(48342)		(50491)				

Figure 8.131

MEANS CONSOLIDATED ESTIMATE

PROJECT: Office Building

LOCATION:

TAKE OFF BY PHD QUANTITIES BY PHD PRICES BY RSM EXTENSIONS BY SLM

CLASSIFICATION:

ARCHITECT:

DESCRIPTION	SOURCE/DIMENSIONS		QUANTITY	UNIT	MATERIAL UNIT COST	MATERIAL TOTAL	LABOR UNIT COST	LABOR TOTAL	EQUIPMENT UNIT COST	EQUIPMENT TOTAL	SUBCONTRACT UNIT COST	SUBCONTRACT TOTAL
Lighting: (Cont'd)												
Conductors:												
THHN Copper #12	16.1	10	120	405	CLF	3.85	1559	16.30	6602			
Boxes & Devices:												
Box - 4" Octagon	16.2	20	002	394	Ea.	.89	351	8.95	3526			
4" Blank Cover	16.2	20	025	394	Ea.	.41	162	2.80	1103			
Box - 4" Square	16.2	20	015	23	Ea.	1.07	25	8.95	206			
Plaster Rings	16.2	20	030	23	Ea.	.63	14	2.80	64			
Switch Box	16.2	20	065	20	Ea.	.93	19	6.65	133			
S.P. Switch 20A	16.2	30	050	20	Ea.	6.95	139	6.65	133			
Switch Plate	16.2	30	260	20	Ea.	2.10	42	2.24	45			
Subtotals							2311		11812			
Sheet 1							48342		50491			
Sheet 2							2311		11812			
Total Lighting							50653		62303			

Figure 8.132

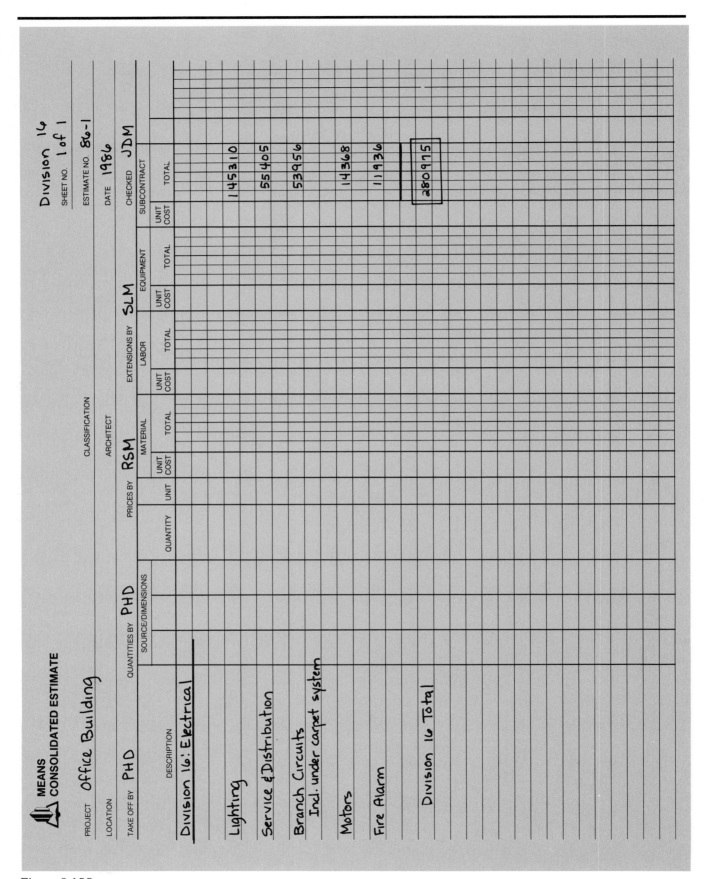

MEANS CONSOLIDATED ESTIMATE

Division 16
SHEET NO. 1 of 1

PROJECT Office Building　　CLASSIFICATION　　ESTIMATE NO. 86-1

LOCATION　　ARCHITECT　　DATE 1986

TAKE OFF BY PHD　　QUANTITIES BY PHD　　PRICES BY RSM　　EXTENSIONS BY SLM　　CHECKED JDM

DESCRIPTION	SOURCE/DIMENSIONS			QUANTITY	UNIT	MATERIAL UNIT COST	MATERIAL TOTAL	LABOR UNIT COST	LABOR TOTAL	EQUIPMENT UNIT COST	EQUIPMENT TOTAL	SUBCONTRACT UNIT COST	SUBCONTRACT TOTAL	
Division 16: Electrical														
Lighting													145310	
Service & Distribution													55405	
Branch Circuits													53956	
Incl. under carpet system														
Motors													14368	
Fire Alarm													11936	
Division 16 Total													280975	

Figure 8.133

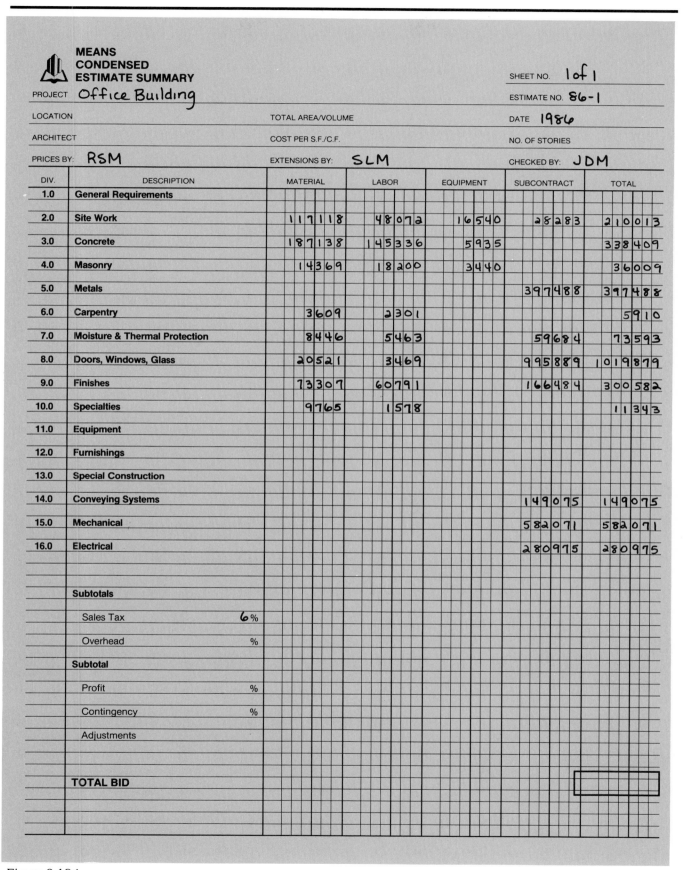

MEANS CONDENSED ESTIMATE SUMMARY

PROJECT: Office Building

ESTIMATE NO. 86-1

LOCATION	TOTAL AREA/VOLUME	DATE 1986
ARCHITECT	COST PER S.F./C.F.	NO. OF STORIES
PRICES BY: RSM	EXTENSIONS BY: SLM	CHECKED BY: JDM

DIV.	DESCRIPTION	MATERIAL	LABOR	EQUIPMENT	SUBCONTRACT	TOTAL
1.0	General Requirements					
2.0	Site Work	117118	48072	16540	28283	210013
3.0	Concrete	187138	145336	5935		338409
4.0	Masonry	14369	18200	3440		36009
5.0	Metals				397488	397488
6.0	Carpentry	3609	2301			5910
7.0	Moisture & Thermal Protection	8446	5463		59684	73593
8.0	Doors, Windows, Glass	20521	3469		995889	1019879
9.0	Finishes	73307	60791		166484	300582
10.0	Specialties	9765	1578			11343
11.0	Equipment					
12.0	Furnishings					
13.0	Special Construction					
14.0	Conveying Systems				149075	149075
15.0	Mechanical				582071	582071
16.0	Electrical				280975	280975
	Subtotals					
	Sales Tax 6%					
	Overhead %					
	Subtotal					
	Profit %					
	Contingency %					
	Adjustments					
	TOTAL BID					

Figure 8.134

MEANS PROJECT OVERHEAD SUMMARY

PROJECT **Office Building**

ESTIMATE NO. **86-1**

LOCATION   ARCHITECT   DATE **1986**

QUANTITIES BY: **EBW**   PRICES BY: **RSM**   EXTENSIONS BY: **SLM**   CHECKED BY: **JDM**

DESCRIPTION	QUANTITY	UNIT	MATERIAL/EQUIPMENT UNIT	MATERIAL/EQUIPMENT TOTAL	LABOR UNIT	LABOR TOTAL	TOTAL COST UNIT	TOTAL COST TOTAL
Job Organization: Superintendent 1.1-22-105	49	wk.			910	44590		
Project Manager								
Timekeeper & Material Clerk 1.1-22-120	40	wk.			495	19800		
Clerical								
Safety, Watchman & First Aid								
Travel Expense: Superintendent								
Project Manager								
Engineering: Layout 1.1-50-120	10	Day			420	4200		
Inspection/Quantities								
Drawings								
CPM Schedule								
Testing: Soil								
Materials	1	LS		7500				
Structural								
Equipment: Cranes								
Concrete Pump, Conveyor, Etc.								
Elevators, Hoists	By Division							
Freight & Hauling								
Loading, Unloading, Erecting, Etc.								
Maintenance								
Pumping								
Scaffolding								
Small Power Equipment/Tools 1.1-48-001	0.5	%		17060				
Field Offices: Job Office Trailer 1.1-58-428/446	11	Mo.	202	2222				
Architect/Owner's Office								
Temporary Telephones								
Utilities	11	Mo.	200	2200				
Temporary Toilets								
Storage Areas & Sheds 1.1-58-557	11	Mo.	80	880				
Temporary Utilities: Heat								
Light & Power 1.1-58-350/355	567	CSF	2.87	1627	7.90	4479		
Water Power 1.1-58-390	567	CSF	49	27783				
PAGE TOTALS				59272		73069		

Figure 8.135

DESCRIPTION	QUANTITY	UNIT	MATERIAL/EQUIPMENT		LABOR		TOTAL COST	
			UNIT	TOTAL	UNIT	TOTAL	UNIT	TOTAL
Total Brought Forward				59272		73069		
Winter Protection: Temp. Heat/Protection 1.1-58-330	567	CSF	14.16	8029	18.75	10631		
Snow Plowing								
Thawing Materials								
Temporary Roads 1.1-58-480	750	SY	.60	450	1.35	1012		
Signs & Barricades: Site Sign	1	LS		750				
Temporary Fences 1.1-58-255	1350	LF	1.51	2038	3.16	4266		
Temporary Stairs, Ladders & Floors								
Photographs								
Clean Up								
Dumpster 2.1-43-060	40	wk.	150	6000				
Final Clean Up 1.1-04-010	56.7	MSF	1.58	90	26	1474		
Continuous - One Laborer	45	wk.			636	28620		
Punch List	0.2	%				6824		
Permits: Building 1.1-36-001/010	1	%	34000					
Misc.								
Insurance: Builders Risk Additional Rider	1	LS		700				
Owner's Protective Liability								
Umbrella								
Unemployment Ins. & Social Security								
(See Estimate Summary)								
Taxes								
City Sales Tax								
State Sales Tax (See Estimate Summary)								
Bonds								
Performance (See Estimate Summary)								
Material & Equipment								
Main Office Expense (See Estimate Summary)								
Special Items								
TOTALS:				111329		125896		

Figure 8.136

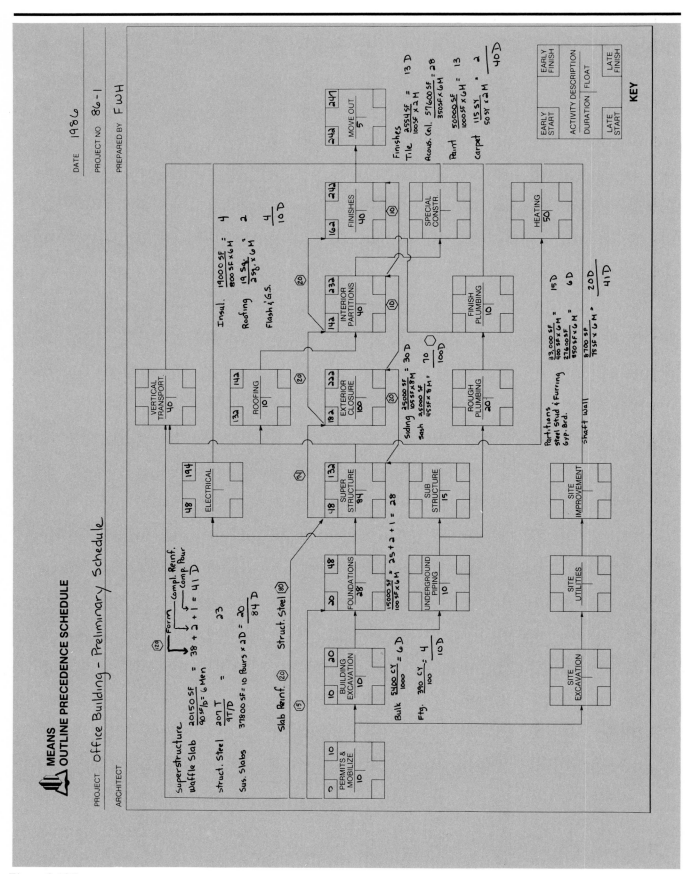

Figure 8.137

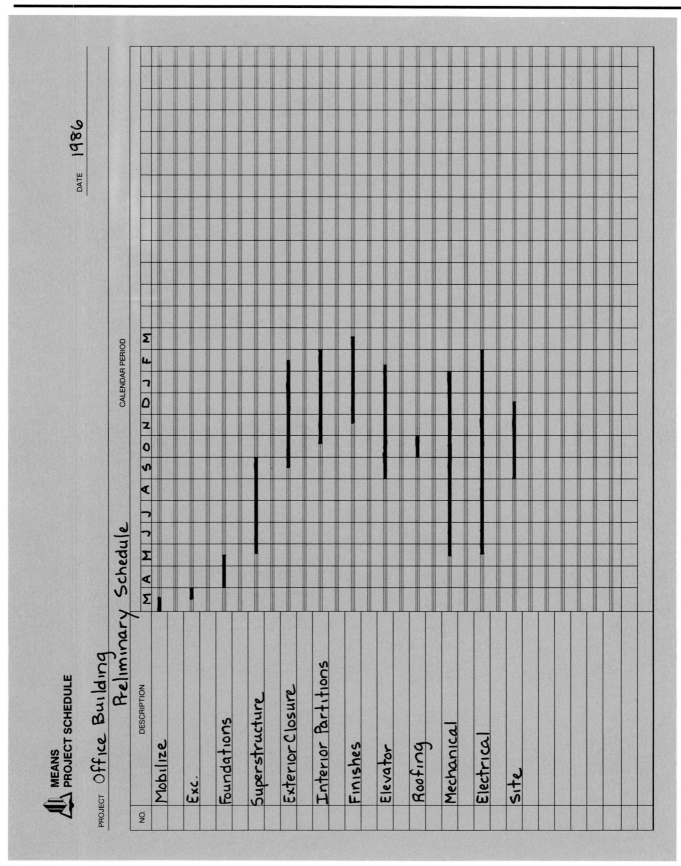

Figure 8.138

303

At this point, all divisions for the building project have been estimated. The preliminary schedule and project overhead summary are complete. Finally, the Estimate Summary sheet can be completed and the final number can be derived. The completed Estimate Summary sheet for the sample estimate is shown in Figure 8.139. Note that the difference between the subtotal of bare costs for all divisions and the "Total Bid" figure is roughly $680,000 — almost 20%. This amount is the sum of all the indirect costs. (See Chapters 4 and 7.)

Sales tax (in this example, 6%) is added to the total bare costs of materials. An additional 10% — for handling and supervision — is added to the material (including tax), equipment and subcontract costs. This is standard industry practice. Bare labor costs, however, are treated differently. As discussed in Chapter 7, office overhead expenses may be more directly attributable to labor. Consequently, the percentage mark-up for labor (45.9%) includes employer-paid taxes and insurance, office overhead and profit. This relationship is shown in Figure 8.140. (Profit may or may not be listed as a separate item.) Since all trades are included in the bare labor subtotal, the percentage used is the average for all skilled workers. The requirements for bonds are determined from the specifications and their costs are obtained from local bonding agencies. Finally a contingency is added if the job warrants. This decision is made when the estimator's role comes to an end and the job of the bidder begins. The decision to add a contingency is often based on the relative detail of the plans and specifications, experience, knowledge of the market and competition, and most likely — a gut feeling. The estimate total, with all indirect costs included, may still not be the same number as that which is *finally* submitted as the bid.

Bid day in a contractor's office is usually a frantic, hectic time. Many subcontractors delay telephoning quotations until the last possible moment in order to prevent the possibility of bid shopping. Subs to subcontractors also withhold quotes in the same way and for the same reason. This situation, in many instances, forces the prime contractor to use a budget or even a "ball park" figure so that the bid sheets can be tabulated to obtain a final number. The importance of the estimator's reviewing all disciplines of the estimate cannot be overstressed. The chaotic atmosphere of bid day can only be compensated by thoroughness, precision and attention to detail during the whole preceding estimating process. If an estimate is poorly prepared and put together, flaws will be amplified at these late stages.

Many general or prime contractors or construction managers use an adjustment column to arrive at a "quote" in the last hour before bid is due. Such adjustments might appear as follows:

Structural Steel	+	$10,000
Mechanical	−	35,000
Partitions	−	10,000
Electrical (Use 2nd Bidder)	+	6,000
Total Deduct		$29,000

MEANS CONDENSED ESTIMATE SUMMARY

PROJECT Office Building

SHEET NO. 1 of 1
ESTIMATE NO. 86-1

LOCATION	TOTAL AREA/VOLUME	DATE 1986
ARCHITECT	COST PER S.F./C.F.	NO. OF STORIES
PRICES BY: RSM	EXTENSIONS BY: SLM	CHECKED BY: JDM

DIV.	DESCRIPTION	MATERIAL	LABOR	EQUIPMENT	SUBCONTRACT	TOTAL
1.0	General Requirements	111329	125896			237225
2.0	Site Work	117118	48072	16540	28283	210013
3.0	Concrete	187138	145336	5935		338409
4.0	Masonry	14369	18200	3440		36009
5.0	Metals				397488	397488
6.0	Carpentry	3609	2301			5910
7.0	Moisture & Thermal Protection	8446	5463		59684	73593
8.0	Doors, Windows, Glass	20521	3469		995889	1019879
9.0	Finishes	73307	60791		166484	300582
10.0	Specialties	9765	1578			11343
11.0	Equipment					
12.0	Furnishings					
13.0	Special Construction					
14.0	Conveying Systems				149075	149075
15.0	Mechanical				582071	582071
16.0	Electrical				280975	280975
	Subtotals	545602	411106	25915	2659949	3642572
	Sales Tax 6 %	32736				32736
	Overhead & Profit 10/45.9/10/10 %	54560	188698	2591	265995	511844
	Subtotal	632898	599804	28506	2925944	4187152
	~~Profit~~ Bond ($ 12/M) %					50246
	Contingency 2 %					84748
	Adjustments					4322146
	TOTAL BID					4323000

QUOTE
$4,294,000
EBW

Figure 8.139

305

Abbr.	Trade	Base Rate Incl. Fringes		Work-ers' Comp. Ins.	Average Fixed Over-head	Subs Over-head	Subs Profit	Subs Total Overhead & Profit		Rate with Subs O & P	
		Hourly	Daily					%	Amount	Hourly	Daily
Skwk	Skilled Workers Average (35 trades)	$20.50	$164.00	9.3%	13.8%	12.8%	10%	45.9%	$ 9.40	$29.90	$239.20
	Helpers Average (5 trades)	15.55	124.40	9.8		13.0		46.6	7.25	22.80	182.40
	Foremen Average, Inside (50¢ over trade)	21.00	168.00	9.3		12.8		45.9	9.65	30.65	245.20
	Foremen Average, Outside ($2.00 over trade)	22.50	180.00	9.3		12.8		45.9	10.35	32.85	262.80
Clab	Common Building Laborers	15.90	127.20	10.1		11.0		44.9	7.15	23.05	184.40
Asbe	Asbestos Workers	22.75	182.00	7.7		16.0		47.5	10.80	33.55	268.40
Boil	Boilermakers	22.75	182.00	6.6		16.0		46.4	10.55	33.30	266.40
Bric	Bricklayers	20.50	164.00	7.6		11.0		42.4	8.70	29.20	233.60
Brhe	Bricklayer Helpers	16.00	128.00	7.6		11.0		42.4	6.80	22.80	182.40
Carp	Carpenters	20.00	160.00	10.1		11.0		44.9	9.00	29.00	232.00
Cefi	Cement Finishers	19.20	153.60	5.9		11.0		40.7	7.80	27.00	216.00
Elec	Electricians	22.40	179.20	4.0		16.0		43.8	9.80	32.20	257.60
Elev	Elevator Constructors	22.65	181.20	5.5		16.0		45.3	10.25	32.90	263.20
Eqhv	Equipment Operators, Crane or Shovel	21.05	168.40	7.2		14.0		45.0	9.45	30.50	244.00
Eqmd	Equipment Operators, Medium Equipment	20.60	164.80	7.2		14.0		45.0	9.25	29.85	238.80
Eqlt	Equipment Operators, Light Equipment	19.45	155.60	7.2		14.0		45.0	8.75	28.20	225.60
Eqol	Equipment Operators, Oilers	17.50	140.00	7.2		14.0		45.0	7.90	25.40	203.20
Eqmm	Equipment Operators, Master Mechanics	21.80	174.40	7.2		14.0		45.0	9.80	31.60	252.80
Glaz	Glaziers	20.15	161.20	7.9		11.0		42.7	8.60	28.75	230.00
Lath	Lathers	20.10	160.80	6.3		11.0		41.1	8.25	28.35	226.80
Marb	Marble Setters	20.10	160.80	7.6		11.0		42.4	8.50	28.60	228.80
Mill	Millwrights	20.75	166.00	6.6		11.0		41.4	8.60	29.35	234.80
Mstz	Mosaic and Terrazzo Workers	19.90	159.20	5.4		11.0		40.2	8.00	27.90	223.20
Pord	Painters, Ordinary	19.25	154.00	7.7		11.0		42.5	8.20	27.45	219.60
Psst	Painters, Structural Steel	20.00	160.00	27.0		11.0		61.8	12.35	32.35	258.80
Pape	Paper Hangers	19.50	156.00	7.7		11.0		42.5	8.30	27.80	222.40
Pile	Pile Drivers	20.10	160.80	17.0		16.0		56.8	11.40	31.50	252.00
Plas	Plasterers	19.90	159.20	7.7		11.0		42.5	8.45	28.35	226.80
Plah	Plasterer Helpers	16.50	132.00	7.7		11.0		42.5	7.00	23.50	188.00
Plum	Plumbers	22.55	180.40	4.8		16.0		44.6	10.05	32.60	260.80
Rodm	Rodmen (Reinforcing)	21.75	174.00	16.8		14.0		54.6	11.90	33.65	269.20
Rofc	Roofers, Composition	18.80	150.40	18.2		11.0		53.0	9.95	28.75	230.00
Rots	Roofers, Tile & Slate	18.95	151.60	18.2		11.0		53.0	10.05	29.00	232.00
Rohe	Roofer Helpers (Composition)	13.75	110.00	18.2		11.0		53.0	7.30	21.05	168.40
Shee	Sheet Metal Workers	22.70	181.60	6.3		16.0		46.1	10.45	33.15	265.20
Spri	Sprinkler Installers	23.25	186.00	5.5		16.0		45.3	10.55	33.80	270.40
Stpi	Steamfitters or Pipefitters	22.75	182.00	4.8		16.0		44.6	10.15	32.90	263.20
Ston	Stone Masons	20.30	162.40	7.6		11.0		42.4	8.60	28.90	231.20
Sswk	Structural Steel Workers	21.70	173.60	19.3		14.0		57.1	12.40	34.10	272.80
Tilf	Tile Layers (Floor)	19.75	158.00	5.4		11.0		40.2	7.95	27.70	221.60
Tilh	Tile Layer Helpers	15.60	124.80	5.4		11.0		40.2	6.30	21.90	175.20
Trlt	Truck Drivers, Light	16.35	130.80	8.6		11.0		43.4	7.10	23.45	187.60
Trhv	Truck Drivers, Heavy	16.60	132.80	8.6		11.0		43.4	7.20	23.80	190.40
Sswl	Welders, Structural Steel	21.70	173.60	19.3		14.0		57.1	12.40	34.10	272.80
Wrck	*Wrecking	15.90	127.20	20.7	↓	11.0	↓	55.5	8.80	24.70	197.60

*Not included in Averages.

Figure 8.140

These deductions or additions may be obtained from last minute phone calls, error corrections or discovered omissions. The final number, or bid price, is, in many cases, arrived at by a principal or senior member of the firm. Bidding strategies are discussed in Chapter 6, but the final quotation is usually determined by personal judgement, good or bad.

Factors that may affect a final decision are: the risk involved, competition from other bidders, thoroughness of the plans and specs, and above all, the years of experience — the qualification to make such a judgment. Some firms are so scientific and calculating, that every quoted price includes a lucky number.

A great deal of success in bidding can be attributed to the proper choice of jobs to bid. A contracting firm can go broke estimating every available job. The company must be able to recognize which jobs are too risky and when the competition is too keen, while not overlooking those which can be profitable. Again, knowledge of the marketplace and *experience* are the keys to successful bidding.

The primary purpose of this text has not been to tell the reader how much an item will cost, but instead, how to develop a consistent and thorough approach to the estimating process. If such a pattern is developed, employing consistency, attention to detail, experience and above all, common sense, accurate costs will follow.

If an estimate is thorough, organized, neat and concise, the benefits go beyond winning contracts. The information and data that is developed will be useful throughout a project — for purchasing, change orders, cost accounting and control and development of historical costs.

APPENDIX

APPENDIX A

Included in this appendix is an R. S. Means' *SPEC-AID*, a publication developed to aid the estimator in preparing all parts of a building project estimate. Each of the sixteen UCI divisions is represented by a complete and thorough check list. These lists are used to record project requirements and to help ensure inclusion of all items in an estimate. In the spring of 1986, R. S. Means will publish a complete book of forms, check lists and aids to the estimator. The book is entitled *Means Forms for Building Construction Professionals*, and will include the following *SPEC-AID*. Sample uses and a full explanation of each type of form will be provided, along with reproducible copies.

SPEC-AID

OUTLINE SPECIFICATION

AND

QUESTIONNAIRE

FOR

PROJECT _____

ADDRESS _____

CITY/STATE/ZIP _____

PREPARED BY _____

_____

DATE _____

R.S. Means Co., Inc.
NEW IDEAS FOR BUILDING

PROJECT SKETCH

1" = _____ Ft.

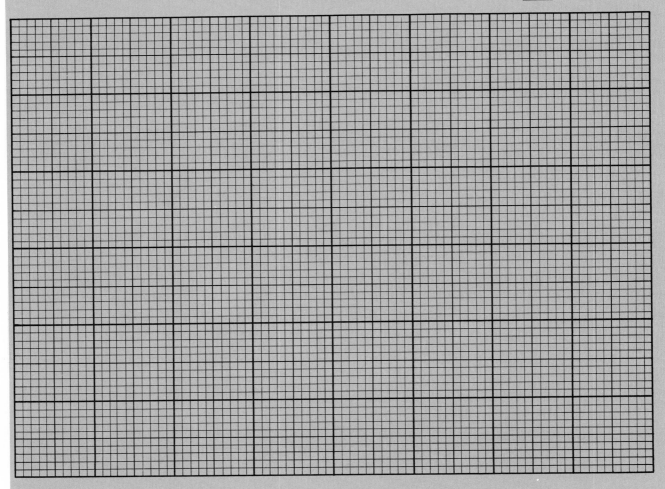

COPYRIGHT 1980

R.S. MEANS COMPANY, INC.
ENGINEERS & ESTIMATORS

100 Construction Plaza
Kingston, MA 02364

TABLE OF CONTENTS

UCI DIVISION NO.	DESCRIPTION	PAGE NO.	UCI DIVISION NO.	DESCRIPTION	PAGE NO.
1	General Requirements	3	11	Equipment	22
2	Site Work	4	12	Furnishings	24
3	Concrete	6	13	Special Construction	25
4	Masonry	8	14	Conveying Systems	27
5	Metals	10	15	Mechanical	28
6	Wood & Plastics	12	16	Electrical	30
7	Moisture Protection	14		Budget Estimate	32
8	Doors, Windows & Glass	16		General Project Notes	outside rear cover
9	Finishes	18		Project Schedule	2
10	Specialties	20		Project Sketch	inside front cover

INSTRUCTIONS FOR USE OF SPEC-AID©

A. A Primary use of SPEC-AID© is to provide construction planners with a detailed check list that will facilitate concurrent precise development of specifications with drawings. (It will assure that all planning groups are talking about the same type and quality of building.)

B. SECTION 1 is a General Project Description which outlines code requirements and basic building parameters. It is usually completed by the project manager, architect or engineer, having responsible knowledge of the appropriate information necessary.

C. SECTIONS 2 thru 16 are arranged according to the CSI and UCI Formats. These section items should be completed by designers or other technical personnel as appropriate. This should be done as early in the design stage as possible.

D. When an item or product is specifically selected or the drawings are detailed around it, identify it by name, type, number, manufacturer, and reference. Use additional sheets as required.

E. The inside front cover has a PROJECT SKETCH set of grid lines to facilitate schematic representation of project phases, column lines, etc. Use of this feature helps to define the scope of the project.

F. The PROJECT SCHEDULE on Page 2 should be one of the first items considered. It can be refined, added to, and revised as the project requirements develop. It is used to show lead time, to coordinate systems, and to visually indicate major project components by events (design, bid, begin construction, etc.), date and duration.

G. The BUDGET ESTIMATE can be summarized on Pages 32 and 33. The systems headings can be coordinated with the PROJECT SCHEDULE on Page 2. By filling in the columns (Quantity, Unit, Unit Price, Total Cost, Cost/S.F., and % of Bldg.), each estimated aspect of the project is shown at a glance. By keeping a complete copy of SPEC-AID© for each project on file, valuable preliminary estimating quantities and costs as well as specifications will be at your fingertips for future reference.

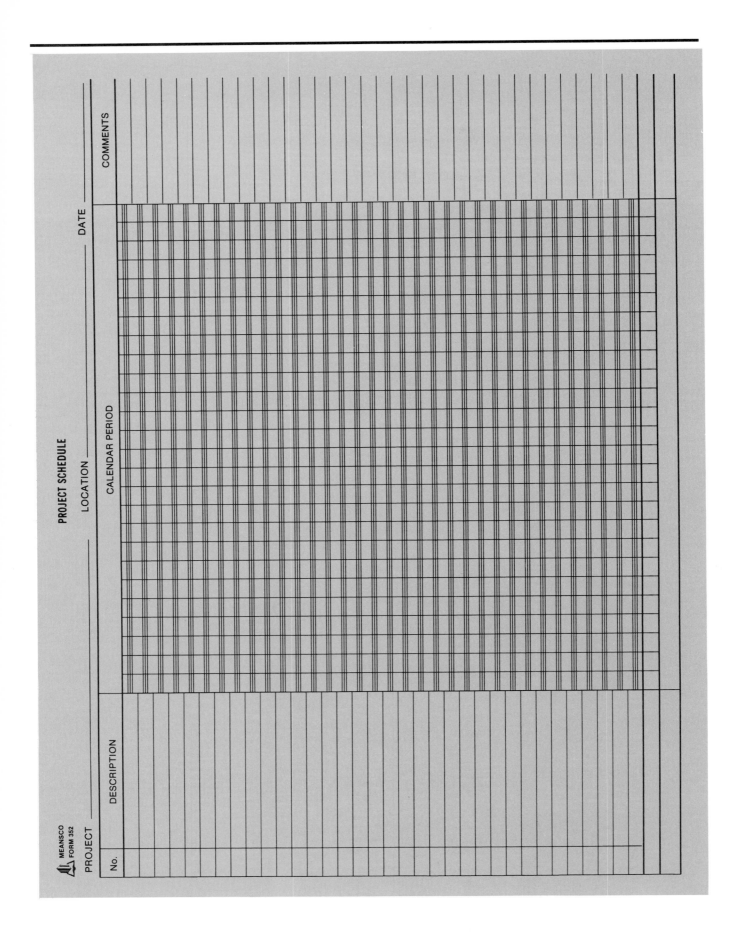

PROJECT SCHEDULE

PROJECT _____ LOCATION _____ DATE _____

No.	DESCRIPTION	CALENDAR PERIOD	COMMENTS

MEANSCO FORM 352

314

GENERAL PROJECT DESCRIPTION

 MEANSCO
FORM 401

DIVISION 1

SPEC-AID

DATE _____

PROJECT _____ LOCATION _____

OWNER _____ **ARCHITECT** _____ **PROJECT MGR.** _____

ENGINEER: Structural _____ Plumbing _____

H.V.A.C. _____ Electrical _____

CONTRACTOR: General _____ Structural _____

Mechanical _____ Electrical _____

BUILDING TYPE _____

BUILDING CAPACITIES: _____

_____

QUALITY ☐ Economy ☐ Average ☐ Good ☐ Luxury Describe _____

SIZE

Ground Floor Area _____ S.F.

Supported Levels (No.) _____x Area/Level _____ S.F.

Supported Levels (No.) _____x Area/Level _____ S.F.

Below Grade Area _____ S.F.

Other Area _____ S.F.

TOTAL GROSS AREA _____ S.F.

Floor to floor height: Maximum _____ Minimum _____ Average _____

Floor to ceiling height: Maximum _____ Minimum _____ Average _____

Floor system depth: Maximum _____ Minimum _____ Average _____

BUILDING CODES ☐ City _____ ☐ County _____

☐ State _____ ☐ National _____

☐ Other _____ Seismic Zone _____

ZONING ☐ Residential ☐ Commercial ☐ Industrial ☐ None ☐ Other _____

DESIGN CRITERIA Live Loads: Roof _____ psf.   End walls _____ psf.   Window openings ___ %

Supported Floor _____ psf.   Side walls _____ psf.   Window openings ___ %

Ground Floor _____ psf.   WIND PRESSURE

Corridors _____ psf.   _____ psf. from _____ to _____ ft.

Balconies _____ psf.   _____ psf. from _____ to _____ ft.

Allow for partitions _____ psf.   _____ psf. from _____ to _____ ft.

Miscellaneous _____ psf.   _____ psf. from _____ to _____ ft.

COMMENTS _____

_____

TYPICAL BAY SPACING _____

STRUCTURAL FRAME ☐ Concrete ☐ Steel ☐ Wood ☐ Wall Bearing ☐ Other _____

Describe _____

_____

FIREPROOFING ☐ None ☐ Columns ___ Hours ☐ Girders ___ Hours ☐ Beams ___ Hours ☐ Floor ___ Hours

ESTIMATING Budget Estimate Due _____ 19 ___ Schematic Estimate Due _____ 19 ___

Preliminary Estimate Due _____ 19 ___ Final Estimate Due _____ 19 ___ at ___ % Working Drawings

LABOR MARKET ☐ Highly Competitive ☐ Normal ☐ Non-Competitive ☐ Unreliable ☐ Union ☐ Non-union

Describe _____

TAXES Tax exempt ☐ No ☐ Yes State ___% County ___ % City ___ % Other ___ %

BOND ☐ Not Required ☐ Required _____

BIDDING Date _____ Start Date _____ Construction Duration _____ Months

☐ Open Competitive ☐ Selected Competitive ☐ Negotiated ☐ Filed Bids _____

CONTRACT ☐ Single ☐ Multiple Describe _____

Multiple Type assigned to General Contractor ☐ No ☐ Yes _____

SITEWORK, EARTHWORK,
Piling & Drainage

MEANSCO FORM 402 DIVISION 2

PAGE 1 OF 2

SPEC-AID   DATE _____

PROJECT _____ LOCATION _____

DEMOLITION SITE: ☐ No ☐ Yes Allowance _____   ☐ Separate Contract
    INTERIOR: ☐ No ☐ Yes ☐ Allowance _____   ☐ Separate Contract
    REMOVAL FROM SITE: ☐ No ☐ Yes Dump Location _____   Distance _____
TOPOGRAPHY ☐ Level ☐ Moderate Grades ☐ Steep Grades Describe _____
SUBSURFACE EXPLORATION ☐ Borings ☐ Test Pits ☐ USDA Maps ☐ Other _____
    Performed by: ☐ Owner ☐ Engineer ☐ Contractor _____
SITE AREA: Total _____ Acres To Clear _____ Acres To Thin _____ Acres Open _____ Acres
CLEARING AND GRUBBING: ☐ No ☐ Light ☐ Medium ☐ Heavy _____
TOPSOIL: ☐ No ☐ Strip ☐ Stockpile ☐ Dispose on Site ☐ Dispose off Site _____ miles ☐ Furnish
    Existing _____ inches deep Final depth _____ inches Describe _____

EARTH WORK 2.1 & 2.3

SOIL TYPE: ☐ Gravel ☐ Sand ☐ Clay ☐ Silt ☐ Rock ☐ Peat ☐ Other _____
    ROCK EXPECTED: ☐ No ☐ Ledge ☐ Boulders ☐ Hardpan Describe _____
    How paid _____
    GROUND WATER EXPECTED: ☐ No ☐ Yes Depth or Elevation _____
    Disposal by ☐ Pumping ☐ Wells ☐ Wellpoints ☐ Other _____
EXCAVATION: ☐ Grade and Fill on Site ☐ Dispose off Site _____ miles ☐ Borrow expected _____ miles
    Quantity involved _____
    Describe _____
    Sheeting required: ☐ No ☐ Yes Describe _____
    Protect existing structures: ☐ No ☐ Yes Describe _____
BACKFILL: Paving Area ☐ No ☐ Yes Area_____ Material _____ inches deep _____% Compaction
    Landscape Area ☐ No ☐ Yes Area _____ Material _____ inches deep _____% Compaction
    Building Area ☐ No ☐ Yes Area _____ Material _____ inches deep _____% Compaction
    Source of Materials _____
WATER CONTROL: ☐ Ditching ☐ Sheet Piling ☐ Pumping ☐ Wells ☐ Wellpoints ☐ Pressure Grouting
    ☐ Chemical grouting ☐ Other _____
    Describe _____
TERMITE CONTROL: ☐ No ☐ Yes Describe _____
SPECIAL CONSIDERATIONS: _____

PILING 2.4

PILES: ☐ No ☐ Yes ☐ Friction ☐ End bearing ☐ Concrete ☐ Pipe, empty ☐ Pipe, concrete filled ☐ Steel
    ☐ Step tapered ☐ Tapered thin shell ☐ Wood Capacity _____ Tons
    Size _____ Length _____ Number Required _____
CAISSONS: ☐ No ☐ Yes ☐ Cased ☐ Uncased Capacity _____
    Size _____ Length _____ Number Required _____
PRESSURE INJECTED FOOTINGS: ☐ No ☐ Yes ☐ Cased ☐ Uncased Capacity _____
    Size _____ Length _____ Number Required _____
SPECIAL CONSIDERATIONS: _____

DRAINAGE 2.5

STORM DRAINS: ☐ No ☐ Yes ☐ Asbestos Cement ☐ Bituminous Fiber ☐ Concrete ☐ Corrugated Metal ☐ _____
    Size and Length _____
    HEADWALL: ☐ No ☐ Yes Type _____ Number _____
    CATCH BASINS: ☐ No ☐ Yes ☐ Block ☐ Brick ☐ Concrete ☐ Precast Size _____ Number _____
    MANHOLES: ☐ No ☐ Yes ☐ Block ☐ Brick ☐ Concrete ☐ Precast Size _____ Number _____
BUILDING SUB DRAINS: ☐ No ☐ Yes Type _____ Length _____
FRENCH DRAINS: ☐ No ☐ Yes Size _____ Length _____
TRENCHES: Swales, etc.: ☐ No ☐ Yes Describe _____
RIP RAP: ☐ No ☐ Yes Describe _____
SPECIAL CONSIDERATIONS: _____

SITEWORK Utilities, Roads and Walks,
Site Improvements

SPEC-AID

UTILITIES 2.5

WATER SUPPLY EXISTING MAIN: ☐ No ☐ Yes Location _____ Size _____

SERVICE PIPING: By Utility ☐ By Others ☐ This Contract _____ Size _____

WELLS: ☐ No ☐ Yes ☐ By Others ☐ This Contract _____ Capacity _____

WATER PUMPING STATION: ☐ No ☐ Yes Type _____ Capacity _____

SEWERS: ☐ No ☐ Yes ☐ By Others ☐ Asbestos Cement ☐ Concrete ☐ Plastic ☐ Vitrified Clay ☐ _____

MANHOLES: ☐ No ☐ Yes ☐ Block ☐ Brick ☐ Concrete ☐ Precast Size _____ Number _____

SEWAGE PUMPING STATION: ☐ No ☐ Yes Type _____ Capacity _____

SEWAGE TREATMENT: ☐ No ☐ Yes ☐ By Others ☐ This Contract ☐ Septic Tank ☐ Package Treatment Plant

Describe _____

SPECIAL CONSIDERATIONS: _____

ROADS AND WALKS 2.6

DRIVEWAYS: ☐ No ☐ Yes ☐ By Others ☐ Bituminous ☐ Concrete ☐ Gravel ☐ _____ Thickness _____

PARKING AREA: ☐ No ☐ Yes ☐ By Others ☐ Bituminous ☐ Concrete ☐ Gravel ☐ _____ Thickness _____

BASE COURSE: ☐ No ☐ Yes ☐ By Others ☐ Gravel ☐ Stone ☐ _____ Thickness _____

CURBS: ☐ No ☐ Yes ☐ By Others ☐ Bituminous ☐ Concrete ☐ Granite ☐ _____ Size _____

PARKING BUMPERS: ☐ No ☐ Yes ☐ By Others ☐ Concrete ☐ Timber _____

PAINTING LINES: ☐ No ☐ Yes ☐ By Others ☐ Paint ☐ Thermo Plastic ☐ Traffic lines ☐ Stalls ☐ _____

GUARD RAIL: ☐ No ☐ Yes ☐ By Others ☐ Cable ☐ Steel ☐ Timber _____

SIDEWALKS: ☐ No ☐ Yes ☐ By Others ☐ Bituminous ☐ Brick ☐ Concrete ☐ Stone _____

Width _____ Thickness _____

STEPS: ☐ No ☐ Yes ☐ Brick ☐ Concrete ☐ Stone ☐ Timber _____

SIGNS: ☐ No ☐ Yes ☐ Stock ☐ Custom _____

TRAFFIC SIGNALS: ☐ No ☐ Yes ☐ By Others _____

SPECIAL CONSIDERATIONS: _____

SITE IMPROVEMENTS 2.7 & 2.8

FENCING: ☐ No ☐ Yes ☐ By Others ☐ Chain link ☐ Aluminum ☐ Steel ☐ Other _____

Height _____ Length _____ Gates _____

FOUNTAINS: ☐ No ☐ Yes ☐ By Others _____

PLANTERS: ☐ No ☐ Yes ☐ By Others ☐ Asbestos Cement ☐ Concrete ☐ Fiberglass ☐ _____

PLAYGROUND EQUIPMENT: ☐ No ☐ Yes ☐ By Others ☐ Benches _____ ☐ Bleachers _____

☐ Bike Rack _____ ☐ Goal Posts _____ ☐ Posts _____

☐ Running track _____

☐ See Saw _____ ☐ Shelters _____ ☐ Slides _____

☐ Swings _____ ☐ Whirlers _____ ☐ _____

PLAYING FIELDS: ☐ No ☐ Yes ☐ By Others _____

RAILROAD WORK: ☐ No ☐ Yes ☐ By Others Weight _____ lb. per L.Y. ☐ New ☐ Relay Length _____

Turnout: ☐ No ☐ Yes _____ ☐ Bumpers _____ ☐ Derails _____

☐ Wheel Stops _____ ☐ Others _____

RETAINING WALLS: ☐ No ☐ Yes ☐ By Others ☐ Gravity Concrete ☐ Cantilever Concrete ☐ Steel Bin ☐ Cribbing

☐ Timber ☐ Other _____ Height _____ Length _____

SPRINKLER SYSTEM: ☐ No ☐ Yes ☐ By Others _____

TENNIS COURTS: ☐ No ☐ Yes ☐ By Others Type _____ Number _____

TRASH CLOSURES: ☐ No ☐ Yes Size _____

LAWNS & PLANTING: ☐ No ☐ Yes ☐ By Others _____ Allowance _____

TOPSOIL: ☐ No ☐ Yes ☐ By Others Depth _____ inches Source _____

SHRUBS: ☐ No ☐ Yes ☐ By Others Describe _____ Allowance _____

TREES: ☐ No ☐ Yes ☐ By Others Describe _____ Allowance _____

SEEDING: ☐ No ☐ Yes ☐ By Others Describe _____

SODDING: ☐ No ☐ Yes ☐ By Others Describe _____ Thickness _____

☐ Ground cover _____ ☐ Edging _____ ☐ Mulching _____

SPECIAL CONSIDERATIONS: _____

CONCRETE Cast in Place

SPEC-AID

DATE _____

PROJECT _____ LOCATION _____

FOUNDATIONS Bearing on: ☐ Rock ☐ Earth ☐ Piles ☐ Caissons ☐ Other _____
Bearing Capacity _____

FOOTINGS PILE CAPS: ☐ No ☐ Yes _____ psi   Size _____
   Forms _____ Reinforcing _____ Waterproofing _____
  SPREAD FOOTINGS: ☐ No ☐ Yes _____ psi   Size _____ Soil Bearing Capacity _____
   Forms _____ Reinforcing _____ Waterproofing _____
  CONTINUOUS FOOTINGS: ☐ No ☐ Yes _____ psi   Size _____
   Forms _____ Reinforcing _____ Waterproofing _____
  GRADE BEAMS: ☐ No ☐ Yes _____ psi   Size _____
   Forms _____ Reinforcing _____ Waterproofing _____
  PIERS: ☐ No ☐ Yes _____ psi   Size _____
   Forms _____ Reinforcing _____ Finish _____

ANCHOR BOLTS: ☐ No ☐ Yes   Size _____
  GROUT column base plates: ☐ No ☐ Yes _____

UNDERSLAB FILL: ☐ No ☐ Yes   Material _____ Depth _____

VAPOR BARRIER: ☐ No ☐ Yes   Material _____ Thickness _____

PERIMETER INSULATION: ☐ No ☐ Yes   Material _____ Dimensions _____

SLAB ON GRADE: ☐ No ☐ Yes _____ psi _____ Thickness _____
  FORMS: ☐ Cold Keyed ☐ Expansion ☐ Other _____ Spacing _____
  REINFORCING: ☐ No ☐ Mesh ☐ Bars _____ Type _____
  FINISH: ☐ Screed ☐ Darby ☐ Float ☐ Broom ☐ Trowel ☐ Granolithic _____
  SPECIAL FINISH: ☐ No ☐ Hardener ☐ Colors ☐ Abrasives ☐ _____

COLUMNS: ☐ No ☐ Round ☐ Square ☐ Rectangular ☐ Precast ☐ Steel ☐ Encased Steel ☐ Lightweight
_____ psi   Size _____
  FORMS: ☐ Optional ☐ Framed Plywood ☐ Plywood ☐ Fiber tube ☐ Steel ☐ Round Fiberglass ☐ _____
  REINFORCING: ☐ No ☐ Square tied ☐ Spirals   Grade _____ Bar Sizes _____ Type Splice _____
  FINISH: ☐ Break Fins ☐ Rubbed ☐ Other _____

ELEVATED SLAB SYSTEM: ☐ No ☐ Flat Plate ☐ Flat Slab ☐ Domes ☐ Pans ☐ Beam & Slab ☐ Lift Slab ☐ Composite
  ☐ Floor Fill ☐ Roof Fill ☐ Standard Weight ☐ Light Weight   Concrete strength _____
  FORMS: ☐ Optional ☐ Plywood ☐ Other _____ Ceiling Height _____
  REINFORCING: ☐ Mesh ☐ Bars   Grade _____ Size: _____
   Post-tension: ☐ No ☐ Simple Spans ☐ Continuous   Spans _____ Depth _____
   ☐ Grouted ☐ Ungrouted   Perimeter conditions _____
  SLAB FINISH: ☐ Screed ☐ Darby ☐ Float ☐ Broom ☐ Trowel ☐ Granolithic ☐ _____
  SPECIAL FINISH: ☐ No ☐ Hardener ☐ Colors ☐ Abrasives ☐ _____
  CEILING FINISH: ☐ No ☐ Break Fins ☐ Rubbed ☐ Other _____

BEAMS: ☐ No ☐ Steel ☐ Encased Steel ☐ Precast ☐ Regular Weight ☐ Light Weight ☐ Steel Composite _____
Description: _____
  FORMS: ☐ Optional ☐ Framed Plywood ☐ Plywood ☐ Steel ☐ Other _____ Ceiling Height _____
  REINFORCING: ☐ Conventional ☐ Post-tension ☐ Simple Span ☐ Continuous Spans _____ Depth _____
   ☐ Grouted ☐ Ungrouted   Perimeter conditions _____

WALLS: ☐ No ☐ Precast ☐ Tilt up ☐ Regular Weight ☐ Light Weight _____ psi   Thickness _____
  FORMS: ☐ Optional ☐ Framed Plywood ☐ Plywood ☐ Steel ☐ Slipform ☐ _____
  REINFORCING: ☐ No ☐ Bars   Grade _____ Clear Height _____
  FINISH: ☐ No ☐ Break Fins ☐ Rubbed ☐ _____

STAIRS: ☐ No ☐ Precast ☐ Ground Cast ☐ Form Cast ☐ Pan Fill Treads ☐ _____
  FORMS: ☐ Plywood ☐ Steel ☐ Prefab Steel, left in place ☐ _____
  REINFORCING: ☐ Conventional   Grade _____
  FINISH: ☐ All Surfaces ☐ Treads ☐ Risers ☐ Abrasives ☐ Nosings _____

CONCRETE Cast in Place Cont'd.,
Precast & Cementitious Decks

SPEC-AID

CAST-IN-PLACE 3.3

REINFORCING SPLICES: ☐ No ☐ Yes ☐ Lap type ☐ Compression only ☐ 125% Yield ☐ Full Tension
☐ Horizontal ☐ Vertical ☐ Special _____
GUNITE: ☐ No ☐ Yes _____
CAST IN PLACE SPECIAL CONSIDERATIONS: _____
_____
_____
_____
_____

COPINGS: ☐ No ☐ Yes Size _____ Finish _____
CURBS: ☐ No ☐ Yes Size _____ Finish _____
JOISTS: ☐ No ☐ Yes Live load _____ psf. Span _____ Size _____
Describe _____
LIFT SLAB: ☐ No ☐ Yes No. Slabs _____ Thickness _____ inches Column Spacing _____
Story Height _____ ☐ Conventional Reinforcing ☐ Post tension _____
LINTELS: ☐ No ☐ Yes ☐ Doors ☐ Windows ☐ Other _____
☐ Conventional reinforcing ☐ Prestressed _____

PRECAST CONCRETE 3.4

PRESTRESSED PRECAST FLOORS: ☐ No ☐ Yes ☐ Plank ☐ Multiple Tee Depth _____ Span _____ Width _____
ROOFS: ☐ No ☐ Yes ☐ Plank ☐ Double Tee ☐ Single Tee Depth _____ Span _____ Width _____
SUPPORTING BEAMS: ☐ No ☐ Yes ☐ Cast in Place ☐ Precast Describe _____
_____
COLUMNS: ☐ No ☐ Yes ☐ Steel ☐ Cast in Place ☐ Precast Size _____
WALLS: ☐ No ☐ Yes ☐ Multiple Tee ☐ Other Thickness _____ Height _____ Width _____
STAIRS: ☐ No ☐ Yes ☐ Treads only ☐ Tread & Riser Units ☐ Complete Stairs ☐ Other _____
Describe _____
TILT UP WALLS: ☐ No ☐ Yes Size _____ Finish _____
WALL PANELS: ☐ No ☐ Yes ☐ Insulated ☐ Regular Weight ☐ Light Weight Panel Size _____
FINISH: ☐ Gray ☐ White ☐ Exposed Aggregate ☐ Other _____
REINFORCING: ☐ Conventional ☐ Prestressed ☐ Plain ☐ Galvanized _____
ERECTION: ☐ No. Stories _____ Maximum lift _____ Overhangs, etc. _____
WINDOW SECTION: ☐ No ☐ Yes ☐ Size _____ Finish _____
WINDOW SILLS: ☐ No ☐ Yes Size _____ Finish _____
PRECAST SPECIAL CONSIDERATIONS: _____
_____
_____
_____
_____

CEMENTITIOUS DECKS 3.5

CONCRETE DECKS: ☐ No ☐ Yes ☐ Cast in Place ☐ Plank ☐ Topping ☐ Cement Fiber ☐ Channel Slab ☐ _____
Depth _____ Span _____ Sub Purlins _____ Roof Pitch _____
CONCRETE FILL: ☐ No ☐ Yes ☐ Regular Weight ☐ Light Weight Type _____ Depth _____
FORMBOARD: ☐ No ☐ Yes Type _____ Depth _____ Spans _____
SUB PURLINS: ☐ No ☐ Yes Span _____ Describe _____
GYPSUM DECKS FLOOR PLANK: ☐ No ☐ Yes Depth _____ Span _____ Underlayment _____
ROOFS: ☐ No ☐ Yes ☐ Cast in Place ☐ Plank Depth _____ Span _____ Pitch _____
OTHER CEMENTITIOUS DECKS: ☐ No ☐ Yes Describe _____

CEMENTITIOUS DECKS: SPECIAL CONSIDERATIONS _____
_____

GENERAL NOTES: CONCRETE SECTION _____
_____
_____

MASONRY
Brickwork

SPEC-AID

DATE _____

PROJECT _____ LOCATION _____

EXTERIOR WALLS: ☐ No ☐ Yes ☐ Load Bearing ☐ Non Load Bearing Story height _____
   Describe _____

INTERIOR WALLS: ☐ No ☐ Yes ☐ Load Bearing ☐ Non Load Bearing Ceiling Height _____
   Describe _____

MORTAR: ☐ Optional ☐ Type K ☐ Type O ☐ Type N ☐ Type S ☐ Type M ☐ Thinset ☐ _____
   ☐ Colors _____ ☐ Other _____

CEMENT BRICK: ☐ No ☐ Yes ☐ Solid ☐ Cavity ☐ Veneer ☐ _____
   Describe _____
   _____ Compressive Strength _____ psi. ASTM No. _____
   Size _____ Bond _____ Joints _____ Reinforcing _____ Ties _____

COMMON BRICK: ☐ No ☐ Yes ☐ Solid ☐ Cavity ☐ Veneer ☐ _____
   Describe _____
   _____ Compressive Strength _____ psi. ASTM No. _____
   Size _____ Bond _____ Joints _____ Reinforcing _____ Ties _____

FACE BRICK: ☐ No ☐ Yes ☐ Solid ☐ Cavity ☐ Veneer ☐ _____
   Describe _____
   _____ Compressive Strength _____ psi. ASTM No. _____
   SIZE: ☐ Standard ☐ Jumbo ☐ Norman ☐ Roman ☐ Engineer ☐ Double ☐ _____
   ALLOWANCE: ☐ No ☐ Yes $ _____ per M delivered ☐ Unglazed ☐ Single Glazed ☐ Double Glazed
   BOND: ☐ Running ☐ Common ☐ English ☐ Flemish ☐ Stack ☐ _____ Headers every _____ course.
   JOINTS: ☐ Concave ☐ Struck ☐ Flush ☐ Raked ☐ Weathered ☐ Stripped ☐ _____
   REINFORCING: ☐ No ☐ Yes Describe _____
   WALL TIES: ☐ No ☐ Yes Describe _____

ANCHOR BOLTS: ☐ No ☐ Yes Size _____

CHIMNEYS: ☐ No ☐ Yes ☐ Regular Brick ☐ Radial Brick Size _____

COLUMNS: ☐ No ☐ Yes Size _____

CONTROL JOINTS: ☐ No ☐ Yes Spacing _____ Material _____

COPINGS ☐ No ☐ Yes ☐ Concrete ☐ Stone ☐ _____ Describe _____

FIRE BRICK: ☐ No ☐ Yes ☐ Low Duty ☐ High Duty Describe _____

FIREPLACES: ☐ No ☐ Yes Describe _____
   Accessories _____

FLOORING: ☐ No ☐ Yes ☐ Laid Flat ☐ Laid on Edge ☐ Pattern _____
   ☐ Regular ☐ Acid Resisting Describe _____

INSULATING BRICK: ☐ No ☐ Yes Describe _____

INSULATION: ☐ No ☐ Yes ☐ Board ☐ Poured ☐ Sprayed Material _____
   Thickness _____ Describe _____

LINTELS: ☐ No ☐ Yes ☐ Block ☐ Precast ☐ Steel Describe _____

MASONRY RESTORATION: ☐ No ☐ Yes ☐ Cut ☐ Recaulk ☐ Repoint ☐ Stucco Finish ☐ _____
   SAND BLAST: ☐ No ☐ Yes Describe _____
   STEAM CLEAN: ☐ No ☐ Yes Describe _____

PIERS: ☐ No ☐ Yes Size _____

PILASTERS: ☐ No ☐ Yes Size _____

REFRACTORY WORK: ☐ No ☐ Yes Describe _____

SIMULATED BRICK: ☐ No ☐ Yes Material _____ Describe _____

STEPS: ☐ No ☐ Yes Describe _____

VENT BOX: ☐ No ☐ Yes ☐ Aluminum ☐ Bronze Size _____

WEEP HOLES: ☐ No ☐ Yes Spacing _____ Describe _____

WINDOW Sills and Stools: ☐ No ☐ Yes ☐ Brick ☐ Concrete ☐ Stone ☐ _____
   Describe _____

MASONRY
Block, Tile & Stone

SPEC-AID

CONCRETE BLOCK: ☐ No ☐ Yes ☐ Exterior ☐ Interior ☐ Regular Weight ☐ Light Weight ☐ Solid ☐ Hollow ☐ Load Bearing
☐ Non Load Bearing Describe _____

_____ Compressive Strength _____ psi. ASTM No. _____

SIZE: _____

FINISH: ☐ Regular ☐ Ground ☐ Ribbed ☐ Glazed ☐ _____

BOND: ☐ Common ☐ Stack ☐ Other _____ Headers every _____ course.

JOINTS: ☐ Concave ☐ Struck ☐ Flush ☐ Raked ☐ Weathered ☐ Stripped ☐ _____

REINFORCING: ☐ No ☐ Yes _____ Strips every _____ course.

WALL TIES: ☐ No ☐ Yes Describe _____

BOND BEAMS: ☐ No ☐ Yes Size _____ Describe _____

   Reinforcing _____ Grout _____

LINTELS: ☐ No ☐ Yes ☐ Precast ☐ Steel ☐ Block Size _____ Describe _____

   Reinforcing _____ Grout _____

COLUMNS: ☐ No ☐ Yes Size _____

PILASTERS: ☐ No ☐ Yes Size _____

GLASS BLOCK: ☐ No ☐ Yes Size _____ Type _____

Special Block _____

Describe _____

GLAZED CONCRETE BLOCK: ☐ No ☐ Yes ☐ Solid ☐ Hollow Type _____

☐ Non Reinforced ☐ Reinforced _____ Strips every _____ course.

Describe _____

GYPSUM BLOCK: ☐ No ☐ Yes ☐ Solid ☐ Hollow Thickness _____ Describe _____

_____

GROUTING: ☐ No ☐ Yes ☐ Block Cores ☐ Bond Beams ☐ Cavity Walls ☐ Door Frames ☐ Lintels ☐ _____

Describe _____

INSULATION: ☐ No ☐ Yes ☐ Board ☐ Poured ☐ Sprayed Material _____

Thickness _____ Describe _____

SOLAR SCREEN: ☐ No ☐ Yes Describe _____

SPECIAL BLOCK: ☐ No ☐ Yes Describe _____

☐ Parge Block ☐ Clean Cavity ☐ Spandrel Flashing _____

SPECIAL CONSIDERATIONS: _____

CERAMIC VENEER: ☐ No ☐ Yes Describe _____

STRUCTURAL FACING TILE: ☐ No ☐ Yes ☐ 6T Series ☐ 8W Series ☐ Other _____

Describe _____

TERRA COTTA: ☐ No ☐ Yes ☐ Floors ☐ Partitions ☐ Fireproofing ☐ Load Bearing ☐ Non Load Bearing

Describe _____

ASHLAR STONE: ☐ No ☐ Yes Type _____ Thickness _____

Describe _____

RUBBLE STONE: ☐ No ☐ Yes ☐ Coarsed ☐ Uncoarsed Type _____ Thickness _____

Describe _____

CUT STONE: ☐ No ☐ Yes ☐ Granite ☐ Limestone ☐ Marble ☐ Sand Stone ☐ Slate ☐ _____

☐ Base _____ ☐ Columns _____ ☐ Coping _____

☐ Curbs _____ ☐ Facing Panels _____

☐ Flooring _____ ☐ Showers _____

☐ Soffits _____ ☐ Stair Treads _____

☐ Stairs _____ ☐ Thresholds _____

☐ Window Sills _____ ☐ Window Stools _____

☐ _____

SIMULATED STONE: ☐ No ☐ Yes Material _____ Describe _____

SPECIAL STONE _____

GENERAL NOTES: MASONRY _____

_____

Left margin labels: BLOCKWORK 4.3   TILE 4.3   STONE WORK 4.4

MEANSCO FORM 405   DIVISION 5

SPEC-AID

DATE _____

PROJECT _____ LOCATION _____

DESIGN CRITERIA: In Division 1 _____
  TYPICAL BAY SPACINGS: _____
_____

  FLOOR TO CEILING HEIGHTS: _____
  BEAM DEPTHS: _____
  ROOF SLOPE: ☐ Flat ☐ Other _____
  EAVE HEIGHT: _____

ANCHOR BOLTS: ☐ No ☐ By Others ☐ Yes Describe _____
_____ Number _____

BASE PLATES: ☐ No ☐ By Others ☐ Yes Describe _____
_____ Number _____

METAL DECKING FLOORS: ☐ No ☐ By Others ☐ Cellular ☐ Non Cellular ☐ Painted ☐ Galv. Depth _____
  ☐ Acoustical ☐ Ventilating Gauge _____ Describe _____

  ROOF DECK: ☐ No ☐ By Others ☐ Cellular ☐ Non Cellular ☐ Painted ☐ Galv. Depth _____
  ☐ Acoustical ☐ Ventilating Gauge _____ Describe _____

STRUCTURAL SYSTEM: ☐ Wall Bearing ☐ Free Standing ☐ Simple Spans ☐ Continuous Spans _____
  ☐ Conventional Design ☐ Plastic Design ☐ Field Welded ☐ Field Bolted ☐ Composite Design
  ☐ Other _____
  TYPE STEEL _____ Grade _____
  ESTIMATED WEIGHTS: Beams _____ Roof Frames _____ Adjustable Spandrel Angles _____
    Girders _____ Girts _____ Hanger Pods _____ Bracing _____
    Columns _____ Connections _____ Other _____
  PAINT: Shop ☐ No ☐ Yes _____ Coats Material _____
    Field Paint ☐ No ☐ Yes ☐ Brush ☐ Roller ☐ Spray _____ Coats Material _____
  GALVANIZING: ☐ No ☐ Yes Thickness _____
  OTHER: _____
FIREPROOFING: ☐ No ☐ Yes ☐ Beams ☐ Columns ☐ Decks ☐ _____ Rating _____ Hr.
  ☐ Concrete Encasement ☐ Spray ☐ Plaster ☐ Drywall ☐ _____
  Describe _____
OPEN WEB JOISTS: ☐ No ☐ Yes ☐ H Series ☐ LH Series ☐ _____
  ESTIMATED WEIGHTS: _____
  BRIDGING ☐ No ☐ Yes ☐ Bolted ☐ Welded ☐ Pod Bridging _____
  PAINT: Shop ☐ Standard ☐ Special _____ Coats Field Paint ☐ No ☐ Yes Describe _____
LIGHT GAUGE JOISTS: ☐ No ☐ Yes Describe _____
LIGHT GAUGE FRAMING: ☐ No ☐ Yes Describe _____
SPECIAL CONSIDERATIONS: _____
_____
_____

FASTENERS: Expansion Bolts _____ High Strength Bolts _____
  Machine Screws _____ Machinery Anchors _____
  Nails _____ Roof Bolts _____
  Sheet Metal Screws _____ Studs _____
  Timber Connectors _____ Toggle Bolts _____
  Welded Studs _____ Other _____

STRUCTURAL METALS 5.1

FASTENERS 5.8

METALS
Miscellaneous & Ornamental

SPEC-AID

AREA WALLS: ☐ No ☐ Yes _____ Gratings _____ Caps _____

BUMPER RAILS: ☐ No ☐ Yes _____

CANOPY FRAMING: ☐ No ☐ Yes _____

CHECKERED PLATE: ☐ No ☐ Trench Covers ☐ Pit Covers ☐ Platforms ☐ _____

COLUMNS: ☐ No ☐ Aluminum ☐ Steel ☐ Square ☐ Rectangular ☐ Round ☐ _____

CONSTRUCTION CASTINGS: ☐ No ☐ Chimney Specialties _____ ☐ Column Bases _____

☐ Manhole Covers _____ ☐ Wheel Guards _____

☐ _____

CORNER GUARDS: ☐ No ☐ Yes _____

CRANE RAIL: ☐ No ☐ Yes _____

CURB ANGLES: ☐ No ☐ Straight ☐ Curved _____

DECORATIVE COVERING: ☐ No ☐ Stock Sections ☐ Custom Sections _____

Doors _____ Walls _____

DOOR Frames: ☐ No ☐ Yes _____ ☐ Protection: ☐ No ☐ Yes _____

EXPANSION JOINTS CEILINGS: ☐ No ☐ Yes _____ Cover Plates: ☐ No ☐ Yes _____

FLOORS: ☐ No ☐ Yes _____ Cover Plates: ☐ No ☐ Yes _____

WALLS: ☐ No ☐ Yes _____ Cover Plates: ☐ No ☐ Yes _____

FIRE ESCAPE: ☐ No ☐ Yes _____ Size _____

Stairs _____ Ladders _____ Cantilever _____

FLOOR GRATING: ☐ No ☐ Aluminum ☐ Steel ☐ Fiberglass ☐ Platforms ☐ Stairs ☐ _____

Type _____ Weight _____

Special Finish _____

LADDERS: ☐ No ☐ Aluminum ☐ Steel ☐ _____

☐ With Cage ☐ No Cage _____ ☐ Inclined Type _____

LAMP POSTS: ☐ No ☐ Yes _____

LINTELS: ☐ No ☐ Yes ☐ Plain ☐ Built-up ☐ Painted ☐ Galvanized _____

_____

LOUVERS: ☐ No ☐ Yes _____

MANHOLE COVERS: ☐ No ☐ Yes _____

MAT FRAMES: ☐ No ☐ Yes _____

OVERHEAD SUPPORTS: ☐ No ☐ Toilet ☐ Partitions ☐ _____

PIPE BUMPERS: ☐ No ☐ Yes _____

PIPE SUPPORTS: ☐ No ☐ Yes _____

RAILINGS: ☐ No ☐ Yes ☐ Aluminum ☐ Steel ☐ Pipe ☐ _____

Balconies: ☐ No ☐ Yes _____

Stairs: ☐ No ☐ Yes _____

Wall: ☐ No ☐ Yes _____

SOLAR SCREENS: ☐ No ☐ Yes _____

STAIRS: ☐ No ☐ Yes ☐ Aluminum ☐ Steel ☐ Stock ☐ Custom ☐ _____

Size _____ Landings _____

SPIRAL: ☐ No ☐ Aluminum ☐ Steel ☐ Stock ☐ Custom ☐ _____

PRE-ERECTED: ☐ No ☐ Yes _____

STAIR TREADS: ☐ No ☐ Yes _____

TRENCH COVERS: ☐ No ☐ Yes _____

WEATHER VANES: ☐ No ☐ Yes _____

WINDOW GUARDS: ☐ No ☐ Bars ☐ Woven Wire ☐ _____

WIRE: ☐ No ☐ Yes _____

WIRE ROPE: ☐ No ☐ Yes _____

SPECIAL CONSIDERATIONS: _____

_____

_____

_____

MISCELLANEOUS AND ORNAMENTAL METALS 5.4

CARPENTRY
Rough and Laminated

MEANSCO FORM 406   DIVISION 6

SPEC-AID

DATE _____

PROJECT _____ LOCATION _____

FRAMING: Type Wood _____ Fiber Stress _____ psi.

BEAMS: ☐ Single ☐ Built up _____ Grade _____
BRACING: ☐ No ☐ Let in ☐ _____
BRIDGING: ☐ Steel ☐ Wood _____
CANOPY FRAMING: _____
COLUMNS _____ Fiber Stress _____ psi.
DOOR BUCKS: ☐ No ☐ Treated ☐ Untreated _____
FLOOR PLANKS _____ Grade _____
FURRING: ☐ Metal ☐ Wood _____
GROUNDS: ☐ No ☐ Casework ☐ Plaster ☐ On Wood ☐ On Masonry _____
JOISTS: ☐ No ☐ Floor ☐ Ceiling _____ Grade _____
LEDGERS: ☐ No ☐ Bolted ☐ Nailed _____
LUMBER TREATMENT: ☐ No ☐ Creosote ☐ Salt Treated ☐ Fire Retardant _____
  ☐ Kiln Dry _____
NAILERS: ☐ No ☐ Treated ☐ Untreated _____
PLATES: _____ **PLATFORM FRAMING:** _____
PLYWOOD TREATMENT: ☐ No ☐ Salt Treated ☐ Fire Retardant _____
POSTS & GIRTS: _____
RAFTERS: ☐ No ☐ Ordinary ☐ Hip _____
ROOF CANTS: ☐ No ☐ Yes _____ **ROOF CURBS:** ☐ No ☐ Yes _____
ROOF DECKS: ☐ No ☐ Yes _____ inches thick _____
ROOF PURLINS: ☐ No ☐ Yes _____
ROOF TRUSSES: ☐ No ☐ Timber Connectors ☐ Nailed ☐ Glued Spaced _____ O.C. Span _____ feet
SHEATHING, ROOF: ☐ No ☐ Plywood ☐ Boards ☐ Wood Fiber ☐ Gypsum _____
  WALL: ☐ No ☐ Plywood ☐ Boards ☐ Wood Fiber ☐ Gypsum _____
SIDING HARDBOARD: ☐ Plain ☐ Primed ☐ Stained _____
  PARTICLE BOARD: _____ WOOD FIBER _____
  PLYWOOD: ☐ Cedar ☐ Fir ☐ Redwood ☐ Marine ☐ Natural ☐ Stained ☐ Plastic Faced ☐ _____

  WOOD: ☐ Cedar ☐ Redwood ☐ White Pine ☐ Bevel ☐ Board & Batten ☐ Channel ☐ T & G ☐ Shiplap _____
    ☐ Natural ☐ Stained _____
SILLS: _____ **SLEEPERS:** _____
SOFFITS: ☐ No ☐ Open ☐ Vented ☐ Plywood _____
STRESSED SKIN PLYWOOD BOX BEAMS: _____ Depth _____
  FLOOR PANELS: ☐ No ☐ Yes _____ Depth _____
  ROOF PANELS: ☐ No ☐ Straight ☐ Curved _____ Depth _____
  FOLDED PLATE: ☐ No ☐ Yes _____ Depth _____
STUDS: ☐ No ☐ Yes _____ Grade _____
SUBFLOOR: ☐ No ☐ Plywood ☐ Boards ☐ Wood Fiber ☐ _____
SUSPENDED CEILING FRAMING: ☐ No ☐ Yes _____
UNDERLAYMENT: ☐ No ☐ Particle Board ☐ Plywood ☐ Wood Fiber ☐ Hardboard _____
SPECIAL CONSIDERATIONS: _____

LAMINATED FRAMING: ☐ Beams ☐ Straight ☐ Curved _____ Span _____
  ☐ Bowstring Trusses ☐ Radial Arch ☐ Tudor Arch ☐ Columns _____
  Span _____ Height _____
  ☐ Industrial Grade ☐ Premium Grade ☐ Exterior Glue ☐ Stain ☐ Varnish ☐ Treated ☐ _____
LAMINATED ROOF DECK: ☐ No ☐ Yes _____ Thickness _____
SPECIAL CONSIDERATIONS: _____

ROUGH CARPENTRY 6.1

LAMINATED 6.3

CARPENTRY
Finish & Millwork

SPEC-AID

BASE: ☐ No ☐ One Piece ☐ Built up ☐ Pine ☐ Hardwood _____

CABINETS: ☐ No ☐ Corner ☐ Kitchen ☐ Toilet Room ☐ Other _____
    ☐ Stock ☐ Custom _____
    ☐ Unfinished ☐ Prefinished _____
    BASE CABINETS: ☐ Softwood ☐ Hardwood ☐ Drawer Units _____
    WALL CABINETS: ☐ Softwood ☐ Hardwood _____
    TALL CABINETS: ☐ Softwood ☐ Hardwood _____
    SPECIAL: _____

CASINGS: ☐ No ☐ Doors ☐ Windows ☐ Beams ☐ Other _____
    ☐ Softwood ☐ Hardwood _____

CEILING BEAMS: ☐ No ☐ Cedar ☐ Pine ☐ Fir ☐ Plastic _____

CHAIR RAIL: ☐ No ☐ Pine ☐ Other _____

CLOSETS: ☐ No ☐ Pole ☐ Shelf ☐ Prefabricated _____

COLUMNS: ☐ No ☐ Square ☐ Round ☐ Solid ☐ Built up ☐ Hollow ☐ Tapered _____
    Diameter _____ Height _____

CONVECTOR COVERS: ☐ No ☐ Yes _____

CORNICE: ☐ No ☐ 1 Piece ☐ 2 Piece ☐ 3 Piece ☐ Pine ☐ Cedar ☐ Other _____

COUNTER TOPS: ☐ No ☐ Plastic ☐ Ceramic Tile ☐ Marble ☐ Suede Finish ☐ Other _____
    ☐ Stock ☐ Custom _____
    ☐ No Splash ☐ Square Splash ☐ Cove Splash _____
    ☐ Self Edge ☐ Stainless Edge ☐ Aluminum Edge _____
    SPECIAL _____

CUPOLAS: ☐ No ☐ Stock ☐ Custom ☐ Wood ☐ Fiberglass ☐ Square ☐ Octagonal Size _____
    ☐ Aluminum Roof ☐ Copper Roof ☐ Other _____

DOORS AND FRAMES: See Division 8 _____

DOOR MOLDINGS: ☐ No ☐ Yes _____

DOOR TRIM: ☐ No ☐ Yes _____

FIREPLACE MANTELS: ☐ No ☐ Beams ☐ Moldings _____
    Size _____

MOLDINGS: ☐ No ☐ Softwood ☐ Hardwood ☐ Metal ☐ Other _____

PANELING HARDBOARD: ☐ No ☐ Tempered ☐ Untempered ☐ Pegboard ☐ Plastic Faced _____
    PLYWOOD, UNFINISHED: ☐ No ☐ Veneer Core ☐ Lumber Core Grade _____ Thick _____
    PLYWOOD, PREFINISHED: ☐ No ☐ Stock ☐ Architectural Finish _____
    SIZE _____
    WOOD BOARDS: ☐ No ☐ Softwood ☐ Hardwood _____

RAILINGS: ☐ No ☐ Stock ☐ Custom ☐ Softwood ☐ Hardwood _____
    ☐ Stairs ☐ Balcony ☐ Porch ☐ Wall ☐ Other _____

SHELVING: ☐ No ☐ Prefinished ☐ Unfinished ☐ Stock ☐ Custom ☐ Plywood ☐ Particle Board ☐ Boards _____
    ☐ Book Shelves _____ ☐ Linen Shelves _____
    ☐ Storage Shelves _____ ☐ Other _____

STAIRS: ☐ No ☐ Prefabricated ☐ Built in Place ☐ Softwood ☐ Hardwood _____
    ☐ Box ☐ Open ☐ Circular _____

THRESHOLDS: ☐ No ☐ Interior ☐ Exterior _____

WAINSCOT: ☐ No ☐ Boards ☐ Plywood ☐ Moldings _____

WINDOWS AND FRAMES: See Division 8 _____

WINDOW TRIM: ☐ No ☐ Yes _____

SPECIAL CONSIDERATIONS: _____

MOISTURE PROTECTION Waterproofing,

MEANSCO FORM 407 DIVISION 7 **Insulation, Shingles, Preformed Roofing & Siding**

SPEC-AID DATE _____

PROJECT _____ LOCATION _____

WATERPROOFING 7.1

BENTONITE: ☐ No ☐ Panels ☐ Granular _____

BITUMINOUS COATING: ☐ No ☐ Brushed ☐ Sprayed ☐ Troweled ☐ 1 Coat ☐ 2 Coat ☐ Protective Board _____

BUILDING PAPER: ☐ No ☐ Asphalt ☐ Polyethylene ☐ Rosin ☐ Kraft ☐ Foil Backed ☐ _____

☐ Roof Deck Vapor Barrier _____

CAULKING: ☐ No ☐ Gun Grade ☐ Knife Grade ☐ Plain ☐ Colors _____

☐ Doors ☐ Windows ☐ _____

CEMENTITIOUS: ☐ No ☐ 1 Coat ☐ 2 Coat Thickness _____ inches Mix _____

CONTROL JOINTS: _____ **EXPANSION JOINTS:** _____

ELASTOMERIC WATERPROOFING: ☐ No ☐ EPDM ☐ Neoprene ☐ PVC ☐ Urethane ☐ _____

LIQUID WATERPROOFING: ☐ No ☐ Silicone ☐ Stearate ☐ _____

MEMBRANE WATERPROOFING: ☐ 1 Ply ☐ 2 Ply ☐ 3 Ply ☐ Felt ☐ Fabric ☐ Elastomeric ☐ _____

METALLIC COATING: ☐ No ☐ Walls _____ in. thick ☐ Floors _____ in. thick

PREFORMED VAPOR BARRIER: ☐ No ☐ Yes _____

SEALANTS: ☐ No ☐ Butyl ☐ Polysulfide ☐ PVC ☐ Urethane ☐ _____

☐ Doors ☐ Windows ☐ _____

SPECIAL WATERPROOFING _____

INSULATION 7.2

BUILDING INSULATION: RIGID: ☐ No ☐ Fiberglass ☐ Polystyrene ☐ Urethane ☐ _____

NON RIGID: ☐ No ☐ Fiberglass ☐ Mineral Fiber ☐ Vermiculite ☐ Perlite ☐ _____

FORM BOARD: ☐ No ☐ Acoustical ☐ Asbestos Cement ☐ Fiberglass ☐ Gypsum ☐ Mineral Fiber ☐ Wood Fiber

☐ Other _____ ☐ Sub purlins _____ Span _____

MASONRY INSULATION: ☐ No ☐ Cavity Wall ☐ Block Cores ☐ Poured ☐ Foamed Type _____

PERIMETER INSULATION: ☐ No ☐ Yes Type _____ Thickness _____

ROOF DECK INSULATION: ☐ No ☐ Fiberboard ☐ Fiberglass ☐ Foamglass ☐ Polystyrene ☐ Urethane ☐ _____

Thickness _____ ☐ **CANTS** _____ Size _____

SPRAYED: ☐ No ☐ Fibrous ☐ Cementitious ☐ Urethane ☐ _____

SPECIAL INSULATION _____

SHINGLES 7.3

SHINGLES: ALUMINUM: ☐ No ☐ Yes _____ **ASBESTOS:** ☐ No ☐ Yes _____

ASPHALT: ☐ No ☐ Class C ☐ Class A ☐ _____ Weight _____ lb. per Sq. _____

CLAY TILE: ☐ No ☐ Plain ☐ Glazed ☐ Spanish ☐ _____ Weight _____ lb. per Sq. _____

CONCRETE TILE: ☐ No ☐ Yes _____ **PORCELAIN ENAMEL:** ☐ No ☐ Yes _____

SLATE: ☐ No ☐ Yes Type _____ Color _____ Exposure _____

WOOD: ☐ No ☐ Roofing ☐ Siding ☐ Fire Retardant Type _____ Grade _____ Exposure _____

SHINGLE UNDERLAYMENT: ☐ No ☐ Asbestos ☐ Asphalt ☐ _____ Weight _____

SPECIAL SHINGLES: _____

PREFORMED ROOFING & SIDING 7.4

ALUMINUM: ☐ No ☐ Roofing ☐ Siding ☐ Painted ☐ Insulated ☐ Sandwich ☐ _____

Thickness _____ Type _____

ASBESTOS CEMENT: ☐ No ☐ Roofing ☐ Siding ☐ Flat ☐ Corrugated ☐ Natural ☐ Painted ☐ Sandwich

☐ Fire Rated Thickness _____ Type _____

EPOXY PANELS: ☐ No ☐ Solid ☐ Plywood Back ☐ Hardboard Back ☐ Exposed Aggregate ☐ _____

FIBERGLASS PANELS: ☐ No ☐ Roofing ☐ Siding ☐ Flat ☐ Corrugated ☐ _____ Thickness _____

METAL FACING PANELS: ☐ No ☐ Field Assembled ☐ Factory Made Insulation _____

Outside Face _____ Inside Face _____

PROTECTED METAL: ☐ No ☐ Roofing ☐ Siding Type _____ Gauge _____

STEEL: ☐ No ☐ Roofing ☐ Siding ☐ Painted ☐ Galvanized ☐ Insulated ☐ Sandwich ☐ _____

Type _____ Gauge _____

VINYL SIDING: ☐ No ☐ Plain ☐ Insulated Type _____

SPECIAL ROOFING & SIDING: _____

_____

MEMBRANE ROOFING 7.4

BUILT UP ROOFING: ☐ No ☐ Tar & Gravel ☐ Asphalt & Gravel ☐ Felt ☐ Mineral Surface ☐ Aggregate
☐ 1 Ply ☐ 2 Ply ☐ 3 Ply ☐ 4 Ply ☐ 5 Ply ☐ Bonded _____ years Roof Pitch _____ Type Deck _____
UNDERLAYMENT: ☐ No ☐ Rosin Paper ☐ Vapor Barrier ☐ _____
ELASTIC SHEET ROOFING: ☐ No ☐ Butyl ☐ Neoprene ☐ _____ Thickness _____
Describe _____
FLUID APPLIED ROOFING: ☐ No ☐ Hypalon Neoprene ☐ Silicone ☐ Vinyl ☐ _____ Thickness _____
Describe _____
ROLL ROOFING: ☐ No ☐ Smooth ☐ Granular _____ Weight _____ lbs. per Sq.
SPECIAL MEMBRANE ROOFING: _____

SHEET METAL WORK 7.6

DOWNSPOUTS: ☐ No ☐ Aluminum ☐ Copper ☐ Lead Coated Copper ☐ Galvanized Steel ☐ Stainless Steel
☐ Steel Pipe ☐ Vinyl ☐ Zinc Alloy ☐ Stock ☐ Custom ☐ _____ Size _____
Describe _____
EXPANSION JOINTS: ☐ No ☐ Roof ☐ Walls ☐ No Curbs ☐ Curbs ☐ Rubber ☐ Metallic ☐ _____
Describe _____
FASCIA: ☐ No ☐ Yes Describe _____ Thickness _____
FLASHING: ☐ No ☐ Aluminum ☐ Asphalt ☐ Copper ☐ Fabric ☐ Lead ☐ Lead Coated Copper ☐ PVC ☐ Rubber
☐ Stainless Steel ☐ Terne ☐ Zinc Alloy ☐ Paper Backed ☐ Mastic Backed ☐ Fabric Backed ☐ _____
Describe _____ Thickness _____

GRAVEL STOP: ☐ No ☐ Aluminum ☐ Copper ☐ PVC ☐ Stainless Steel ☐ _____
☐ With Fascia ☐ No Fascia ☐ Natural ☐ Painted Thickness _____ Face Height _____
GUTTERS: ☐ No ☐ Aluminum ☐ Copper ☐ Lead Coated Copper ☐ Galvanized Steel ☐ Stainless Steel _____
☐ Vinyl ☐ Wood ☐ Zinc Alloy ☐ _____ Thickness _____
☐ Box Type ☐ K Type ☐ Half Round ☐ Stock ☐ Custom ☐ _____ Size _____
LOUVERS: ☐ No ☐ Yes _____
MANSARD: ☐ No ☐ Yes _____ Thickness _____
METAL ROOFING: ☐ No ☐ Copper ☐ Copper Bearing Steel ☐ Lead ☐ Lead Coated Copper ☐ Stainless Steel
☐ Terne ☐ Zinc Alloy ☐ _____ Size _____ Thickness _____
☐ Standing Seam ☐ Flat Seam ☐ Batten Seam ☐ _____ Weight _____ lbs. per Sq.

UNDERLAYMENT: ☐ No ☐ 15 lb. Felt ☐ 30 lb. Felt ☐ Rosin Paper ☐ _____
REGLET: ☐ No ☐ Aluminum ☐ Copper ☐ Galvanized Steel ☐ Stainless Steel ☐ Zinc Alloy ☐ _____
Thickness _____ Counter Flashing: ☐ No ☐ Yes _____ Thickness _____
SOFFIT: ☐ No ☐ Yes _____ Thickness _____
SPECIAL SHEET METAL WORK: _____

ROOF ACCESSORIES 7.8

CEILING HATCHES: ☐ No ☐ Steel ☐ Galvanized ☐ Painted ☐ Aluminum ☐ _____
Size _____
ROOF DRAINS: ☐ No ☐ In Plumbing ☐ Yes _____
ROOF HATCHES: ☐ No ☐ Steel ☐ Galvanized ☐ Painted ☐ Aluminum ☐ _____
☐ Insulated ☐ Not Insulated ☐ With Curbs ☐ No Curbs ☐ _____ Size _____
SMOKE HATCHES: ☐ No ☐ Yes _____
SNOW GUARDS: ☐ No ☐ Yes _____
SKYLIGHTS: ☐ No ☐ Domes ☐ Vaulted ☐ Ridge Units ☐ Field Fabricated ☐ Glass ☐ Plastic ☐ Single ☐ Double
☐ Sandwich Panels ☐ With Curbs ☐ No Curbs ☐ _____ Size _____
SMOKE VENTS: ☐ No ☐ Yes _____
SKYROOFS: ☐ No ☐ Yes _____
VENTILATORS: ☐ No ☐ In Ventilating ☐ Stationary ☐ Spinners ☐ Motorized
SPECIAL ROOF ACCESSORIES _____

DOORS, WINDOWS & GLASS
Doors, Entrances, Store Fronts & Windows

MEANSCO FORM 408   DIVISION 8

SPEC-AID

DATE _____

PAGE 1 OF 2

PROJECT _____ LOCATION _____

DOORS 8.1-8.2

HOLLOW METAL FRAMES: ☐ No ☐ Baked Enamel ☐ Galvanized ☐ Porcelain Enamel _____

HOLLOW METAL DOORS: ☐ No _____ ☐ Core _____ ☐ Labeled _____

ALUMINUM FRAMES: ☐ No ☐ Clear ☐ Bronze ☐ Black _____

ALUMINUM DOORS AND FRAMES: ☐ No ☐ Yes _____ Frames _____

WOOD FRAMES: ☐ No ☐ Exterior ☐ Interior ☐ Custom ☐ With Sill ☐ Vinyl covered ☐ Pine ☐ Oak

WOOD DOORS: ☐ No _____ Core ☐ Labeled _____ Frames _____

INTERIOR DOOR FRAMES: ☐ No ☐ Aluminum ☐ Hollow Metal ☐ Steel ☐ Wood ☐ Prehung ☐ Stock ☐ Custom ☐ _____

CUSTOM DOORS: ☐ No ☐ Swing ☐ Bi-Passing ☐ Bi-Folding _____ Frames _____

ACCORDIAN FOLDING DOORS: ☐ No ☐ Yes _____ Frames _____

SPECIAL DOORS 8.3

ACOUSTICAL DOORS: ☐ No ☐ Yes _____ Decibels _____ Frames _____

COLD STORAGE: ☐ No ☐ Manual ☐ Power ☐ Sliding ☐ Hinged _____

COUNTER DOORS: ☐ No ☐ Aluminum ☐ Steel ☐ Wood _____ Frames _____

DARK ROOM DOORS: ☐ No ☐ Revolving ☐ 2 way ☐ 3 way _____

FLOOR OPENING DOORS: ☐ No ☐ Aluminum ☐ Steel ☐ Single ☐ Double ☐ Commercial ☐ Industrial _____

GLASS DOORS: ☐ No ☐ Sliding ☐ Swing _____ Frames _____

HANGAR DOORS: ☐ No ☐ Bi-Fold ☐ Other ☐ Electric _____

JALOUSIE DOORS: ☐ No ☐ Plain Glass ☐ Tempered Glass _____

KALAMEIN: ☐ No ☐ Yes ☐ Labeled _____ Frames _____

KENNEL DOORS: ☐ No ☐ 2 way Swinging _____

OVERHEAD DOORS: ☐ No ☐ Regular Duty ☐ Heavy Duty ☐ Stock ☐ Custom ☐ One Piece ☐ Sectional ☐ Manual ☐ Electric
☐ Aluminum ☐ Fiberglass ☐ Steel ☐ Wood ☐ Hardboard ☐ Commercial ☐ Residential Size _____

ROLLING DOORS EXTERIOR: ☐ No ☐ Manual ☐ Electric ☐ Labeled _____

ROLLING DOORS INTERIOR: ☐ No ☐ Manual ☐ Electric ☐ Labeled _____ Frames _____

ROLLING GRILLES: ☐ No ☐ Manual ☐ Electric ☐ Aluminum ☐ Steel _____

SERVICE DOOR FRAMES: ☐ No ☐ Aluminum ☐ Hollow Metal ☐ Steel ☐ Wood ☐ Stock ☐ Custom _____

SERVICE DOORS: ☐ No ☐ Stock ☐ Custom _____ ☐ Transoms _____ ☐ Sidelights _____ ☐ Aluminum
☐ Hollow Metal _____ Core _____ ☐ Kalamein _____ ☐ Steel _____ ☐ Wood _____
Core _____ ☐ Labeled _____ ☐ Special Finish _____

SHOCK ABSORBING DOORS: ☐ No ☐ Flexible ☐ Rigid _____ Frames _____

SLIDING DOORS: ☐ No ☐ Glazed ☐ Unglazed ☐ Aluminum ☐ Steel ☐ Wood _____

SWING DOORS: ☐ No ☐ Single ☐ Double _____

TELESCOPING DOOR: ☐ No ☐ Manual ☐ Electric _____

TINCLAD DOORS: ☐ No ☐ Manual ☐ Electric _____

VAULT FRONT DOORS: ☐ No ☐ Stainless Steel ☐ Time Lock ☐ 1 Hr. Test ☐ 2 Hr. Test ☐ 4 Hr. Test _____

SPECIAL EXTERIOR DOORS: ☐ No ☐ Yes _____

SPECIAL INTERIOR DOORS: ☐ No ☐ Yes _____

ENTRANCE 8.4

BALANCED DOORS: ☐ No ☐ Economy ☐ Premium ☐ Aluminum ☐ Stainless Steel _____

REVOLVING DOORS: ☐ No ☐ Stock ☐ Custom ☐ Manual ☐ Electric ☐ Diameter _____

ENTRANCE UNITS: ☐ No ☐ Aluminum ☐ Bronze ☐ Glass ☐ Hollow Metal ☐ Stainless Steel ☐ Wood ☐ Steel ☐ Stock _____
☐ Custom ☐ Balanced ☐ Sidelights ☐ Transoms Special Finish _____

ENTRANCE FRAMES: ☐ No ☐ Aluminum ☐ Hollow Metal ☐ Steel ☐ Wood ☐ Stainless Steel ☐ Stock ☐ Custom _____

STORE FRONTS: ☐ No ☐ Sliding ☐ Fixed ☐ Institutional Grade ☐ Monumental Grade ☐ Commercial Grade _____

WINDOWS 8.5-8.6

WINDOWS: _____ % of Exterior walls _____

PROJECTED: ☐ No ☐ Glazed ☐ Unglazed ☐ Aluminum ☐ Steel ☐ Wood _____

SINGLE HUNG: ☐ No ☐ Glazed ☐ Unglazed ☐ Aluminum ☐ Steel ☐ Wood _____

SLIDING: ☐ No ☐ Glazed ☐ Unglazed ☐ Aluminum ☐ Steel ☐ Wood _____

SECURITY WINDOWS: ☐ No ☐ Yes _____

328

DOORS, WINDOWS & GLASS

Windows, Hardware, Weatherstripping, Glass & Glazing

SPEC-AID

CASEMENT: ☐ No ☐ Fixed _____% Vented ☐ Aluminum ☐ Steel ☐ Wood _____

PICTURE WINDOW: ☐ No ☐ Glazed ☐ Unglazed ☐ Aluminum ☐ Steel ☐ Wood _____

DOUBLE HUNG: ☐ No ☐ Glazed ☐ Unglazed ☐ Aluminum ☐ Steel ☐ Wood _____

SPECIAL WINDOWS: ☐ No ☐ Yes _____

SCREENS: ☐ No ☐ Aluminum ☐ Steel ☐ Wood _____

FINISH HARDWARE ALLOWANCE: ☐ No ☐ Yes _____

    Exterior Doors _____

    Interior Doors _____

AUTOMATIC OPENERS: ☐ No ☐ 1 way ☐ 2 way ☐ Double Door ☐ Activating Carpet

AUTOMATIC OPERATORS: ☐ No ☐ Sliding ☐ Swing ☐ Controls _____

BUMPER PLATES: ☐ No ☐ U Channel ☐ Teardrop _____

DOOR CLOSERS: ☐ No ☐ Regular ☐ Fusible Link ☐ Concealed ☐ Heavy Use _____

DOOR STOPS: ☐ No ☐ Yes _____

FLOOR CHECKS: ☐ No ☐ Single Acting ☐ Double Acting _____

HINGES: ☐ No ☐ Butt ☐ Pivot ☐ Spring ☐ Frequency _____

KICK PLATES: ☐ No ☐ Yes _____

LOCK SET: ☐ No ☐ Cylindrical ☐ Mortise ☐ Heavy Duty ☐ Commercial ☐ Residential _____

PANIC DEVICE: ☐ No ☐ Yes ☐ Exit Only ☐ Exit & Entrance _____

PUSH-PULL DEVICE: ☐ No ☐ Yes ☐ Bronze ☐ Aluminum ☐ Other _____

CABINET HARDWARE: ☐ No ☐ Yes _____

WINDOW HARDWARE: ☐ No ☐ Yes _____

SPECIAL HARDWARE: ☐ No ☐ Yes _____

THRESHOLD: ☐ No ☐ Yes _____

WEATHER STRIPPING DOORS: ☐ No ☐ Zinc ☐ Bronze ☐ Stainless Steel ☐ Spring Type ☐ Extruded Sections

    WINDOWS: ☐ No ☐ Zinc ☐ Bronze _____

ACOUSTICAL GLASS: ☐ No ☐ Yes _____ Thickness _____

FACETED GLASS: ☐ No ☐ Yes _____ Thickness _____

GLAZING: ☐ No ☐ Putty ☐ Flush ☐ Bead ☐ Gasket ☐ Butt ☐ Riglet ☐ _____

INSULATED GLASS: ☐ No ☐ Standard ☐ Non-Standard _____ Thickness _____

LAMINATED GLASS: ☐ No ☐ Yes _____ Thickness _____

MIRRORS: ☐ No ☐ Plate ☐ Sheet ☐ Transparent ☐ Incl. Frames ☐ No Frames ☐ _____

    Door Type _____ Wall Type _____

OBSCURE GLASS: ☐ No ☐ Yes _____ Thickness _____

PLATE GLASS: ☐ No ☐ Clear ☐ Tinted ☐ Tempered _____ Thickness _____

PLEXIGLASS: ☐ No ☐ Masked ☐ Unmasked _____ Thickness _____

POLYCARBONATE: ☐ No ☐ Masked ☐ Unmasked _____ Thickness _____

REFLECTIVE: ☐ No ☐ Clear ☐ Tinted _____ Thickness _____

SAND BLASTED: ☐ No ☐ Yes _____ Thickness _____

SHEET OR FLOAT GLASS: ☐ No ☐ Clear ☐ Gray _____ Thickness _____

SPANDREL GLASS: ☐ No ☐ Plain ☐ Insulated ☐ Sandwich _____ Thickness _____

STAINED GLASS: ☐ No ☐ Yes _____

VINYL GLAZING: ☐ No ☐ Yes _____ Thickness _____

WINDOW GLASS: ☐ No ☐ DSA ☐ DSB ☐ Tempered _____ Thickness _____

WIRE GLASS: ☐ No ☐ Yes _____ Thickness _____

SPECIAL GLAZING: ☐ No ☐ Yes _____

CURTAIN WALLS: ☐ No ☐ Yes _____

WINDOW WALLS: ☐ No ☐ Yes _____

FINISH HARDWARE 8.7

GLASS & GLAZING 8.8

WINDOW/CURTAIN WALLS 8.9

MEANSCO FORM 409   DIVISION 9

SPEC-AID

DATE _____

PROJECT _____ LOCATION _____

LATH 9.1

FURRING: CEILING: ☐ No ☐ Wired Direct ☐ Suspended _____

PARTITIONS: ☐ No ☐ Load Bearing ☐ Non Load Bearing _____ Thickness _____

WALLS: ☐ No ☐ Yes _____

GYPSUM LATH: ☐ No ☐ Walls ☐ Ceilings ☐ Regular ☐ Foil Faced ☐ Fire Resistant ☐ Moisture Resistant _____

_____ Thickness _____

METAL LATH: ☐ No ☐ Diamond ☐ Rib ☐ _____ Weight _____

☐ Painted ☐ Galvanized ☐ Paper Backed _____

☐ Walls ☐ Ceilings ☐ Suspended ☐ Partitions ☐ Load Bearing ☐ Non Load Bearing _____

DRYWALL 9.2

DRYWALL FINISHES: ☐ Taped & Finished ☐ Thin Coat Plaster ☐ Prime Coat ☐ Electric Heat Compound ☐ _____

MOUNTINGS: ☐ Nailed ☐ Screwed ☐ Laminated ☐ Clips ☐ _____

BEAMS: ☐ No _____ Layers _____ Thickness _____

CEILINGS: ☐ No ☐ Standard ☐ Fire Resistant ☐ Water Resistant _____ Thickness _____

COLUMNS: ☐ No _____ Layers _____ Thickness _____

PARTITIONS: ☐ No ☐ Wood Studs ☐ Steel Studs _____ Layers _____ Thickness _____

PREFINISHED: ☐ No ☐ Standard ☐ Fire Resistant _____ Thickness _____

SOFFITS: ☐ No _____ Layers _____ Thickness _____

SOUND DEADING BOARD: ☐ No Type _____ Thickness _____

WALLS: ☐ No _____ Layers _____ Thickness _____

PLASTER 9.1

PLASTER FINISHES: ☐ 1 Coat ☐ 2 Coat ☐ 3 Coat ☐ Gypsum ☐ Perlite ☐ Vermiculite ☐ Wood ☐ _____

BEAMS: ☐ No _____ **CEILINGS:** ☐ No _____

COLUMNS: ☐ No _____ **SOFFITS:** ☐ No _____

PARTITIONS: ☐ No ☐ Wood Studs ☐ Steel Studs ☐ Solid ☐ Hollow _____

WALLS: ☐ No _____

SPECIAL PLASTER: _____

SPRAYED ACOUSTICAL: ☐ No ☐ Yes _____ Thickness _____

FIREPROOFING: ☐ No ☐ Yes _____ Thickness _____

STUCCO: ☐ No ☐ On Mesh ☐ Masonry _____

TILE 9.3

CAST STONE: ☐ No ☐ Glazed ☐ Unglazed ☐ Waxed _____ Thickness _____

CERAMIC TILE BASE: ☐ No ☐ Cove ☐ Sanitary ☐ _____ Set _____ Height _____

FLOORS: ☐ No ☐ _____ Set ☐ Natural Clay ☐ Porcelain ☐ Conductive _____ Color Group _____

WALLS: ☐ No ☐ _____ Set ☐ Interior ☐ Exterior ☐ Glazed ☐ Crystalline Glazed ☐ _____

☐ Unmounted ☐ Backmounted _____

PANELS: ☐ No ☐ Yes _____

GLASS MOSAICS: ☐ No ☐ Yes _____ Color Group _____

METAL TILE: ☐ No ☐ Aluminum ☐ Copper ☐ Stainless Steel _____

PLASTIC TILE: ☐ No ☐ Yes _____ Thickness _____

QUARRY TILE BASE: ☐ No ☐ Cove ☐ Sanitary _____ Height _____

FLOOR: ☐ No _____ Set Size _____ Color _____

STAIRS: ☐ No ☐ Treads ☐ Risers _____

WAINSCOT: ☐ No _____ Set Size _____

TERRAZZO 9.3

CAST IN PLACE TERRAZZO BASE: ☐ No ☐ Yes _____ **CURB:** ☐ No ☐ Yes _____

FLOOR: ☐ No ☐ Bonded ☐ Unbonded ☐ Gray Cement ☐ White Cement ☐ Conventional ☐ Venetian _____

☐ Conductive ☐ Monolithic ☐ Epoxy ☐ _____

Divider Strips: ☐ No ☐ Brass ☐ Zinc _____ Spacing _____

STAIRS: ☐ No ☐ Yes _____ **WAINSCOT:** ☐ No ☐ Yes _____

PRECAST TERRAZZO BASE: ☐ No ☐ Yes _____ **CURB:** ☐ No ☐ Yes _____

FLOOR TILES: ☐ No Size _____ Thickness _____

STAIRS: ☐ No ☐ Treads ☐ Risers ☐ Stringers ☐ Landings _____

WAINSCOT: ☐ No ☐ Yes _____ Thickness _____

FINISHES Acoustical, Flooring,
Painting & Wall Covering

SPEC-AID

ACOUSTICAL 9.5

BARRIERS: ☐ No ☐ Aluminum ☐ Foil ☐ Mesh ☐ Lead ☐ Leaded Vinyl _____

ACOUSTICAL BARRIERS: ☐ No ☐ Yes _____

CEILINGS: ☐ No ☐ Boards ☐ Tile ☐ Cemented ☐ Stapled ☐ On Suspension ☐ _____
☐ Fiberglass ☐ Mineral Fiber ☐ Wood Fiber ☐ Metal Pan _____
☐ Fire Rated ☐ Ventilating ☐ _____ Ceiling Height _____
☐ Luminous Panels _____ ☐ Access Panels _____

SUSPENSION SYSTEM: ☐ No ☐ T Bar ☐ Z Bar ☐ Carrier Channels ☐ _____

STRIP LIGHTING: ☐ No ☐ Yes _____ Foot Candles _____

SPECIAL ACOUSTICAL _____

FLOORING 9.6

BRICK FLOORING: ☐ No ☐ Yes _____

CARPET: ☐ No ☐ Yes ☐ with Padding ☐ with Backing ☐ _____ Allowance _____
Type: ☐ Acrylic ☐ Nylon ☐ Polypropylene ☐ Wool ☐ Tile ☐ _____ Face Weight _____
Padding: ☐ No ☐ Yes _____ Backing: ☐ No ☐ Yes _____

COMPOSITION FLOORING: ☐ No ☐ Acrylic ☐ Epoxy ☐ Mastic ☐ Neoprene ☐ Polyester ☐ ____
☐ Regular Duty ☐ Heavy Duty _____ Thickness _____

CONCRETE FLOOR TOPPING: ☐ No ☐ In Concrete ☐ Yes _____

RESILIENT FLOORS: BASE: ☐ No ☐ Rubber ☐ Vinyl _____ Height _____
ASPHALT TILE: ☐ No ☐ Yes _____ Color Group _____
CONDUCTIVE TILE: ☐ No ☐ Yes _____ Thickness _____
CORK TILE: ☐ No ☐ Yes _____ Thickness _____
LINOLEUM: ☐ No ☐ Yes _____ Thickness _____
POLYETHYLENE: ☐ No ☐ Yes _____
POLYURETHANE: ☐ No ☐ Yes _____ Thickness _____
RUBBER TILE: ☐ No ☐ Yes _____ Thickness _____
VINYL: ☐ No ☐ Sheet ☐ Tile _____ Thickness _____
VINYL ASBESTOS TILE: ☐ No ☐ Yes _____ Color Group _____

STAIR COVERING: ☐ No ☐ Risers ☐ Treads ☐ Landings ☐ Nosings ☐ Rubber ☐ Vinyl _____

STEEL PLATES: ☐ No ☐ Cement Bed ☐ Epoxy Bed _____

WOOD FLOOR: ☐ No ☐ Block ☐ Strip ☐ Parquetry ☐ Unfinished ☐ Prefinished ☐ Stock ☐ Custom ____
FIR: ☐ No ☐ Flat Grain ☐ Vertical Grain _____ Size _____
GYM: ☐ No ☐ Yes Type _____
MAPLE: ☐ No ☐ Yes Grade _____ Size _____
OAK: ☐ No ☐ Red ☐ White Grade _____ Size _____
OTHER: ☐ _____ Grade _____ Size _____
FINISH REQUIRED: ☐ No ☐ Yes _____

WOOD BLOCK FLOOR: ☐ No ☐ Creosoted ☐ Natural _____ Thickness _____

PAINTING AND WALL COVERING 9.8

SPECIAL COATINGS: ☐ No ☐ Floor ☐ Wall _____

PAINTING: ☐ No ☐ Regular ☐ Fireproof ☐ Fire Retardant ☐ Brush ☐ Roller ☐ Spray _____
CASEWORK: ☐ No _____ Coats _____ CEILINGS: ☐ No _____ Coats _____
DOORS: ☐ No _____ Coats _____ TRIM: ☐ No _____ Coats _____
WALLS, Exterior: ☐ No _____ Coats _____ INTERIOR WALLS: ☐ No _____ Coats _____
WINDOWS: ☐ No _____ Coats _____ PIPING: ☐ No _____ Coats _____
OTHER: _____
STRUCTURAL STEEL: ☐ No ☐ Yes _____ MISCELLANEOUS METALS: ☐ No ☐ Yes _____

WALL COVERING: ☐ No ☐ Cork Tile _____ ☐ Metal Foil _____
☐ Flexible Wood Veneers _____ ☐ Vinyl _____ Weight _____
☐ Wall Paper _____ ☐ Murals _____
☐ Other _____

GUARDS, CORNER: ☐ No ☐ Rubber ☐ Steel ☐ Vinyl _____
WALL: ☐ No ☐ Rubber ☐ Steel ☐ Vinyl _____

SPECIALTIES

SPEC-AID   DATE _____

PROJECT _____ LOCATION _____

BATHROOM ACCESSORIES: ☐ No ☐ Curtain Rod _____ ☐ Dispensers _____ ☐ Grab Bar _____
☐ Hand Dryer _____ ☐ Medicine Cabinet _____ ☐ Mirror _____ ☐ Robe Hook _____
☐ Soap Dispenser _____ ☐ Shelf _____ ☐ Tissue Dispenser _____ ☐ Towel Bar _____
☐ Tumbler Holder _____ ☐ Wall Urn _____ ☐ Waste Receptical _____ ☐ _____
☐ _____

BULLETIN BOARD: ☐ No ☐ Cork ☐ Vinyl Cork ☐ Unbacked ☐ Backed ☐ Stock ☐ Custom ☐ Tan ☐ _____
☐ Framed ☐ No Frames ☐ Changeable Letter ☐ _____ Thickness _____

CANOPIES: ☐ No ☐ Free Standing ☐ Wall Hung ☐ Stock ☐ Custom _____

CHALKBOARD: ☐ No ☐ Cement Asbestos ☐ Hardboard ☐ Metal _____ Ga. ☐ Slate _____ in. thick ☐ Tempered Glass _____
☐ Treated Plastic ☐ _____ ☐ Unbacked ☐ Backed with _____
☐ No Frames ☐ Frames ☐ Chalk Tray ☐ Map Rail ☐ _____
☐ Built in Place ☐ Prefabricated _____
☐ Portable ☐ Reversible ☐ Swing Wing ☐ Sliding Panel _____

CHUTES LINEN: ☐ No ☐ Aluminum ☐ Aluminized Steel ☐ Stainless Steel ☐ _____ Ga. Diameter _____
☐ Bottom Collector ☐ Sprinklers
MAIL: ☐ No ☐ Aluminum ☐ Bronze ☐ Stainless ☐ _____ Size _____ ☐ Bottom Collector
PACKAGE: ☐ No ☐ Aluminum ☐ Bronze ☐ Stainless _____
RUBBISH: ☐ No ☐ Aluminum ☐ Aluminized Steel ☐ Stainless Steel ☐ _____ Ga. Diameter _____
☐ Bottom Collector ☐ Sprinklers _____

COMPARTMENTS & CUBICLES: ☐ No ☐ Hospital _____ ☐ Office _____
☐ Shower _____ ☐ Toilet _____ ☐ _____
CONTROL BOARDS: ☐ No ☐ Yes

DECORATIVE GRILLES AND SCREENS: ☐ No ☐ Yes _____

DIRECTORY BOARDS: ☐ No ☐ Exterior ☐ Interior ☐ Aluminum ☐ Bronze ☐ Stainless ☐ Lighted _____
Desbribe _____

DISAPPEARING STAIRS: ☐ No ☐ Stock ☐ Custom ☐ Manual ☐ Electric _____ Ceiling Height _____

DISPLAY CASES: ☐ No ☐ Economy ☐ Deluxe _____

FIRE EXTINGUISHERS: ☐ No ☐ CO₂ ☐ Dry Chemical ☐ Foam ☐ Pressure Water ☐ Soda Acid ☐ _____
☐ Aluminum ☐ Copper ☐ Painted Steel ☐ Stainless Steel ☐ _____ Size _____
CABINETS: ☐ No ☐ Aluminum ☐ Painted Steel ☐ Stainless Steel ☐ _____
HOSE EQUIPMENT: ☐ No ☐ Blanket ☐ Cabinets ☐ Hose _____ Size _____
PROTECTION SYSTEM: ☐ No ☐ Yes _____

FIREPLACE, PREFABRICATED: ☐ No ☐ Economy ☐ Deluxe ☐ Wall Hung ☐ Free Standing _____

FLAGPOLES: ☐ No ☐ Aluminum ☐ Bronze ☐ Fiberglass ☐ Stainless ☐ Steel ☐ Wood ☐ Tapered ☐ Sectional _____
☐ Ground Set ☐ Wall Set ☐ Counterbalanced ☐ Outriggers _____ Height _____
BASES: ☐ No ☐ Economy ☐ Deluxe _____
FOUNDATION: ☐ No ☐ Yes _____

FOLDING GATES: ☐ No ☐ Scissors Type ☐ Vertical Members ☐ Stock ☐ Custom _____ Opening _____

LOCKERS: ☐ No ☐ No Locks ☐ Keyed ☐ Combination _____ Tier Size _____ Height _____
ATHLETIC: ☐ No ☐ Basket ☐ Ventilating ☐ Overhead _____ Size _____
BENCHES: ☐ No ☐ Yes _____
SPECIAL LOCKERS: _____

MAIL SPECIALTIES BOXES: ☐ No ☐ Front Loading ☐ Rear Loading ☐ Aluminum ☐ Stainless ☐ _____
Size _____
LETTER SLOT: ☐ No ☐ Yes _____ COUNTER WINDOW: ☐ No ☐ Yes _____
DIRECTORY: ☐ No ☐ Yes _____ KEY KEEPER _____
OTHER: _____

SPECIALTIES
Incl. Partitions

SPEC-AID

ACCORDION FOLDING PARTITIONS: ☐ No ☐ Acoustical ☐ Non Acoustical _____ Weight _____ psf.
Ceiling Height _____ Describe _____

FOLDING LEAF PARTITIONS: ☐ No ☐ Acoustical ☐ Non Acoustical _____ Weight _____ psf.
Ceiling Height _____ Describe _____

HOSPITAL PARTITIONS: ☐ No ☐ Metal ☐ Curtain Track _____

MOVABLE OFFICE PARTITIONS: ☐ No ☐ Acoustical ☐ Non Acoustical ☐ Asbestos Cement ☐ Hardboard
☐ Laminated Gypsum ☐ Plywood ☐ _____
☐ With Glass ☐ No Glass Describe _____ Partition Height _____
SPECIAL FINISH: _____
DOORS: ☐ No ☐ Yes Type _____ Finish _____ Size _____

OPERABLE PARTITIONS: ☐ No ☐ Yes Type _____

PORTABLE PARTITIONS: ☐ No ☐ Acoustical ☐ Non Acoustical _____ Weight _____ psf.
Partition Height _____ Describe _____

SHOWER PARTITIONS: ☐ No ☐ Fiberglass ☐ Glass ☐ Marble ☐ Metal ☐ _____ Finish _____
☐ Stock ☐ Custom ☐ Economy ☐ Deluxe Size _____
DOORS: ☐ No ☐ Glass ☐ Tempered Glass ☐ Plastic ☐ Curtain Only _____ Size _____
RECEPTORS: ☐ No ☐ Concrete ☐ Metal ☐ Plastic ☐ Terrazzo _____ Size _____
TUB ENCLOSURE: ☐ No ☐ Stock ☐ Custom ☐ Economy ☐ Deluxe _____ Size _____

TOILET PARTITIONS: ☐ No ☐ Fiberglass ☐ Marble ☐ Metal ☐ Slate ☐ Wood ☐ _____
☐ Floor Mounted ☐ Wall Hung ☐ Ceiling Hung _____
Special Finish _____
DOORS: ☐ No ☐ Yes _____
SCREENS: ☐ No ☐ Full Height ☐ Urinal ☐ Floor Mounted ☐ Wall Hung ☐ Ceiling Hung _____

WOVEN WIRE PARTITIONS: ☐ No ☐ Walls ☐ Ceilings Panel Width _____ Height _____
DOORS: ☐ No ☐ Sliding ☐ Swing _____ Windows: ☐ No ☐ Yes _____
☐ Painted ☐ Galvanized _____

OTHER PARTITIONS: _____

PARTS BINS: ☐ No ☐ Yes _____

SCALES: ☐ No ☐ Built in ☐ Portable ☐ Beam Type ☐ Dial Type _____ Capacity _____
Platform Size _____ Material _____ Foundations _____
Accessory Items _____

SHELVING, STORAGE: ☐ No ☐ Metal ☐ Wood _____

SIGNS: INDIVIDUAL LETTERS: ☐ No ☐ Aluminum ☐ Bronze ☐ Plastic ☐ Stainless ☐ Steel ☐ _____
☐ Cast ☐ Fabricated Describe _____
PLAQUES: ☐ No ☐ Aluminum ☐ Bronze _____
SIGNS: ☐ No ☐ Metal ☐ Plastic ☐ Lighted _____

SUN CONTROL DEVICES: ☐ No ☐ Yes _____

TELEPHONE ENCLOSURES: ☐ No ☐ Indoor ☐ Outdoor _____

TURNSTILES: ☐ No ☐ Yes _____

VENDING MACHINES: ☐ No ☐ Yes _____

WARDROBE SPECIALTIES: ☐ No ☐ Yes _____

OTHER SPECIALTIES: _____
_____
_____
_____
_____

PARTITIONS 10.1

ARCHITECTURAL EQUIPMENT

MEANSCO FORM 411   DIVISION 11

SPEC-AID   DATE _____

PROJECT _____ LOCATION _____

APPLIANCES, RESIDENTIAL: ☐ No ☐ Yes Allowance _____ ☐ Separate Contract
  ☐ Cook Tops _____ ☐ Compactors _____ ☐ Dehumidifier _____ ☐ Dishwasher _____
  ☐ Dryer _____ ☐ Garbage Disposer _____ ☐ Heaters, electric _____
  ☐ Hood _____ ☐ Humidifier _____ ☐ Ice Maker _____ ☐ Oven _____
  ☐ Refrigerator _____ ☐ Sump Pump _____ ☐ Washing Machine _____ ☐ Water Heater _____
  ☐ Water Softener _____ ☐ _____

AUTOMOTIVE EQUIPMENT: ☐ No ☐ Yes Allowance _____ ☐ Separate Contract
  ☐ Hoists _____ ☐ Lube _____ ☐ Pumps _____ ☐ _____

BANK EQUIPMENT: ☐ No ☐ Yes Allowance _____
  ☐ Counters _____ ☐ Safes _____ ☐ Vaults _____ ☐ Windows _____
  ☐ _____

CHECK ROOM EQUIPMENT: ☐ No ☐ Yes Allowance _____ ☐ Separate Contract
  Describe _____

CHURCH EQUIPMENT: ☐ No ☐ Yes Allowance _____ ☐ Separate Contract
  ☐ Altar _____ ☐ Baptistries _____ ☐ Bells & Carillons _____ ☐ Confessionals _____
  ☐ Organ _____ ☐ Pews _____ ☐ Pulpit _____ ☐ Spires _____
  ☐ Wall Cross _____ ☐ _____

COMMERCIAL EQUIPMENT: ☐ No ☐ Yes Allowance _____ ☐ Separate Contract
  Describe _____

DARKROOM EQUIPMENT: ☐ No ☐ Yes Allowance _____ ☐ Separate Contract
  Describe _____

DATA PROCESSING EQUIPMENT: ☐ No ☐ Yes Allowance _____ ☐ Separate Contract
  Describe _____

DENTAL EQUIPMENT: ☐ No ☐ Yes Allowance _____ ☐ Separate Contract
  ☐ Chair _____ ☐ Drill _____ ☐ Lights _____ ☐ X-Ray _____
  ☐ _____

DOCK EQUIPMENT: ☐ No ☐ Yes Allowance _____ ☐ Separate Contract
  ☐ Bumpers _____ ☐ Boards _____ ☐ Door Seal _____ ☐ Levelers _____
  ☐ Lights _____ ☐ Shelters _____ ☐ _____

FOOD SERVICE EQUIPMENT: ☐ No ☐ Yes Allowance _____ ☐ Separate Contract
  ☐ Bar Units _____ ☐ Cooking Equip. _____ ☐ Dishwashing Equip. _____ ☐ Food Prep. _____
  ☐ Food Serving _____ ☐ Refrigerated Cases _____ ☐ Tables _____ ☐ _____

GYMNASIUM EQUIPMENT: ☐ No ☐ Yes Allowance _____ ☐ Separate Contract
  ☐ Basketball Backstops _____ ☐ Benches _____ ☐ Bleachers _____
  ☐ Divider Curtain _____ ☐ Gymnast Equip. _____ ☐ Mats _____ ☐ Scoreboards _____
  ☐ _____

INDUSTRIAL EQUIPMENT: ☐ No ☐ Yes Allowance _____ ☐ Separate Contract
  Describe _____

LABORATORY EQUIPMENT: ☐ No ☐ Yes Allowance _____ ☐ Separate Contract
  ☐ Casework _____ ☐ Counter Tops _____ ☐ Hoods _____ ☐ Sinks _____
  ☐ Tables _____ ☐ _____

LAUNDRY EQUIPMENT: ☐ No ☐ Yes Allowance _____ ☐ Separate Contract
  ☐ Dryers _____ ☐ Washers _____ ☐ _____

LIBRARY EQUIPMENT: ☐ No ☐ Yes Allowance _____ ☐ Separate Contract
  ☐ Book Shelves _____ ☐ Book Stacks _____ ☐ Card Files _____ ☐ Carrels _____
  ☐ Charging Desks _____ ☐ Racks _____ ☐ _____

MEDICAL EQUIPMENT: ☐ No ☐ Yes Allowance _____ ☐ Separate Contract
  ☐ Casework _____ ☐ Exam Room _____ ☐ Incubators _____ ☐ Patient Care _____
  ☐ Radiology _____ ☐ Sterilizers _____ ☐ Surgery Equip. _____ ☐ Therapy Equip. _____
  ☐ _____

ARCHITECTURAL EQUIPMENT

SPEC-AID

MORTUARY EQUIPMENT: ☐ No ☐ Yes Allowance _____ ☐ Separate Contract
Describe _____

MUSICAL EQUIPMENT: ☐ No ☐ Yes Allowance _____ ☐ Separate Contract
Describe _____

OBSERVATORY EQUIPMENT: ☐ No ☐ Yes Allowance _____ ☐ Separate Contract
Describe _____

PARKING EQUIPMENT: ☐ No ☐ Yes Allowance _____ ☐ Separate Contract
☐ Automatic Gates _____ ☐ Booths _____ ☐ Control Station _____
☐ Ticket Dispenser _____ ☐ Traffic Detectors _____
☐ _____

PLAYGROUND EQUIPMENT: In Division 2 _____

PRISON EQUIPMENT: ☐ No ☐ Yes Allowance _____ ☐ Separate Contract
☐ Ceiling Lining _____ ☐ Wall Lining _____ ☐ Bar Walls _____ ☐ Doors _____
☐ Bunks _____ ☐ Lavatory _____ ☐ Water Closet _____ ☐ _____

RESIDENTIAL EQUIPMENT: ☐ No ☐ Yes Allowance _____ ☐ Separate Contract
☐ Kitchen Cabinets (Also Div. 6) _____ ☐ Lavatory Cabinets _____ ☐ Kitchen Equipment _____
☐ Laundry Equip. _____ ☐ Unit Kitchens _____ ☐ Vacuum Cleaning _____ ☐ _____
☐ _____

SAFES: ☐ No ☐ Yes Allowance _____ ☐ Separate Contract
☐ Office _____ ☐ Money _____ ☐ _____ Rating _____
Describe _____

SAUNAS: ☐ No ☐ Yes Allowance _____ ☐ Separate Contract
☐ Built in Place ☐ Prefabricated Size _____ Describe _____
☐ Heater _____ ☐ Seats _____ ☐ Timer _____ ☐ _____

SCHOOL EQUIPMENT: ☐ No ☐ Yes Allowance _____ ☐ Separate Contract
☐ Arts & Crafts _____ ☐ Audio-Visual _____ ☐ Language Labs _____ ☐ Vocational _____
☐ Wall Benches _____ ☐ Wall Tables _____ ☐ _____
☐ _____

SHOP EQUIPMENT: ☐ No ☐ Yes Allowance _____ ☐ Separate Contract
Describe _____

STAGE EQUIPMENT: ☐ No ☐ Yes Allowance _____ ☐ Separate Contract
Describe _____

STEAM BATHS: ☐ No ☐ Yes Allowance _____ ☐ Separate Contract
Describe _____

SWIMMING POOL EQUIPMENT: ☐ No ☐ Yes Allowance _____ ☐ Separate Contract
☐ Diving Board _____ ☐ Diving Stand _____ ☐ Life Guard Chair _____ ☐ Ladders _____
☐ Heater _____ ☐ Lights _____ ☐ Pool Cover _____ ☐ Slides _____
☐ _____

UNIT KITCHENS: ☐ No ☐ Yes Allowance _____ ☐ Separate Contract
Describe _____

VACUUM CLEANING, CENTRAL: ☐ No ☐ Yes Allowance _____ ☐ Separate Contract
☐ _____ Valves Describe _____

WASTE DISPOSAL COMPACTORS: ☐ No ☐ Yes _____
INCINERATORS: ☐ No ☐ Electric ☐ Gas Type Waste _____ Capacity _____

SPECIAL EQUIPMENT: _____
_____
_____
_____
_____
_____
_____

FURNISHINGS

MEANSCO FORM 412   DIVISION 12

SPEC-AID   DATE _____

PROJECT _____ LOCATION _____

ARTWORK: ☐ No ☐ Yes Allowance _____ ☐ Separate Contract
  ☐ Murals _____ ☐ Paintings _____ ☐ Photomurals _____ ☐ Sculptures _____
  ☐ Stained Glass _____ ☐ _____
INTERIOR LANDSCAPING: ☐ No ☐ Yes Allowance _____
BLINDS, EXTERIOR: ☐ No ☐ Yes Allowance _____ ☐ Separate Contract
  ☐ Solid ☐ Louvered ☐ Aluminum ☐ Nylon ☐ Vinyl ☐ Wood ☐ _____
  Describe _____
BLINDS, INTERIOR: ☐ No ☐ Yes Allowance _____ ☐ Separate Contract
  FOLDING: ☐ No ☐ Stock ☐ Custom ☐ Wood ☐ _____
    Describe _____
  VENETIAN: ☐ No ☐ Stock ☐ Custom ☐ Aluminum ☐ Plastic ☐ Steel ☐ Wood ☐ _____
    Describe _____
  VERTICAL: ☐ No ☐ Aluminum ☐ Cloth ☐ Vinyl ☐ _____
    Describe _____
  OTHER: _____
CABINETS: ☐ No ☐ Yes Allowance _____ ☐ Separate Contract
  ☐ Classroom _____
  ☐ Dormitory _____
  ☐ Hospital _____
  ☐ _____
CARPETS: In Division 9 _____
DORMITORY UNITS: ☐ No ☐ Yes Allowance _____ ☐ Separate Contract
  ☐ Beds _____ ☐ Desks _____ ☐ Wardrobes _____ ☐ _____
  ☐ _____
DRAPERY & CURTAINS: ☐ No ☐ Yes Allowance _____ ☐ Separate Contract
  Describe _____
_____
FLOOR MATS: ☐ No ☐ Yes Allowance _____ ☐ Separate Contract
  ☐ Recessed ☐ Non Recessed _____
  ☐ Link ☐ Solid _____
FURNITURE: ☐ No ☐ Yes Allowance _____ ☐ Separate Contract
  ☐ Beds _____ ☐ Chairs _____ ☐ Chests _____ ☐ Desks _____
  ☐ Sofas _____ ☐ Tables _____ ☐ _____
  ☐ _____
SEATING AUDITORIUM: ☐ No ☐ Yes Allowance _____ ☐ Separate Contract
  Describe _____
  CLASSROOM: ☐ No ☐ Yes Allowance _____ ☐ Separate Contract
  Describe _____
  STADIUM: ☐ No ☐ Yes Allowance _____ ☐ Separate Contract
  Describe _____
SHADES: ☐ No ☐ Yes Allowance _____ ☐ Separate Contract
  ☐ Stock ☐ Custom ☐ Lightproof ☐ Fireproof _____
  ☐ Cotton ☐ Fiberglass ☐ Vinyl ☐ Woven Aluminum ☐ _____
  Describe _____
WARDROBES: ☐ No ☐ Yes Allowance _____ ☐ Separate Contract
  ☐ Classroom _____ ☐ Dormitory _____ ☐ Hospital _____ ☐ _____
  Describe _____
OTHER FURNISHINGS: _____
_____
_____

SPECIAL CONSTRUCTION

MEANSCO FORM 413   DIVISION 13

SPEC-AID

DATE _____

PROJECT _____ LOCATION _____

ACOUSTICAL ECHO CHAMBER: ☐ No ☐ Yes Allowance _____ ☐ Separate Contract
Describe _____
ENCLOSURES: ☐ No ☐ Yes Allowance _____ ☐ Separate Contract
Describe _____
PANELS: ☐ No ☐ Yes Allowance _____ ☐ Separate Contract
Describe _____

AIR CURTAINS: ☐ No ☐ Yes Allowance _____ ☐ Separate Contract
☐ Heated Air ☐ Unheated Air ☐ Recirculating ☐ Non Recirculating ☐ _____
Describe _____

AIR INFLATED BUILDINGS: ☐ No ☐ Yes Describe _____

ANECHOIC CHAMBERS: ☐ No ☐ Yes Allowance _____ ☐ Separate Contract
Describe _____

AUDIOMETRIC ROOMS: ☐ No ☐ Yes Allowance _____ ☐ Separate Contract
Describe _____

BOWLING ALLEYS: ☐ No ☐ Yes Allowance _____ ☐ Separate Contract
Describe _____

BROADCASTING STUDIO: ☐ No ☐ Yes Allowance _____ ☐ Separate Contract
Describe _____

CHIMNEYS: ☐ No ☐ Yes Allowance _____ ☐ Separate Contract
CONCRETE: ☐ No ☐ Unlined ☐ Lined ☐ _____ Diameter _____ Height _____
METAL: ☐ No ☐ Insulated ☐ Not Insulated ☐ U.L. Listed ☐ Not U.L. Listed ☐ _____
Describe _____ Diameter _____ Height _____
RADIAL BRICK: ☐ No ☐ Unlined ☐ Lined ☐ _____ Diameter _____ Height _____
FOUNDATION: ☐ No ☐ Yes _____

CLEAN ROOMS: ☐ No ☐ Yes Allowance _____ ☐ Separate Contract
Describe _____

COMFORT STATIONS: ☐ No ☐ Yes Describe _____

DARK ROOMS: ☐ No ☐ Yes Allowance _____ ☐ Separate Contract
Describe _____

DOMES, OBSERVATION: ☐ No ☐ Yes Allowance _____ ☐ Separate Contract
Describe _____

GARAGE: ☐ No ☐ Yes Describe _____ Cars _____

GARDEN HOUSE: ☐ No ☐ Yes Allowance _____ ☐ Separate Contract
Describe _____

GRANDSTAND: ☐ No ☐ Yes Describe _____ Seats _____

GREENHOUSE: ☐ No ☐ Yes Allowance _____ ☐ Separate Contract
Describe _____

HANGARS: ☐ No ☐ Yes Describe _____ Planes _____

HYPERBARIC ROOMS: ☐ No ☐ Yes Allowance _____ ☐ Separate Contract
Describe _____

INCINERATORS (See also Division 10): ☐ No ☐ Yes Allowance _____ ☐ Separate Contract
Describe _____ Capacity _____

INSULATED ROOMS: ☐ No ☐ Yes Allowance _____ ☐ Separate Contract
DOORS: ☐ No ☐ Cooler ☐ Freezer ☐ Manual ☐ Electric _____
☐ Galvanized ☐ Stainless Describe _____
COOLERS: ☐ No ☐ Yes Describe _____
FREEZERS: ☐ No ☐ Yes Describe _____
PARTITIONS: ☐ No ☐ Yes ☐ Stock ☐ Custom Describe _____
OTHER: _____

SPECIAL CONSTRUCTION

SPEC-AID

INTEGRATED CEILINGS: ☐ No ☐ Yes Module _____ Ceiling Height _____

   LIGHTING: ☐ No ☐ Yes Describe _____ Foot Candles _____

   HEATING: ☐ No ☐ Yes Describe _____

   VENTILATING: ☐ No ☐ Yes Describe _____

   AIR CONDITIONING: ☐ No ☐ Yes Describe _____

MUSIC PRACTICE ROOMS: ☐ No ☐ Yes Allowance _____ ☐ Separate Contract

   Describe _____

PEDESTAL FLOORS: ☐ No ☐ Yes Allowance _____ ☐ Separate Contract

   ☐ Aluminum ☐ Plywood ☐ Steel ☐ _____ Panel Size _____ Height _____

   ☐ High Density Plastic ☐ Vinyl Tile ☐ V.A. Tile ☐ _____

   Describe _____

PORTABLE BOOTHS: ☐ No ☐ Yes Allowance _____ ☐ Separate Contract

   Describe _____

PREFABRICATED STRUCTURES: ☐ No ☐ Yes Allowance _____ ☐ Separate Contract

   Describe _____

RADIATION PROTECTION, FLUOROSCOPY ROOM: ☐ No ☐ Yes _____

   NUCLEAR REACTOR: ☐ No ☐ Yes _____

   RADIOLOGICAL ROOM: ☐ No ☐ Yes _____

   X-RAY ROOM: ☐ No ☐ Yes _____

   OTHER: _____

RADIO FREQUENCY SHIELDING: ☐ No ☐ Yes Allowance _____ ☐ Separate Contract

   Describe _____

RADIO TOWER: ☐ No ☐ Yes Allowance _____ ☐ Separate Contract

   ☐ Guyed ☐ Self Supporting Wind Load _____ psf. _____ Height _____

   Foundations _____

SAUNAS AND STEAM ROOMS: ☐ No ☐ Yes Allowance _____ ☐ Separate Contract

   Describe _____

SILOS: ☐ No ☐ Yes Allowance _____ ☐ Separate Contract

   ☐ Concrete ☐ Steel ☐ Wood ☐ _____ Diameter _____ Height _____

   Foundations _____

SQUASH & HAND BALL COURTS: ☐ No ☐ Yes Allowance _____ ☐ Separate Contract

   Describe _____

STORAGE VAULTS: ☐ No ☐ Yes Allowance _____ ☐ Separate Contract

   Describe _____

SWIMMING POOL ENCLOSURE: ☐ No ☐ Yes Allowance _____ ☐ Separate Contract

   Describe _____

SWIMMING POOL EQUIPMENT: In Division 11 _____

SWIMMING POOLS: ☐ No ☐ Yes Allowance _____ ☐ Separate Contract

   ☐ Aluminum ☐ Concrete ☐ Gunite ☐ Plywood ☐ Steel ☐ _____

   ☐ Lined ☐ Unlined _____

   DECK: ☐ No ☐ Concrete ☐ Stone _____ Size _____

   BATH HOUSES: ☐ No ☐ Yes _____ Fixtures _____

TANKS: ☐ No ☐ Yes Allowance _____ ☐ Separate Contract

   ☐ Concrete ☐ Fiberglass ☐ Steel ☐ Wood ☐ _____ Capacity _____

   ☐ Fixed Roof ☐ Floating Roof ☐ _____ Height _____

   Foundations: _____

THERAPEUTIC POOLS: ☐ No ☐ Yes Describe _____

VAULT FRONT: ☐ No ☐ Yes Allowance _____ ☐ Separate Contract

   Describe _____ Hour Test _____

ZOO STRUCTURES: ☐ No ☐ Yes Describe _____

OTHER SPECIAL CONSTRUCTION: _____

CONVEYING SYSTEMS

SPEC-AID

DATE _____

PROJECT _____ LOCATION _____

ASH HOIST: ☐ No ☐ Yes Allowance _____ ☐ Separate Contract
Describe _____

CONVEYERS: ☐ No ☐ Yes Allowance _____ ☐ Separate Contract
Describe _____

CORRESPONDENCE LIFT: ☐ No ☐ Yes Allowance _____ ☐ Separate Contract
Describe _____

DUMBWAITERS: ☐ No ☐ Yes Allowance _____ ☐ Separate Contract
Capacity _____ Size _____ Number _____ Floors _____
Stops _____ Speed _____ Finish _____
Describe _____

ELEVATORS, FREIGHT: ☐ No ☐ Yes Allowance _____ ☐ Separate Contract
☐ Hydraulic ☐ Electric ☐ Geared ☐ Gearless ☐ _____
Capacity _____ Size _____ Number _____ Floors _____
Stops _____ Speed _____ Finish _____
Machinery Location _____ Door Type _____
Signals _____ Special Requirements _____

ELEVATORS, PASSENGER: ☐ No ☐ Yes Allowance _____ ☐ Separate Contract
☐ Hydraulic ☐ Electric ☐ Geared ☐ Gearless ☐ _____
Capacity _____ Size _____ Number _____ Floors _____
Stops _____ Speed _____ Finish _____
Machinery Location _____ Door Type _____
Signals _____ Special Requirements _____

ESCALATORS: ☐ No ☐ Yes Allowance _____ ☐ Separate Contract
Capacity _____ Size _____ Number _____ Floors _____
Story Height _____ Speed _____ Finish _____
Machinery Location _____ Incline Angle _____
Special Requirements _____

HOISTS & CRANES: ☐ No ☐ Yes Allowance _____ ☐ Separate Contract
Describe _____

LIFTS: ☐ No ☐ Yes Allowance _____ ☐ Separate Contract
Describe _____

MATERIAL HANDLING SYSTEMS: ☐ No ☐ Yes Allowance _____ ☐ Separate Contract
☐ Automated ☐ Non Automated ☐ _____
Describe _____

MOVING STAIRS & SIDEWALKS: ☐ No ☐ Yes Allowance _____ ☐ Separate Contract
Capacity _____ Size _____ Number _____ Floors _____
Story Height _____ Speed _____ Finish _____
Machinery Location _____ Incline Angle _____
Special Requirements _____

PNEUMATIC TUBE SYSTEM: ☐ No ☐ Yes Allowance _____ ☐ Separate Contract
☐ Automatic ☐ Manual ☐ _____ Size _____ Stations _____
Length _____ Special Requirements _____

VERTICAL CONVEYER: ☐ No ☐ Yes Allowance _____ ☐ Separate Contract
☐ Automatic ☐ Non Automatic ☐ _____
Describe _____

OTHER CONVEYING: _____

MECHANICAL, Plumbing

MEANSCO FORM 415   DIVISION 15

SPEC-AID   DATE _____

PROJECT _____ LOCATION _____

BUILDING DRAINAGE: Design Rainfall _____ ☐ Roof Drains _____ ☐ Court Drains _____
    ☐ Floor Drains _____ ☐ Yard Drains _____ ☐ Lawn Drains _____ ☐ Balcony Drains _____
    ☐ Area Drains _____ ☐ Sump Drains _____ ☐ Shower Drains _____ ☐ _____
    ☐ DRAIN PIPING: Size _____ Describe _____
    ☐ DRAIN GATES _____ ☐ CLEAN OUTS _____ ☐ GREASE TRAPS _____

SANITARY SYSTEM: ☐ No ☐ Yes ☐ Site Main _____ ☐ Manholes _____
    ☐ Sump Pumps _____ ☐ Bilge Pumps _____ ☐ Ejectors _____
    ☐ Soils, Stacks _____ ☐ Wastes, Vents _____ ☐ _____

DOMESTIC COLD WATER: ☐ No ☐ Water Meters _____ ☐ Lawn Sprinkler Connection _____
    ☐ Water Softening _____ ☐ Water Filtering _____
    ☐ Boiler Feed Water _____ ☐ Conditioning Apparatus _____
    ☐ Standpipe System _____ ☐ Hose Bibbs _____
    ☐ Pressure Tank _____ ☐ Booster Pumps _____
    ☐ Reducing Valves _____ ☐ _____

DOMESTIC HOT WATER: ☐ No ☐ Electric ☐ Gas ☐ Oil ☐ Solar _____
    ☐ Boiler _____ ☐ Conditioner _____ ☐ Fixture Connections _____
    ☐ Storage Tanks _____ Capacity _____
    ☐ Pumps _____

PIPING: ☐ No ☐ Yes Material _____
    ☐ Air Chambers _____ ☐ Escutcheons _____ ☐ Expansion Joints _____
    ☐ Shock Absorbers _____ ☐ Hangers _____
    ☐ Valves _____ ☐ Paint _____

SPECIAL PIPING: ☐ No ☐ Compressed Air _____ ☐ Vacuum _____
    ☐ Oxygen _____ ☐ Nitrous Oxygen _____
    ☐ Carbon Dioxide _____ ☐ Process Piping _____

INSULATION COLD: ☐ No ☐ Yes Material _____ Jacket _____
    HOT: ☐ No ☐ Yes Material _____ Jacket _____

FIXTURES BATHTUB: ☐ No ☐ C.I. ☐ Steel ☐ Fiberglass ☐ _____ Color _____
    ☐ Curtain ☐ Rod ☐ Enclosure ☐ Wall Shower _____
    DRINKING FOUNTAIN: ☐ No ☐ Yes ☐ Wall Hung ☐ Pedestal _____
    HOSE BIBB: ☐ No ☐ Yes Describe _____
    LAVATORY: ☐ No ☐ China ☐ C.I. ☐ Steel ☐ _____ Color _____
        ☐ Wall Hung ☐ Legs ☐ Acid Resisting _____
    SHOWER: ☐ No ☐ Individual ☐ Group ☐ Heads ☐ _____ Size _____
    Compartment: ☐ No ☐ Metal ☐ Stone ☐ Fiberglass ☐ _____ ☐ Door ☐ Curtain
    Receptor: ☐ No ☐ Plastic ☐ Metal ☐ Terrazzo ☐ _____
    SINKS: ☐ No ☐ Kitchen _____ ☐ Janitor _____
        ☐ Laundry _____ ☐ Pantry _____
        ☐ _____
    URINALS: ☐ No ☐ Floor Mounted ☐ Wall Hung _____
    SCREENS: ☐ No ☐ Floor Mounted ☐ Wall Hung _____
    WASH CENTERS: ☐ No ☐ Yes Describe _____
    WASH FOUNTAINS: ☐ No ☐ Floor Mounted ☐ Wall Hung _____ Size _____
    Describe _____
    WATER CLOSETS: ☐ No ☐ Floor Mounted ☐ Wall Hung Color _____
    Describe _____
    WATER COOLERS: ☐ No ☐ Floor Mounted ☐ Wall Hung _____ Capacity _____ gph.
    ☐ Water Supply ☐ Bottle ☐ Hot ☐ Compartment _____
    OTHER FIXTURES: _____

PLUMBING 15.1 to 15.4

MECHANICAL, Plumbing, cont'd.
Heating, Ventilating & Air Conditioning

SPEC-AID

PLUMBING

FIRE PROTECTION: ☐ Carbon Dioxide System _____ ☐ Standpipe _____
☐ Sprinkler System ☐ Wet ☐ Dry _____ Spacing _____
☐ Fire Department Connection _____ ☐ Building Alarm _____
☐ Hose Cabinets _____ ☐ Hose Racks _____
☐ Roof Manifold _____ ☐ Compressed Air Supply _____
☐ Hydrants _____ ☐ _____
SPECIAL PLUMBING _____

GAS SUPPLY SYSTEM: ☐ No ☐ Natural Gas ☐ Manufactured Gas _____
PIPE: Schedule _____ FITTINGS _____
SHUTOFFS: _____ MASTER CONTROL VALVE: _____
INSULATION: _____ PAINT: _____
OIL SUPPLY SYSTEM: ☐ No ☐ Tanks ☐ Above Ground ☐ Below Ground _____
☐ Steel ☐ Plastic ☐ _____ Capacity _____
HEATING PLANT: ☐ No ☐ Electric ☐ Gas ☐ Oil ☐ Solar _____
☐ Boilers _____ ☐ Pumps _____
☐ PRV Stations _____ ☐ Piping _____
☐ Heat Pumps _____
COOLING PLANT: ☐ No ☐ Yes _____ Tons _____
CHILLERS: ☐ Steam ☐ Water ☐ Air _____
CONDENSER — COMPRESSOR ☐ Air ☐ Water _____
PUMPS _____ COOLING TOWERS _____
SYSTEM TYPE: _____
☐ Single Zone _____ ☐ Multi-Zone _____
☐ All Air _____ ☐ Terminal Reheat _____
☐ Double Duct _____ ☐ Radiant Panels _____
☐ Fan Coil _____ ☐ Unit Ventilators _____
☐ Perimeter Radiation _____ ☐ _____
AIR HANDLING UNITS: Area Served _____ Number _____
Total CFM _____ % Outside Air _____
Cooling, Tons _____ Heating, MBH _____
Filtration _____ Supply Fans _____
Economizer _____
FANS: ☐ No ☐ Return ☐ Exhaust ☐ _____
Describe _____
DISTRIBUTION: DUCTWORK _____ Material _____
TERMINALS: ☐ Diffusers _____ ☐ Registers _____
☐ Grilles _____ ☐ Hoods _____
VOLUME DAMPERS: _____
TERMINAL BOXES: ☐ High Velocity _____ ☐ With Coil _____
☐ Double Duct _____ ☐ _____
COILS: _____
☐ Preheat _____ ☐ Reheat _____
☐ Cooling _____ ☐ _____
PIPING: See Previous Page _____
INSULATION: COLD: ☐ No ☐ Yes Material _____ Jacket _____
HOT: ☐ No ☐ Yes Material _____ Jacket _____
AUTOMATIC TEMPERATURE CONTROLS: _____
AIR & HYDRONIC BALANCING: _____
SPECIAL HVAC: _____

HEATING, VENTILATING & AIR CONDITIONING 15.5 to 15.7

ELECTRICAL

MEANSCO FORM 416   DIVISION 16

SPEC-AID

DATE _____

PROJECT _____ LOCATION _____

INCOMING SERVICE: □ Overhead   □ Underground

	PRIMARY	SECONDARY
Voltage _____		
Unit Sub-Station & Size _____		
Number of Manholes _____		
Feeder Size _____		
Length _____		
Conduit _____		
Duct _____		
Concrete: □ No □ Yes _____		
Other _____		

BUILDING SERVICE: Size _____ Amps Switchboard _____
PANELS: □ Distribution _____ Lighting _____ Power _____
Describe _____

MOTOR CONTROL CENTER: Furnished by _____
Describe _____

BUS DUCT: □ No □ Yes Size _____ Amps Application _____
Describe _____

CABLE TRAY: □ No □ Yes Describe _____

EMERGENCY SYSTEM: □ No □ Yes Allowance _____ □ Separate Contract
GENERATOR: □ No □ Diesel □ Gas □ Gasoline _____ Size _____ KW
TRANSFER SWITCH: □ No □ Yes Number _____ Size _____ Amps
AREA PROTECTION RELAY PANELS: □ No □ Yes _____
OTHER _____

CONDUIT: □ No □ Yes □ Aluminum _____
□ Electric Metallic Tubing _____
□ Galvanized Steel _____
□ Plastic _____

WIRE: □ No □ Yes □ Type Installation _____
□ Armored Cable _____
□ Building Wire _____
□ Metallic Sheath Cable _____
□ _____

UNDER FLOOR DUCT: □ No □ Yes Describe _____

HEADER DUCT: □ No □ Yes Describe _____

TRENCH DUCT: □ No □ Yes Describe _____

UNDERGROUND DUCT: □ No □ Yes Describe _____

EXPLOSION PROOF AREAS: □ No □ Yes Describe _____

MOTORS: □ No □ Yes Total H.P. _____ No. of Fractional H.P. _____ Voltage _____
□ 1/2 to 5 H.P. _____   □ 7-1/2 to 25 H.P. _____   □ Over 25 H.P. _____
Describe _____
Starters: Type _____
Supplied by: _____

ELECTRICAL

SPEC-AID

TELEPHONE SYSTEM: ☐ No ☐ Yes Service Size _____ Length _____

    MANHOLE: ☐ No ☐ Yes Number _____ Termination _____

    CONCRETE ENCASED: ☐ No ☐ Yes ☐ Rigid Galv. ☐ Duct ☐ _____

FIRE ALARM SYSTEM: ☐ No ☐ Yes Service Size _____ Length _____ Wire Type _____

    CONCRETE ENCASED: ☐ No ☐ Yes ☐ Rigid Galv. ☐ Duct ☐ _____

    ☐ Stations _____ ☐ Horns _____ ☐ Lights _____ ☐ Combination _____

    DETECTORS: ☐ Rate of Rise _____ ☐ Fixed _____ ☐ Smoke _____

    Describe _____ Insulation _____ Wire Size _____

    ☐ Zones _____ ☐ Conduit _____ ☐ E.M.T. _____ ☐ Empty _____

    Describe _____

WATCHMANS TOUR: ☐ No ☐ Yes ☐ Stations _____ ☐ Door Switches _____

    ☐ Alarm Bells _____ ☐ Key Re-sets _____ ☐ _____

    ☐ Conduit _____ ☐ E.M.T. _____ ☐ Wire _____ ☐ Empty _____

    Describe _____

CLOCK SYSTEM: ☐ No ☐ Yes ☐ Electronic ☐ Wired ☐ _____

    ☐ Single Dial _____ ☐ Double Dial _____ ☐ Program Bell _____

    ☐ Conduit _____ ☐ E.M.T. _____ ☐ Empty _____

    Describe _____

SOUND SYSTEM: ☐ No ☐ Yes Type _____ Speakers _____

    ☐ Conduit _____ ☐ Cable _____ ☐ E.M.T. _____ ☐ Empty _____

    Describe _____

TELEVISION SYSTEM: ☐ No ☐ Yes Describe _____

    ☐ Antenna _____ ☐ Closed Circuit _____ ☐ Teaching _____ ☐ Security _____

    ☐ Learning Laboratory _____ ☐ _____

    ☐ Conduit _____ ☐ E.M.T. _____ ☐ Wire _____ ☐ Empty _____

LIGHTNING PROTECTION: ☐ No ☐ Yes Describe _____

LOW VOLTAGE SWITCHING: ☐ No ☐ Yes Describe _____

SCOREBOARDS: ☐ No ☐ Yes Describe _____ Number _____

COMFORT SYSTEMS: ☐ No ☐ Electric Heat ☐ Snow Melting ☐ _____

    Describe _____

OTHER SYSTEMS: _____

_____

(side label: ELECTRICAL SYSTEMS 16.0 to 16.8)

LIGHTING FIXTURES: ☐ No ☐ Yes Allowance _____ ☐ Separate Contract

    ☐ Economy ☐ Commercial ☐ Deluxe ☐ Explosion Proof ☐ _____

    ☐ Incandescent _____

_____ Foot Candles _____

    ☐ Fluorescent _____

_____ Foot Candles _____

    ☐ Mercury Vapor _____

_____ Foot Candles _____

    ☐ _____ Foot Candles _____

    ☐ Step Lighting _____ ☐ Planter Lighting _____ ☐ Fountain Lighting _____

    ☐ Site Lighting _____ ☐ Poles _____ ☐ Area Lighting _____ ☐ Flood Lighting _____

    Dimming System: ☐ No ☐ Yes ☐ Incandescent ☐ Fluorescent _____

    Ceilings: ☐ T Bar ☐ Concealed Spline ☐ _____

    Emergency Battery Units: ☐ No ☐ Lead Acid ☐ Nickel Cadmium ☐ 6 Volt _____ 12 Volt _____

    Describe _____

SPECIAL CONSIDERATIONS: _____

_____

(side label: LIGHTING 16.6)

SYSTEMS ESTIMATE SUMMARY

MEANSCO FORM 103

PROJECT	NET AREA		S.F.	SHEET NO.
LOCATION	GROSS AREA		S.F.	ESTIMATE NO.
ARCHITECT	RATIO: NET TO GROSS			DATE
OWNER	GROSS VOLUME		C.F.	NO. OF STORIES

PRICES BY	EXTENSIONS BY	CHECKED BY

NO.	SYSTEM DESCRIPTION	QUANTITY	UNIT	UNIT PRICE	TOTAL COST	COST/S.F.
1.01	SUB-STRUCTURE					
.11	Spread Footings					
.21	Strip Footings					
.31	Grade Beams					
.41	Foundation Walls					
.51	Slab on Grade					
.61	Building Excavation					
3.01	SUPERSTRUCTURE					
.11	Floor Systems					
.21	Roof Systems					
.31	Columns					
.41	Structural Walls					
.42	Shear Walls					
.51	Stairs					
4.01	EXTERIOR CLOSURE					
.11	Bearing Walls					
.21	Curtain Walls					
.31	Fenestration					
.41	Glass and Glazing					
5.01	ROOFING					
.11	Covering					
.21	Openings					
.31	Insulation					
.41	Special Systems					
.51	Gutters, Downspouts, Flashing					
6.01	INTERIOR CONSTRUCTION					
.11	Fixed Partitions					
.21	Miscellaneous Partitions					
.31	Doors					
.41	Interior Finishes					
.51	Floor Coverings					
.61	Ceilings					
7.01	CONVEYING SYSTEMS					
.11	Elevators					
.21	Escalators					
.31	Lifts and Hoists					
.32	Conveyors					
.33	Pneumatic Tubes					
.34	Other Systems					
8.01	PLUMBING SYSTEMS					
.11	Drainage Rough-In					
.21	Supply Rough-In					
.31	Fixtures and Hardware					
.41	Equipment					
.51	Fire Protection					
.61	Special Sub-Systems					
8.02	H.V.A.C. SYSTEMS					
.11	Energy Conversion					
.12	Heat Generation Equipment					
.13	Cooling Generation Equipment					
.21	Energy Distribution					
.22	Piping					
.23	Insulation					
.24	Heating Dist. Equipment with Insulation					

NO.	SYSTEM DESCRIPTION	QUANTITY	UNIT	UNIT PRICE	TOTAL COST	COST/S.F.
.25	Cooling Distribution Equipment					
.31	Air Handling System					
.32	Sheet Metal					
.34	Registers, Grilles & Diffusers					
.35	Air Handling Equipment					
.41	Temperature Control System					
.51	Special Sub-Systems					
9.01	ELECTRICAL SYSTEMS					
.11	Emergency Power					
.21	Lighting					
.31	Power					
.41	Electrical Circuits					
.51	Service and Distribution					
.61	Sub-Systems					
.71	Communications Systems					
	BASIC BUILDING SUB-TOTAL					
10.01	FIXED EQUIPMENT					
11.01	SPECIAL FOUNDATIONS					
.11	Special Excavation					
.21	Piles (Bearing/Friction)					
.31	Caissons					
.41	Mat Construction					
.51	Sheeting & Shoring					
.61	Dewatering					
.71	Special Waterproofing					
	BUILDING TOTAL COST, SUB-TOTAL					
12.01	SITE CONSTRUCTION					
.11	Site Improvement					
.12	Grading & Landscaping					
.13	Site Structures & Paving					
.21	Site Utilities					
.22	Plumbing Site Work					
.23	H.V.A.C. Site Work					
.24	Electrical Site Work					
	CONSTRUCTION COST, SUB-TOTAL					
13.01	CONSTRUCTION RELATED COSTS & CONDITIONS					
.11	General Conditions					
.21	Special Requirements					
.31	Overhead & Insurance					
.41	Profit and Fees					
	ESTIMATED CONSTRUCTION CONTRACT AWARD					
14.01	Contingencies					
.11	Construction & Design _____ %					
.12	Scope & Information Increase _____ %					
.13	Field Change Orders _____ %					
.21	Escalation to Bid Date _____/_____ 19 _____ _____ %					
.31	Probable Bond Cost _____ %					
	TOTAL ESTIMATED CONSTRUCTION COST					
15.01	PROJECT RELATED COSTS					
.11	Site Costs					
.21	Design & Review Costs					
.31	Management & Inspection Costs					
.41	Furnishings & Fixtures					
	ESTIMATED TOTAL PROJECT COST					
	ESTIMATE PROJECTED TO A BID DATE OF					

APPENDIX B

The following tables have been developed to assist in estimating the carpentry portion of the estimate. The tables primarily apply to rough carpentry. The factors used for determining quantities include waste allowances. However, items such as bands, plates, double joists or studs, and corners must be taken off and added separately. In most of the tables, factors are provided to determine quantities of nails for each type of framing. These tables should be used with discretion, taking into account any unique or unusual project requirements.

Flat Roof Framing			
Joist Size	Inches on Center	Board Feet per Square Feet of Roof Area	Nails Lbs. per MBM
2" x 6"	12"	1.17	10
	16"	.91	10
	20"	.76	10
	24"	.65	10
2" x 8"	12"	1.56	8
	16"	1.21	8
	20"	1.01	8
	24"	.86	8
2" x 10"	12"	1.96	6
	16"	1.51	6
	20"	1.27	6
	24"	1.08	6
2" x 12"	12"	2.35	5
	16"	1.82	5
	20"	1.52	5
	24"	1.30	5
3" x 8"	12"	1.82	5
	16"	1.82	5
	20"	1.52	5
	24"	1.30	5
3" x 10"	12"	2.94	4
	16"	2.27	4
	20"	1.90	4
	24"	1.62	4

Pitched Roof Framing

Rafters Including Collar Ties, Hip and Valley Rafters, Ridge Poles

Spacing Center to Center

Rafter Size	12"		16"		20"		24"	
	Board Feet per Square Feet of Roof Area	Nails Lbs. per MBM	Board Feet per Square Feet of Roof Area	Nails Lbs. per MBM	Board Feet per Square Feet of Roof Area	Nails Lbs. per MBM	Board Feet per Square Feet of Roof Area	Nails Lbs. per MBM
2" x 4"	.89	17	.71	17	.59	17	.53	17
2" x 6"	1.29	12	1.02	12	.85	12	.75	12
2" x 8"	1.71	9	1.34	9	1.12	9	.98	9
2" x 10"	2.12	7	1.66	7	1.38	7	1.21	7
2" x 12"	2.52	6	1.97	6	1.64	6	1.43	6
3" x 8"	2.52	6	1.97	6	1.64	6	1.43	6
3" x 10"	3.13	5	2.45	5	2.02	5	1.78	5

Hip and Valley Rafter Ratios

Ratios of Hip or Valley Length to Run of Common Rafter for Various Slopes

Roof Slope			Roof Slope		
Rise	Run	Ratio	Rise	Run	Ratio
3	12	1.4361	9	12	1.6008
4	12	1.4530	10	12	1.6415
4.5	12	1.4631	11	12	1.6853
5	12	1.4743	12	12	1.7321
6	12	1.5000	13	12	1.7815
7	12	1.5298	14	12	1.8333
8	12	1.5635	15	12	1.8875

Roof Slope Ratios

Ratios of Rafter Length to Run for Various Slopes

Rise	Run	Ratio	Rise	Run	Ratio
3	12	1.0308	9	12	1.2500
4	12	1.0541	10	12	1.3017
4.5	12	1.0680	11	12	1.3566
5	12	1.0833	12	12	1.4142
6	12	1.1180	13	12	1.5366
7	12	1.1577	14	12	1.5366
8	12	1.2019	15	12	1.6008

Cross Bridging

Cross Bridging - Board Feet per Square Feet of Floors, Ceiling or Flat Roof Area
Nails - Pounds per MBM of Bridging

Joist Size	Spacing	1" x 3"		1" x 4"		2" x 3"	
		Bd. Ft.	Nails	Bd. Ft.	Nails	Bd. Ft.	Nails
2" x 8"	12"	.04	147	.05	112	.08	77
	16"	.04	120	.05	91	.08	61
	20"	.04	102	.05	77	.08	52
	24"	.04	83	.05	63	.08	42
2" x 10"	12"	.04	.36	.05	103	.08	71
	16"	.04	114	.05	87	108	58
	20"	.04	98	.05	74	.08	50
	24"	.04	80	.05	61	.08	41
2" x 12"	12"	.04	127	.05	96	.08	67
	16"	.04	108	.05	82	.08	55
	20"	.04	94	.05	71	.08	48
	24"	.04	78	.05	59	.08	39
3" x 8"	12"	.04	160	.05	122	.08	84
	16"	.04	127	.05	96	.08	66
	20"	.04	107	.05	81	.08	54
	24"	.04	86	.05	65	.08	44
3" x 10"	12"	.04	146	.05	111	.08	77
	16"	.04	120	.05	91	.08	62
	20"	.04	.02	.05	78	.08	52
	24"	.04	83	.05	63	.08	42

Siding						
Type of Siding	Size	Exposure	Board Feet per Square Feet of Wall Area	Lbs. Nails per MBM of Siding		
				Stud Spacing		
				16"	20"	24"
Plain Bevel Siding	1/2" x 4"	2-1/2"	1.60	17	13	11
		2-3/4"	1.45			
	1/2" x 6"	4-1/2"	1.33	11	9	7
		4-3/4"	1.26			
		5"	1.20			
	1/2" x 8"	6-1/2"	1.23	8	7	6
		7"	1.14			
Plain Bevel Bungalow Siding	5/8" x 8"	6-1/2"	1.23	14	11	9
		7"	1.14			
	5/8" x 10"	8-1/2"	1.18	16	13	11
		9"	1.11			
	3/4" x 8"	6-1/2"	1.23	14	11	9
		7"	1.14			
	3/4" x 10"	8-1/2"	1.18	16	13	11
		9"	1.11			
	3/4" x 12"	10-1/2"	1.14	14	11	9
		11"	1.09			
Drop or Rustic Siding	3/4" x 4"	3-1/4"	1.23	27	22	18
	3/4" x 6"	5-1/16"	1.19	18	15	12
		5-3/16"	1.17			

	Furring				
	Board Feet Per Square Feet of Wall Area				Lbs. Nails per MBM of Furring
	Spacing Center to Center				
Size	12″	16″	20″	24″	
1″ x 2″	.18	.14	.11	.10	55
1″x 3″	.28	.21	.17	.14	37

Wall Board					
Includes Fiber Board, Gypsum Board and Plywood, Used as Underflooring, Sheathing, Plaster Base, or as Drywall Finish					
Factors		Nail			
Used for Underflooring, Sheathing and Plaster Base	Used for Exposed Dry Wall Finish	Pounds of Nails per 1000 Sq. Ft. of Wallboard			
		Joist, Stud of Rafter Spacing			
		12″	16″	20″	24″
1.05	1.10	7	6	5	4

			Floor Framing		
	Floor Joists			Blocking Over Main Bearing	
Joist Size	Inches on Center	Board Feet per Square Feet of Floor Area	Nails Lbs. per MBM	Board Feet per Square Feet of Floor Area	Nails Lbs. per MBM Blocking
2" x 6"	12"	1.28	10	.16	133
	16"	1.02	10	.03	95
	20"	.88	10	.03	77
	24"	.78	10	.03	57
2" x 8"	12"	1.71	8	.04	100
	16"	1.36	8	.04	72
	20"	1.17	8	.04	57
	24"	1.03	8	.05	43
2" x 10"	12"	2.14	6	.05	79
	16"	1.71	6	.05	57
	20"	1.48	6	.06	46
	24"	1.30	6	.06	34
2" x 12"	12"	2.56	5	.06	66
	16"	2.05	5	.06	47
	20"	1.77	5	.07	39
	24"	1.56	5	.07	29
3" x 8"	12"	2.56	5	.04	39
	16"	2.05	5	.05	57
	20"	1.77	5	.06	45
	24"	1.56	5	.06	33
3" x 10"	12"	3.20	4	.05	72
	16"	2.56	4	.07	46
	20"	2.21	4	.07	36
	24"	1.95	4	.08	26

Board Sheathing and Subflooring						
			Diagonal			
			Lbs. Nails per MBM Lumber			
		Board Feet per Square Foot of Area	Joist, Stud or Rafter Spacing			
Type	Size		12"	16"	20"	24"
Surface 4 Sides (S4S)	1" x 4"	1.22	58	46	39	32
	1" x 6"	1.18	39	31	25	21
	1" x 8"	1.18	30	23	19	16
	1" x 10"	1.17	35	27	23	19
Tongue and Groove (T&G)	1" x 4"	1.36	65	51	43	36
	1" x 6"	1.26	42	33	27	23
	1" x 8"	1.22	31	24	20	17
	1" x 10"	1.20	36	28	24	19
Shiplap	1" x 4"	1.41	67	53	45	37
	1" x 6"	1.29	43	33	28	23
	1" x 8"	1.24	31	24	20	17
	1" x 10"	1.21	36	28	24	19

Board Sheathing and Subflooring						
			Right Angles			
			Lbs. Nails per MBM Lumber			
		Board Feet per Square Foot of Area	Joist, Stud or Rafter Spacing			
Type	Size		12"	16"	20"	24"
Surface 4 Sides (S4S)	1" x 4"	1.19	60	47	40	33
	1" x 6"	1.15	40	31	26	22
	1" x 8"	1.15	30	23	20	17
	1" x 10"	1.14	36	28	24	19
Tongue and Groove (T & G)	1" x 4"	1.32	66	52	44	36
	1" x 6"	1.23	43	33	28	23
	1" x 8"	1.19	32	24	21	17
	1" x 10"	1.17	37	29	24	20
Shiplap	1" x 4"	1.38	69	55	46	38
	1" x 6"	1.26	44	34	29	24
	1" x 8"	1.21	32	25	21	17
	1" x 10"	1.18	37	29	25	20

Ceiling Joists			
Joist Size	Inches on Center	Board Feet per Square Feet of Ceiling Area	Nails Lbs. per MBM
2" x 4"	12"	.78	17
	16"	.59	19
	20"	.48	19
2" x 6"	12"	1.15	11
	16"	.88	13
	20"	.72	13
	24"	.63	13
2" x 8"	12"	1.53	9
	16"	1.17	9
	20"	.96	9
	24"	.84	9
2" x 10"	12"	1.94	7
	16"	1.47	7
	20"	1.21	7
	24"	1.04	7
3" x 8"	12"	2.32	6
	16"	1.76	6
	20"	1.44	6
	24"	1.25	6

Exterior Wall Stud Framing					
		Studs Including Corner Bracing		Horizontal Bracing Midway Between Plates	
Stud Size	Inches on Center	Board Feet per Square Feet of Ext. Wall Area	Lbs. Nails per MBM of Stud Framing	Board Feet per Square Feet of Ext. Wall Area	Lbs. Nails per MBM of Bracing
2" x 3"	16"	.78	30	.03	117
	20"	.74	30	.03	97
	24"	.71	30	.03	85
2" x 4"	16"	1.05	22	.04	87
	20"	.98	22	.04	72
	24"	.94	22	.04	64
2" x 6"	16"	1.51	15	.06	59
	20"	1.44	15	.06	48
	24"	1.38	15	.06	43

Partition Stud Framing

Stud Size	Studs Including Sole and C Plates			Horizontal Bracing in All Partitions		Horizontal Bracing in Bearing Partitions Only	
	Inches on Center	Board Feet per Square Feet of Partition Area	Lbs. Nails per MBM of Stud Framing	Board Feet per Square Feet of Partition Area	Lbs. Nails per MBM of Bracing	Board Feet per Square Feet of Partition Area	Lbs. Nails per MBM of Bracing
2" x 3"	12"	.91	25	.04	145	.01	145
	16"	.83	25	.04	111	.01	111
	20"	.78	25	.04	90	.01	90
	24"	.76	25	.04	79	.01	79
2" x 4"	12"	1.22	19	.05	108	.02	108
	16"	1.12	19	.05	87	.02	87
	20"	1.05	19	.05	72	.02	72
	24"	1.02	19	.05	64	.02	64
2" x 6"	16"	1.02	19			.04	59
	20"	1.29	16			.04	48
	24"	1.22	16			.04	43
2" x 4" Staggered	8"	1.69	22				
3" x 4"	16"	1.35	17				
2" x 4" 2" Way	16"	1.08	19